THE
VIVAXIS
CONNECTION

Books by Judy Jacka

A Philosophy of Healing
A-Z of Natural Therapies
Meditation—the Most Natural Therapy
Healing Through Earth Energies
Frontiers of Natural Therapies
Healing Yourself Naturally

Judy Jacka, N.D.

THE VIVAXIS CONNECTION

Healing Through Earth Energies

HAMPTON ROADS

PUBLISHING COMPANY, INC.

The Vivaxis Connection: Healing through Earth Energies
Judy Jacka

Cover design by Marjoram Productions
Cover painting by Lisa Podgur Cuscuna
Illustrations by Julia McLeish

For information write:

Hampton Roads Publishing Company, Inc.
1125 Stoney Ridge Road
Charlottesville, VA 22902

Or call: 804-296-2772
FAX: 804-296-5096
e-mail: hrpc@hrpub.com
Web site: www.hrpub.com

If you are unable to order this book from your local
bookseller, you may order directly from the publisher.
Quantity discounts for organizations are available.
Call 1-800-766-8009, toll-free.

Library of Congress Catalog Card Number: 00-102566

ISBN 1-57174-208-5

10 9 8 7 6 5 4 3 2 1

Printed on acid-free paper in the United States

Dedication

This book is dedicated to the memory of
Frances Nixon,
who was a true pioneer of the healing energies
available from planet Earth.

Acknowledgments

Because of the unusual and complex nature of Earth energies, this has been the most difficult of all my books to write. I am particularly grateful to my friends Linda Stevenson and Ian Dunlop for the many useful suggestions they made following their reading of the first draft of this revised edition of the initial work, *Healing through Earth Energies*. My thanks also to D. N. Pettipas, who supplied me with valuable material from the early writings of Fran Nixon. Especial thanks are due to Julia McLeish for her labor over the peculiar details needed for many of the diagrams and drawings. Last but not least, my thanks to the students of the Vivaxis connection I have taught over a twenty-year period and who persevered to master this most unusual science. They have proved to me that the exercises in this book are relevant and meaningful in our daily life.

Table of Contents

Introduction

As a practicing natural therapist with over twenty-five years of clinical experience, I have found the science of Vivaxis to be a remarkable development in restoring and harmonizing body energies. This book presents twenty-nine exercises that can empower individuals to correct their own health without requiring medical supervision and with virtually no cost involved. This concept of the Vivaxis was pioneered forty years ago by a Canadian researcher named Frances Nixon.

Vivaxis science is a natural therapy, but it is far ahead of the more common natural therapies. It examines the source of those vibrational therapies that form the basis of vitamin and mineral therapy, homeopathy, flower essences, acupuncture, and color therapy, among many other therapies. Most natural therapies are based on the concept of balancing and restoring energy and we know that energy can manifest in various frequencies or vibrations.

The Vivaxis is a sphere of energy established at a geophysical point in

The Vivaxis is a sphere of energy established at a geophysical point in connection with the growing fetus at some point of time during the last two months of pregnancy. Each individual is linked by a two-way circuit to the Earth via their own Vivaxis throughout life, despite how far they may travel from this location. We could say that we have an invisible umbilical cord of energy attaching us to the Earth via our Vivaxis.

connection with the growing fetus at some point of time during the last two months of pregnancy. Each individual is linked by a two-way circuit to the Earth via their own Vivaxis throughout life, despite how far they may travel from this location. We could say that we have an invisible umbilical cord of energy attaching us to the Earth via *our* Vivaxis.

Ill health develops when interference with the energy flows of our Vivaxis occurs. The interference may be chemical, electromagnetic, or psychological. The end result is a diminished or chaotic flow of energy through the body that affects the immune and nervous systems. Indeed, any organs or tissues may be affected.

I have found this work with Earth energies to be easily repeatable by those who practice it carefully, despite the fact that it is a very new and pioneering adventure. This suggests to me that we are dealing with a true science. You will see from the many exercises in part 2 that we can establish double-blind trials in some significant areas, and that this has already been done on a small scale.

Over the years, I have learned many practical ways to use Earth energies to restore health to myself, to my clients, and to the environment around me. I call this the Vivaxis connection. The great advantage of this work with Earth energies is that it costs nothing and can be accomplished by each individual for himself or herself. It is especially useful during times of illness, stress, and travel or at any time when you are thrown completely back on your own resources without therapeutic assistance.

It was twenty years ago that the late Frances Nixon from Vancouver Island, Canada, introduced me to this science of Earth energies. At the time, I had no idea of the adventure that was to unfold. I can say that my study of Earth energies remains the most amazing aspect of health and healing I have encountered during thirty-five years of study in the area of natural therapies.

The story begins when I was introduced to Fran's discoveries by an Australian chiropractor who had attended one of her Canadian seminars. At that time, I was developing the Southern School of Natural Therapies in Melbourne, Australia, and lecturing on naturopathic philosophy and the principles of natural therapies. My major aim was to build a bridge between energy, as understood by orthodox science, and the vitalistic concept of natural therapies. The foundation of natural therapy rests on restoring and balancing the energies of the body, and I was always on the lookout for scientific material on the subject of vitality to present to students.

I was impressed that Fran Nixon had evoked the interest of several Canadian and American physicists. Like a scientist, she followed a meticulous routine of checking and rechecking all her material before publishing and teaching her discoveries. The nature of her work convinced me she was dealing with subtle energies that are increasingly viewed as providing the blueprint for growth and regrowth, or healing.

In 1979, I wrote to Fran and asked if she would be prepared to do a workshop in Australia. She was delighted to accept and came for two months, during which time she conducted a two-week seminar on our property at Kinglake in the Great Dividing Range north of Melbourne on the south coast of Australia. Only ten people showed interest in attending this seminar. However, when I described her work in a leading health journal, I received more letters and inquiries about the subject than I had received from any of my previous books and articles on health and healing.

For the last twenty years, I have taught this subject, which Fran named the science of Vivaxis. Vivaxis means the axis of life. The Vivaxis could be considered as a small sphere of energies at a particular geographical point. We are connected to this point by a two-way flow of energy, or umbilicus, to our personal energy field. This is our Vivaxis connection. Before Fran died in August 1985, I assisted her with her work in Canada and she asked me to carry on her work. Fran was a purist, whereas my interest in the healing arts is quite eclectic, so I have always combined an interest in Earth energies with an interest in other aspects of health and healing. Hence, this book is not just about the science of Vivaxis, but it also includes other findings about Earth energies and the relationship of Earth energies to many aspects of health and healing.

One of the main aims of this book is to train you to use your own subtle energy body as the instrument for finding, comparing, assessing, and using energies. This science of Earth energies currently is largely beyond the capacity of physics to measure and may remain so. However, the energies described are still in the physical realm and appear to be closely related to the laws of gravitation, magnetism, and electricity as manifested on this planet. So physical instruments can indirectly measure subtle energies via the electromagnetic field that surrounds and interpenetrates all living beings. The Earth energies studied in this work are therefore geophysical in the sense that they are found in relation to the ground on which we walk but are more subtle than solids, liquids, and gases.

The term "etheric" is often used for these more subtle energies, and this term means those energies associated with the blueprint underlying all physical form. Another term used for such energies is "morphogenetic fields," as coined by scientist Rupert Sheldrake. Engineer and scientist William Tiller from Stanford University defines etheric energies as the more subtle counterpart of electromagnetic fields and uses the term "magnetoelectric" for the etheric realm. Etheric fields carry the patterns for growth in all the kingdoms in nature. We can therefore view our own electromagnetic field as the mirror image of the etheric or magnetoelectric fields. I believe that the Vivaxis and associated phenomena include both etheric and electromagnetic energies and that the etheric energies are the more subtle of the two.

We need to be able to clearly distinguish these Vivaxis energies, subjective as they are at present, from the psychic energy that operates in the "astral" realm. The astral realm is largely created by human desires and is therefore largely illusory in one sense although real enough when we are immersed in it. Therefore, an emphasis on this level of consciousness combined with our particular mental conditioning can distort our work with Vivaxis energies. The New Age movement has emphasized psychic phenomena, whereas although Vivaxis energies are subtle, they are a subtle *physical* phenomena. A study of our whole psychic constitution is therefore essential to distinguish Vivaxis phenomena from the psychic realm. For this reason, I have included sections in the first few chapters on our subtle constitution and the spinal energy centers known as the chakras.

One faculty we use in sensing energies is related to the ancient technique of dowsing, sometimes called the radiesthetic, or kinesthetic, sense. I explore this ability early in the book. In studying dowsing, I became aware of previous research related to how it can find various substances such as water and mineral deposits below the surface of the planet. The field of dowsing extends into radionics, where practitioners use this subtle sense to diagnose disease and "broadcast" healing frequencies. We will look at this area as an aid to understanding the subject of human vibrations and frequencies.

While working with Vivaxis energies, I became aware of other types of Earth energies, including ley lines and the Hartmann and Curry grids, and I found that these subjects have already been somewhat explored by European dowsers. I discuss them toward the end of part 1, the theory part of the book. It is important to include some information about these other grids and the ley lines because the topic of Vivaxis does not just feature our connection with the energy field of the Earth. It includes electromagnetic and etheric layers that, Fran discovered, emanate all the life-giving frequencies we need for health. We will learn to use these layers in part 2. To do this, we also need to understand a bit about the Hartmann and Curry grids, because we need to avoid such systems and find neutral ground when we attempt to absorb the life-giving frequencies.

I make no apology that the bulk of this book is devoted to the discoveries of Fran Nixon. In writing this book, I have reviewed all her self-published work and have continued to be astounded by the implications and applications of her findings. While there are a number of publications on different aspects of Earth energies such as feng shui and ley lines, none of these works are based on a system that minutely diagnoses and corrects the relationship between the individual and the Earth.

The closest parallel would be the traditional Chinese medical system encompassing the five-element theory and associated concordances. Traditional Chinese medicine encourages us to rebalance our energies by choosing particular foods, sounds, colors, and surroundings according to our constitution. The Ayurvedic medicine model from India also selects food and remedies according to body type and temperament. However, in the discoveries of Fran Nixon, we have a system of diagnosis and treatment that enables each individual to find and correct energy variations from the gross to the most subtle energy disturbances without acupuncture needles, supplements, or foods.

I have often wondered why Fran's extraordinary discoveries have not been more widely spread. The focus of the New Age movement has been on psychic phenomena and hence on astral or psychic experience. We see this emphasis in the many rebirthing techniques, past-life regressions, meditation trainings, aura readings, and astrological or Tarot readings. There have been few individuals or groups that have endeavored to focus purely on subtle *physical* energies. Even so, these subtle energies are intrinsic to our health and well-being because they condition our physical bodies.

My training in the Trans-Himalayan teachings transmitted by H. P. Blavatsky and Alice Bailey, together with the study of natural therapies, has attracted me to these subtle physical (or etheric) energies, as they are known in the West. The more subtle part of our physical body consists of these energies that Fran Nixon researched throughout her career. The etheric world forms an interface between our physical brain consciousness and our different levels of consciousness. We cannot transmit these subtle states or be a reliable instrument unless our etheric body and its associated electromagnetic field is balanced and in order.

This book is in three parts. Part 1 contains Fran's discoveries, generally in chronological sequence of discovery. As Fran made each new discovery, earlier techniques were superseded, but it is of value to understand the whole tapestry of her discoveries. Therefore, I have included her initial discoveries. She devised detailed exercises for each discovery, which are included in part 2. You will find it a very useful adventure to undertake these exercises, as they will gradually reveal your energy connections with the planet and solar system. You will also gradually experience a growing awareness of your body energies; you will know how to tell immediately when something in the environment affects you adversely and why; and you will learn simple techniques that will improve your health and energy levels quickly. Of course the biggest bonus is that this Vivaxis work costs nothing. All of us have a Vivaxis connection.

Your Vivaxis studies will help you understand how other natural therapies work, because they are all based on energy as medicine. The exercises in part 2 will help to restore your body energies so that you absorb minerals and vitamins more adequately from your food and supplements. This partly results from the enhancement of all the organs that can take place if you receive energies freely through your Vivaxis. Memory and concentration can also be greatly improved by correcting the disturbed receptors in your cranial (head) area.

We live in a very polluted world, and the exercises I describe will help you to both monitor and correct the pollution in your immediate environment. This pollution is chemical and electromagnetic. You may also be familiar with information about other forms of pollution such as radon gas, which comes from fissures in rock under the ground. We need to know that there are, in addition to pollutants, also beneficial energies that we can use whenever necessary in our immediate environment for health and healing.

The story begins with the central discovery by Fran of the Vivaxis connection whereby our electromagnetic/etheric energy field is connected to the electromagnetic/etheric energy field of the Earth via a sphere of energies created shortly before our birth. In this book, we study how all disease involves a disturbance to our Vivaxis.

The story begins with the central discovery by Fran of the Vivaxis connection whereby our electromagnetic/etheric energy field is connected to the electromagnetic/etheric energy field of the Earth via a sphere of energies created shortly before our birth. Our personal energy field, or aura, consists of a number of layers and could be described as electromagnetic/etheric (the Vivaxis field), astral (feelings and desires), mental (our thoughts), buddhic (intuitions and pure reason), and atmic (spiritual will). (See figure 12, page 76.) The energy field of the Earth has similar layers formed from the collective units in all the kingdoms in nature. However, in the case of the Earth, the human kingdom will be the main contributor to the mental and spiritual fields.

In this book, we study how all disease involves a disturbance to our Vivaxis, and the reader is introduced to the many techniques Fran discovered to restore this connection and to enhance our energies. Her second major discovery was that energy flows in *layers* of the Earth and that there are many uses we can make of these layers, including energizing our bodies, purifying water and food, and inactivating harmful frequencies in our environment. As the Earth becomes more polluted, these techniques will gain further in value.

A most interesting part of Fran's discoveries relate to her mapping of the body receptors for energy as these receptors receive energies from our Vivaxis and the energy layers of the planet. Some of these receptors correspond to acupuncture points charted by traditional Chinese medicine. (See figure 1.) There are thousands of these points, and they are mainly arranged bilaterally on the body's meridian system. There are twelve main meridians that run longitudinally on the body, so these points appear on both sides of this longitudinal division.

Fran added to our understanding by demonstrating how each receptor point responds to particular mineral frequencies essential for health, such as iron, calcium, magnesium, chromium, and so on. Of special significance is her finding that each receptor or acupuncture point is connected to our Vivaxis and therefore receives mineral frequencies from the Earth via our Vivaxis. Each receptor is like a tiny transformer able to receive the subtle currents that flow if the right mineral frequencies are present in the receptor and if it is correctly tuned to our Vivaxis. We are indeed electrical beings, and our electromagnetic field is associated with thousands of these energy receptors.

Fran found the brain receptors to be very important for many body functions, such as movement, memory, and creative thinking. If the brain or other receptors connected to body organs become disturbed by psychic, chemical, or electromagnetic factors, they no longer transmit energy but subside into a chaotic state. This disrupted energy in the receptor could be likened to a short circuit in a household gadget—it no longer functions. In all cases of paralysis, there are disrupted receptors that in many cases can be corrected. Imagine the possibilities for

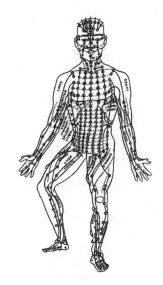

Figure 1. Acupuncture meridians, or energy channels, run the length of the body, on the front, back, and sides. Each meridian has numerous treatment points (indicated in the figures by the numbered black circles) at which a treatment with tiny acupuncture needles may be applied. Up to 1000 different acupuncture points have been identified. Fran Nixon's research showed that many of these points correspond to body sites at which important activities in the Vivaxis model take place.

corrective work if these basic techniques were accepted in conventional medicine. Fran described cases in which she retrained paralyzed people to walk again after helping them to find and correct their disturbed receptors.

All body functions, both voluntary and involuntary, are associated with these receptors, which are all related to different mineral frequencies. You can learn to diagnose disturbed receptors and the techniques for their correction in part 2.

In part 2, we start with cleansing exercises, a step that prepares us to find particular compass directions for elements. The research indicates that we can trace more than twenty common elements with vibrational frequencies and energy flows to particular compass directions. In other words, each element on our planet has a connection, or vector, to a particular compass direction on our planet. This introduces the vibrational concept of the universe that features so strongly in all natural therapies.

We learn about the rhythms and tides produced on our planet by other celestial bodies as well as the techniques we can use for charting some of these interactions. The effect of these various tides and rhythms on our health is significant. We explore the key elements that feature in our bodies and that need to be balanced for health. I describe techniques for finding and assessing these important elements. This leads to perhaps the key adventure of the book: how to find and use the energy layers on the Earth that contain all the frequencies necessary for our life.

After we learn to mark the energy layers, we are in a position to find and use our Vivaxis. Our Vivaxis is located at a particular point on the planet and connects us with health-giving frequencies throughout our life. The inherent skills we use to find the energy layers and our Vivaxis relate to the magnetic properties of the pineal gland in the brain. Understanding this connection helps us appreciate the link between our energy centers and the energy layers; I developed this latter work in recent years. For individuals who have extreme energy confusion in their bodies, I indicate how to create a new Vivaxis. The final exercises in part 2 are devised for those who wish to help family, friends, and clients and, most important, to protect the therapist from taking on the client's energy disturbances.

Techniques for promoting a healthy environment at work and home are described in part 3. This section includes purification of food and water and skills to evaluate the effects of earthquakes, radiation, and electromagnetic fields. I explain how we can check for geopathic stress, or Earth pathology, and how to evaluate our homes and offices for what is called "Sick Building Syndrome." Geopathic stress, or Earth sickness, has always been explored in Chinese culture through feng shui and is now beginning to be researched by some Western architects who are concerned with placing their buildings on geologically healthy sites. They can thus prevent the factors in the Earth that may contribute to Sick Building Syndrome. Building materials that do not conduct health-giving energies (such as some plastics and polymers) also contribute to Sick Building Syndrome. Poor air-conditioning is another cause of unhealthy buildings. The science of Vivaxis can help diagnose Sick Building Syndrome and explain how to heal our buildings.

It probably will be easiest to master this new science of the Vivaxis connection if you read the theory part through once without worrying if you do not understand every term and concept. There are many new ideas and concepts about our energies in part 1 that need to be gradually absorbed and used. Get the big picture first and the details will fall into place later. Then you can read the theory through more slowly the second time and proceed with the exercises in parts 2 and 3.

In the twenty-first century, there may be times of planetary crisis when humanity will be completely thrown back on its resources for health and healing with nothing else but the Earth we stand on. We will then rejoice that we can use Mother Earth for healing and preserving the body for our soul and spirit. The Vivaxis connection is our healing link, for our spirit will eventually return to higher realms, but our body comes from and is dependent on the provisions of our planet Earth.

Glossary of Terms

AREALOHA FORCES: A term coined by Fran Nixon for forces that relate to the true north and south poles and that can be harnessed via sea salt and soda to promote health and balance.

ASTRAL: Denotes energies associated with our feelings and psychic activities such as clairvoyance and clairaudience. The astral body is our vehicle for emotional expression.

AURA: The surrounding fields of energy that originate from the human being or animal and that may include etheric, astral or emotional, mental, and spiritual energies.

BRAIN RECEPTOR: A term used by Fran Nixon to denote a point on the skull that receives and transmits energy.

CHAKRAS: A Sanskrit word meaning "wheel," the term being used for the energy centers in the human or animal energy field.

CURRY GRID: An energy grid described by Dr. Manfred Curry that covers the surface of the Earth and is charged in an electromagnetic sense. The lines are between eleven and twelve feet apart. The lines are diagonal to those of the Hartmann grid (see below).

DOWSING: A method of searching for water or minerals with a divining rod.

ENERGY LAYERS, FLOWS, OR BANDS: The terms used by Fran Nixon to denote the successive layers of energy around the Earth that are positioned like skins of an onion and that are separated by about eight to twelve feet (three to four meters).

ETHERIC BODY: The vehicle for etheric energy for plant, animal, or human and that provides the pattern, or blueprint, for growth and regrowth.

ETHERIC ENERGY: A common name given to the energy that underlies all physical bodies.

FORCE FLOWS: The term used by Fran Nixon to describe the different energies that carry the health-giving life frequencies in the energy layers. There are also detrimental force flows carrying frequencies, such as lead and cadmium, that are inimical to life.

GEOPATHIC STRESS: Areas of pathology in the Earth, such as underground water streams and oil deposits, that can have injurious effects on our health. The term is also often used to cover human-made Earth sickness, such as occurs from exposure to power lines.

GRAVITATIONAL FORCE FLOW AND ELEMENTS: Force flows carrying frequencies that are associated with the gravitational forces of the Moon and Sun. This force flow is also associated with the gravitational layer of our energy field (or aura) and with our Vivaxis.

HARTMANN GRID: A global grid identified by Dr. Ernst Hartmann with lines that run north/south and east/west. They are two to three meters or six to ten feet apart and diagonal to those of the Curry grid (see above).

INACTIVATING: A term used by Fran to mean the removal of chaotic energies from our environment.

ION FLOW: The flow of negative and positive ions in the body that gives a basic indication of flow in the energy field. In physics, an ion is a charged particle.

KIRLIAN PHOTROGRAPHY: The placing of the subject to be photographed in a high-frequency field without the need for any external light source.

L-FIELDS: (Life Fields) were so named by Harold Saxton Burr and refer to the energy fields that underlie the physical body and which provide the blueprint for the growth of all our physical tissues and organs.

LEY LINE: A track on the surface of the Earth that is understood to carry energy from one place to another. The lines have been found to form a grid with lines about two kilometers, or one mile, apart.

MAGNETIC ELEMENTS AND FORCE FLOWS: Force flows carrying the frequencies for elements such as iron, copper, silver, gold, nickel, and selenium. This flow is also associated with the magnetic layer of our energy field or aura.

MAJOR PERIOD: A term used by fisherman in some countries for the high tide; the period lasts for about one and a half hours.

MINOR PERIOD: A term used by fishermen for the low tide; the period lasts for about twenty minutes.

RADIESTHETIC SENSE: The ability to sense etheric energies.

RADIONICS: The practice of energy healing from a distance, using an instrument transmitting the frequencies that can correct disease patterns via a photograph, blood spot, or sample of hair from the subject.

RECEPTORS: The word used by Fran Nixon for tiny energy transmitters on the surface of the body that have been found to be similar to acupuncture points. They are associated with particular mineral frequencies.

SOLUNAR FLOW: The period of about six hours between high and low tides.

VECTOR: A line representing force or velocity.

VEGATEST: A patented electronic device that measures skin resistance.

VIVAXIS: A sphere of energy created during the last weeks before birth that connects our etheric and electromagnetic energy fields with that of the Earth. This sphere of energies is about the size of the fetus and remains in that geographical location where it was formed no matter how far we travel from it. We are connected to this sphere by a two-way flow of energy, or circuit, throughout life.

PART ONE

The Vivaxis Theory

CHAPTER 1

The Vivaxis Discovery

In 1961 Frances Nixon discovered a phenomenon claimed by some physicists to be equal to the discoveries of Albert Einstein. She named this discovery the Vivaxis, which means "axis of life." Her research took place after she had retired with her forester husband to Thetis Island, an idyllic place off Vancouver Island in British Columbia, Canada. Fran had always been a lateral, intuitive thinker, and because of her training and work in art, she was sensitive to the finer energies in nature. As a result of her husband's work in forestry, Fran spent many years of isolation in the Canadian forests and was able to explore some of nature's subtler energies. Sketching and painting the flora and fauna of her environment enhanced Fran's skills of observation.

There was no piped water to their retirement property, and Fran taught herself to dowse energies. Dowsing is an ancient art whereby the practitioner uses a degree of clairsentience, or extrasensory touch, to examine the environment. A pendulum, a metal rod, or, traditionally, forked willow twigs, are aids often used for this purpose. In her dowsing experiments on Thetis Island, Fran used an angled wire made of galvanized iron. (See figure 2.) It is known as a dip wire, because it dips up and down when you test energies.

Figure 2. The first instrument to measure Vivaxis energies. The dip wire was made of galvanized wire. The angle of the bottom hook was relative to the magnetic parameters at the testing site.

Adapted from *Vivaxis Manual* by Frances Nixon, 1974.

When the dip wire was resting on the center of her right index finger pad, it moved a number of times on either the horizontal or vertical plane, depending on how she held her left hand. She realized there was an interplay of energies between her two hands. When she held various insulating objects in her left hand such as wood, paper, or lead, Fran found the objects had no effect on the dip wire. She picked a leaf from a nearby plant to see the effect of holding a living object in her hand. Instead of recording the usual vertical dips, the wire now pulled vigorously in a horizontal direction toward the mother plant from which she had plucked the leaf. Repeated experiments with other plants revealed the same "homing" characteristic. Fran felt this pattern of energies contained definite information, and a fascination to understand the phenomenon grew in her.[1] Fran postulated that all living things might have a homing characteristic, an energy connection to their point of origin, just as this single leaf had for its mother plant.

First Discovery of Human Vivaxis Energies

In 1961 Fran was helping to relieve the pain of a friend dying from cancer by using magnetic waves from blocks of ice placed near the woman's painful areas. Fran's friend was convinced that healing required the use of our own magnetic sense to test energies. Together they discussed the possibility of a person somehow aligning with their own energies to enhance their health and well-being. Fran's friend created in her the spark of desire to probe these secrets of the universe further. Immediately after the death of her friend, Fran awakened one morning with the strong impression that we must learn to harness our own energies for healing.[2]

---

[1] Frances Nixon, *Vivaxis Manual, Part 1* (British Columbia, Canada: Chemainus Publishers, 1974), p. 5.
[2] Frances Nixon, *Born to Be Magnetic*, vol.1 (British Columbia, Canada: Magnetic Publishers, 1971), p. 24.

Fran used two old-fashioned bathroom chains to find her own Vivaxis, or energy point of origin, in the following way. Standing erect and with feet apart, she turned slowly clockwise a few degrees at a time and noted the movement in the chains held in each hand. At the point where she faced her birthplace in Vancouver City, the chains swung back and forth in an alternating movement. The same movement took place when she faced in the opposite direction, and when she turned at right angles to Vancouver, the chains swung in unison.

This early-morning discovery was the first step toward the realization that we can influence our subtle body energies by aligning to our Vivaxis, our energy point of connection. Fran was able to help her husband with a long-standing back and muscular problem by alignment to his Vivaxis. Early in her research, she found that the Vivaxis energies to and from the body traveled in both horizontal and vertical planes.[3]

Fran's subsequent research proved we are permanently connected by energy links to the Vivaxis sphere of energies formed at some time in the last weeks before our birth. Fran named this sphere of energies the Vivaxis from the Latin words "viva," meaning life, and "axis," meaning a central line around which a rotating body moves. She observed that a person's life force rotated about this central point.

Fran's subsequent research proved we are permanently connected by energy links to the Vivaxis sphere of energies formed at some time in the last weeks before our birth. Fran named this sphere of energies the Vivaxis from the Latin words "viva," meaning life, and "axis," meaning a central line around which a rotating body moves. She observed that a person's life force rotated about this central point. The Vivaxis sphere

[3] Frances Nixon, *Vivaxis Manual, Part 1*, p. 18.

5

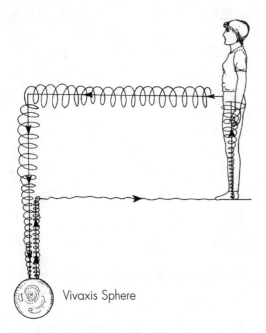

Vivaxis Sphere

Figure 3. The two-way flow of our Vivaxis waves. The Vivaxis sphere, which is the size of the fetus, will be located at a place where the mother spent time in the last few weeks of pregnancy. It is usually formed a few weeks before birth. The position of the Vivaxis will remain in the same position despite how far we travel from its site. There will be a two-way flow of energy between our body and our Vivaxis—the incoming flow travels vertically until it reaches our current altitude, then horizontally until it reaches our left foot, and then moves vertically up our left leg. The outgoing flow moves horizontally out our right hand and returns to the Vivaxis.

remains permanently vibrating in the same geographic position however far away a person travels, remaining even after death. The size of the Vivaxis is the same as the curled-up fetus in the mother's uterus. As suggested, the two-way link to the Vivaxis from the person may be over a thousand miles in length, depending on how far the individual travels from their Vivaxis.

Fran worded a more technical description of the Vivaxis as follows: "A Vivaxis is created when a group of ambient forces relative to time and space are drawn into a common core. It is a sudden fusion of forces that are grounded to the Earth, usually through a solid that is a suitable conductor. The atomic particles within the Vivaxis energy sphere become aligned and magnetized to the geophysical field in which the Vivaxis is created. There is a magnetizing of energies, which causes a wave link to be established between the Vivaxis and its entity owner. This wave-link remains constant regardless of distance."[4]

Our bones are the chief carriers of our Vivaxis forces, possibly because our skeleton is the most stable part of our physical body. A permanent magnetic alignment is introduced into the atomic structure of our bones as they solidify before birth at the geographical point of the

---

[4] *Ibid.*, p. 7.

Vivaxis. This point is usually near our birthplace, but its actual placement depends on where the mother was located at the time the Vivaxis was formed. Near the time of birth, when this process in the bones takes place, the magnetic pattern becomes fixed in the bones and acquires the specific magnetic characteristics of that position on the Earth's surface.[5] By means of this connection, we can detect a two-way link to our own individual Vivaxis. The energies flow toward us from our Vivaxis via the left hand and foot and toward the Vivaxis via the right hand and foot.[6] (See figure 3.) This is our Vivaxis connection.

As the Vivaxis is established at some imprecisely known time during the last weeks of pregnancy, it may not be situated in the home of the mother, but it might be found at a location visited by the mother in the weeks before the birth. It is interesting to speculate on the possible health effects from this geographical position. There could be the future possibility of industrial development with noise, chemical, and electronic pollution at the site of our Vivaxis. This may cause an input of chaotic energies to our energy field via our Vivaxis connection. The individual concerned may suffer severe exhaustion, pain, and general imbalance of their own energies. This means that some individuals may perhaps suffer disrupting effects to their health from the human-made technology near their Vivaxis. Fortunately, as you will discover, we can relocate our Vivaxis quite easily. However, this process is only undertaken after we have explored other, more immediate, causes of ill health. (See exercise 11.)

The Vivaxis connections of a living person has the two-way link as follows: a vertical wave can be detected flowing either directly above or below the person's

---

[5] Nixon, *Born to Be Magnetic*, vol. 1, p. 13.
[6] *Ibid.*, pp. 30, 108.

Vivaxis, depending on whether they are situated above or below their Vivaxis in terms of altitude. A permanent horizontal wave can also be noted. Fran discovered that the energies flowing toward a person from their Vivaxis flowed in a vertical direction up or down until reaching the same level above sea level as the person and then in a horizontal direction until reaching the receiving foot and hand of the person.

Fran found that the magnetic energies flow in a vertical direction and that if a person is standing above the level of their Vivaxis, they receive these energies through the left forefinger and if below their Vivaxis, through the left fourth finger. The energies flow horizontally back to the Vivaxis through the fingers of the right hand.

The discovery of these vertical and horizontal waves is related to Fran's demonstration that our bodies have both an electric and magnetic field at right angles to each other. This is very basic teaching in the area of electromagnetism, but it had never been demonstrated in connection with the human body at that time in the early 1960s. Fran was probably the first to demonstrate that the human body is electrical in nature and that it has an electromagnetic field. Electromagnetism is one of the basic forces in the universe as discovered by physics. One of the other well-known forces is gravity. Electromagnetism features in every atom of our universe and causes the relation between particles in the atom and between atoms, and it therefore can be described as a cohesive force. I have already mentioned that Vivaxis energies include both electromagnetic and etheric energies.

Just as physics has established that electric fields are at right angles to magnetic fields when considering a current carried by a wire, Fran found a similar phenomena when distinguishing between the gravitational (electric) and magnetic fields of the human body. This is amazing, especially since she has described how we can demonstrate this to our own satisfaction. The interesting fact is that when we face directly toward our Vivaxis, these two fields, electric and magnetic, are synchronized. Both fields then have vectors, or directions, of force toward the Vivaxis instead of being at right angles to each other.

When our Vivaxis is disturbed by certain environmental conditions, we suffer from static and the direction of the Vivaxis appears to be at right angles to its normal direction. Fran reasoned that this phenomenon happens when the environmental electromagnetic field overpowers our own energy field in a detrimental sense. This can occur as a result of earthquakes, electrical storms, or when we are subject to human-made electromagnetic interference. Even standing under an electric light will temporarily cause this effect. Through these observations, we begin to understand what humanity has done to our planetary environment and to our health.

It appears that all creatures have magnetic waves linking them directly to a geographic point established shortly before birth, providing life-giving forces in a two-way magnetic link. As children of Mother Earth, it is understandable that our energy field is connected through a bundle of energy to the energy field of the Earth. Fran later discovered that if we destroy our Vivaxis, another one is made immediately, thus keeping our connection to the Earth. We can speculate that in some cases of unexplained death, the Vivaxis may have been profoundly disturbed without a new connection having taken place. We can wonder what effect extraplanetary travel has on astronauts with respect to their Vivaxis.

After death a two-way link will no longer connect the Vivaxis with the animal or human, as they no longer have a physical and energy body. However, the Vivaxis sphere will still be present. This is a hard subject to research on a large scale, because we would have to know the exact place of the Vivaxis to test whether it disappears at some stage after death.

To maintain health and remain connected to our Vivaxis, it is not necessary to find its exact location. We only need to find the exact *direction* to our Vivaxis. In theory, we could find the place by following this direction to its source through continual checking and testing en route. However, even if we lived only a few miles from the place of residence of our mother during pregnancy, this would be quite a challenge on foot. We could do it by car, but this would be very difficult to perform accurately on any road that is close to the disturbing effect of power lines, because their emissions would distort our detections. Also, the effect on our energies while traveling in the car would tend to give inaccurate recordings until we had grounded ourselves again by walking around for a while on Earth. This is a point to remember when doing any Vivaxis testing after traveling by car, train, or plane.

However, a number of persons who live in country areas and who have lived close to their birthplace have been able to find their Vivaxis, and this has provided valuable information. For general purposes, it is unnecessary to find the actual place of one's Vivaxis. We soon learn to test whether there is a clear channel. In this day of pervasive technology, our Vivaxis waves will probably pass by electric cables, wires, microwave transmitters, and machines and yet in most cases, our energies stay intact.

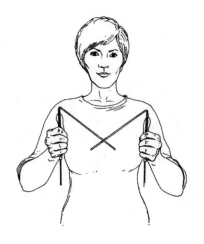

Figure 4. The use of angle wires to find our Vivaxis. When we are directly facing our Vivaxis, the points of the wires cross evenly. We should not think of anything but our Vivaxis during the process.

Early in Fran's research, the use of angle wires made from soft steel provided the means of charting the waves. A piece eighteen inches long was bent in half to make an exact ninety degree angle, and one half was enclosed in a copper sleeve of about six inches long and one quarter of an inch in diameter. The ends of the wire were sharpened to a point and kept free of rust. The wires were held (see figure 4) with the points of the wire crossed when the tester faced directly toward their Vivaxis. The wires were used in a form of self-dowsing for checking disturbances in both the body and environment. Does the dowser have to state he wants the wires to show the Vivaxis direction? Definitely not. This is what I mean by distinguishing between etheric/Vivaxis energies and psychic stuff. The emotions and mind must be kept out.

However, by the time Fran came to Australia to teach our group, she was training people to use their own arms and hands without the use of wires. She had discovered that certain mineral frequencies, such as lead, which are involved with the galvanizing process in the wire and copper pipe, caused distortions in some of the recording practices. She regarded the use of the arm and hand as more accurate.

Sick or debilitated persons often have some impediment in the link to their Vivaxis. Fran found that this blockage could be emotional, chemical, biophysical, or electromagnetic. Later in the book I describe simple techniques to resolve these problems.

The phenomenon of a Vivaxis is not confined to living creatures. A number of physical processes can create a Vivaxis and can cause a permanent two-way link between the object of the experiment and its Vivaxis. Examples of nonhuman Vivaxes are those associated with magnets and lightning strikes. The characteristics of each Vivaxis will be the existence of both a horizontal and vertical wave at the site of the Vivaxis. In each case, the Vivaxis is the sphere of energies at the original site of its manifestation—the connecting link occurs when the physical person or object moves to another area.

Case History of a Person Needing a New Vivaxis

Many years ago, a close relative of mine had a nervous and mental breakdown at age fifty-eight. Although Albert had no actual organic diseases, he chose to stay in bed for nine months, only rising to use the bathroom and to eat. At his own request, he underwent many types of healing, including natural therapies and magnetic, color, and spiritual healing. I perceived that his energy field was a seething mass of chaotic energies and suggested that a new Vivaxis be made. Albert had suffered a severe electric shock at age nineteen during his apprenticeship as an electrical engineer. So, he may have had a foreign Vivaxis feeding into his energy field for almost forty years before his nervous breakdown. We chose the quiet garden of a friend whose property had sufficient slope to mark the energy bands.

This new Vivaxis was established, but my relative did not feel particularly enthusiastic, probably because he had believed for nine months that he would soon die. However, within a few days his outlook improved and within a few weeks he completely regained his health and interest in life. He returned to a busy consulting practice and maintained his health and consulting practice for another nineteen years until a year before his death at the age of seventy-six.

This story shows how crucial it is to have a clear connection to our Vivaxis. This man had no identifiable organic disease, and yet he developed profoundly disturbing symptoms as a result of the chaotic energies from foreign sources affecting his own energy field and Vivaxis energies.

Creating an Artificial Vivaxis

The following examples illustrate how easily a Vivaxis is formed. Artificial Vivaxes are just as permanent as those connected with a human being. This phenomenon suggests that although Vivaxis energies in the human can be influenced by thought and emotion, the phenomenon is also related to the laws of physics.

For instance, when a bar of steel is magnetized by stroking it with a magnet, a Vivaxis will be formed at the site of stroking. In this case, the new magnet (the steel bar) has two Vivaxes—one at its place of magnetizing and the other connected to the Vivaxis of the first magnet at its original site. This is because the energies introduced to the bar of steel are influenced by the energies from the Vivaxis of the original magnet.

Another example relates to the vegetable kingdom. Seeds in a sprouting tray will have a fixed vector, or direction, to their place of sprouting after a few days of watering. They generally retain this Vivaxis after having been transplanted to another place. This is a simple experiment that anyone can do after learning to test for the horizontal and vertical waves associated with a Vivaxis. (See exercise 11.)

We can also create a Vivaxis by drawing two lines. I have found this to be a simple yet revealing way to illustrate the basic phenomenon of a Vivaxis. A Vivaxis is formed when we take a piece of paper and draw two lines about one inch long from opposite ends of the paper in quick succession toward a common center point. After a few seconds, this two-inch line will have a Vivaxis from its center-point with both a horizontal and vertical wave that can be demonstrated by the tester.

A Vivaxis is also created when magnetizing a steel bar by placing it in a coiled wire carrying a direct electric current (DC). The diameter of the Vivaxis is determined by the length of the steel bar. During the life of the magnet, there is a flow of energy waves containing both a horizontal and vertical direction between the magnet and its position of origin—its Vivaxis. No matter how far away the magnet is placed from this point, we can find a horizontal and vertical wave.[7]

A large Vivaxis is always created by a lightning strike. This creates a very strong and permanent Vivaxis, and the radius of the Vivaxis is proportional to the length of the tree trunk or pole. The constant electrical potential of four hundred volts per square meter is a measure of the

---

[7] Nixon, *Born to Be Magnetic*, vol. 2 (British Columbia, Canada: Magnetic Publishers, 1973), p. 91.

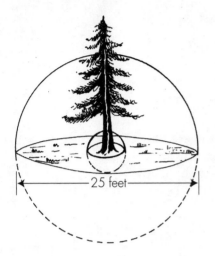

25 feet

Figure 5. A Vivaxis cre-
ated by a lightning
strike. The width of the
Vivaxis created by the
lightning strike is twenty-
five feet.

Adapted from *Born to Be
Magnetic* by Frances Nixon,
vol. 2, 1973

electrical tension between the surface of
the Earth and the ionosphere. So we are
always bathed in Earth's electromagnetic
field, and periodically there is a discharge.

A buildup of positive ions in the
atmosphere following hot weather and
winds causes static and an imbalanced
condition of ion flow. (Ions are charged
particles.) This situation is balanced out in
a thunderstorm when millions of electrical volts are discharged in certain locations. Vertical structures such as steel
towers and even trees attract such a discharge, which is why we are advised to keep indoors during a storm. During an electrical storm, negative ions are
produced and the balance between negative and positive
ions in the atmosphere and Earth's surface is restored.

At the site of a lightning strike, Fran discovered a permanent Vivaxis of enormous proportions (see figure 5) and
she undertook an intriguing experiment. While staying
with her in Canada, I witnessed and took part in a
repetition of this experiment. It involved the transfer of a
lightning Vivaxis to another site through space, using the
Vivaxis connection. Fran undertook this experiment to
indicate how the energy from a large Vivaxis can be trans-
ferred. The following steps were undertaken.

A calcium tablet was placed in a paper cup over neutral ground. Several perforations were made in the bottom
of the cup for drainage purposes. A pinch of ascorbic acid
was dissolved in half a cup of fresh seawater and then
poured over the calcium tablet. (Fran found that the acid
contributed to the formation of the Vivaxis.) The solution
drained through the perforations, and the tablet was
allowed to dry. We were then able to record a small
Vivaxis of about six inches in diameter. The Vivaxis registered as a chaotic circulating motion in the recording arm
of the person (the arm that was doing the testing or

dowsing) who was testing the space around the tablet. A vertical wave was also recorded.

The calcium tablet was then transported to the site of the lightning strike four miles away, whereupon we recorded that the energy at the site of the original Vivaxis had expanded to about twenty-five feet in diameter. This phenomenon occurred because the lightning Vivaxis was transported to the Vivaxis site of the calcium tablet via the wave links of the calcium tablet to the site of its own Vivaxis. Our energy fields felt disturbed and chaotic after a short time of standing near this enlarged Vivaxis. We were affected by blurred vision and were unable to record normal ion flow on our bodies after only sixty seconds of contact with this field.

The calcium tablet was then returned to its base site. Fran found that it was now wave-linked to *two* Vivaxes, with a dividing line down its center marking the connection to each Vivaxis. We then understood how disturbing it is to become linked to a foreign Vivaxis, especially a powerful one. Foreign means any Vivaxis apart from that of the subject. The tablet was then destroyed along with its disrupting Vivaxis.

Fran asked two clairvoyants to observe the two-way Vivaxis energy flow from the tablet to the site of the tree. They both drew pictures of the effects and did not compare notes until finishing their observations. They both described two streams of energy ten inches wide and separated by several inches. The center of each flow moved in rapid spiraling motions and radiated sparkling colors of vivid hues. They also described the huge energy field around the tree. Fran concluded from her researches that Vivaxis waves are responsible for transporting the energy of one Vivaxis to another.[8] This extraordinary experiment

---

[8] Nixon, *Search for Vivaxis*, Part 2 (British Columbia, Canada: Magnetic Publishers, 1979), p. 14.

indicates to some extent the relationship between the electromagnetic phenomenon of our planet and Vivaxis energies.

The lightning strike is just one example of geophysical electromagnetism that can be demonstrated to affect our own energies via Vivaxis connections.

The center point, or most important exercise, derived from all of Fran's research involves the benefit from regular alignment to our Vivaxis. The purpose for this alignment is twofold—to remove harmful foreign energies from our energy field and to absorb health-giving energies.

From these examples, it can be seen that both human and nonhuman Vivaxes are permanent spheres of energy of varying sizes, according to the size of the entity concerned. There will be a permanent two-way link to the subject concerned that is not dependent on the distance from the original location. As mentioned earlier, the energies travel vertically until they reach the altitude of the subject and then horizontally until they reach the left foot of the subject. Once you have developed the ability to test horizontal and vertical waves, it is simple to evaluate these forces associated with a Vivaxis.

Aligning to Our Vivaxis

The center point, or most important exercise, derived from all of Fran's research involves the benefit from regular alignment to our Vivaxis. The purpose for this alignment is twofold—to *remove* harmful foreign energies from our energy field and to *absorb* health-giving energies. In particular, Fran found these latter energies contain the frequencies for the minerals that form the basic building blocks of our cells and tissues. Such alignment appears to have the capacity to enhance the absorption of minerals and vitamins in our diet. Frequencies will be explained in detail in the next chapter, but

basically I am referring here to the wavelength, or resonance, of each element in our bodies.

The many sources of pollution created since the
industrial age appear to have impaired the mechanisms by
which humans absorb life-giving frequencies. Of special
note is electrical pollution from power lines, computer
screens, cellular phone towers, and many forms of medical diagnostic equipment. The full effect and eradication
of these factors will be described later in the book.

Fran described the alignment to our Vivaxis as like
tuning into *our own* radio station. If we do not align (or
channel) in exactly the correct degree, we do not receive
the right station.[9] (The methods for finding our Vivaxis
direction are detailed in part 2.) Over the years, Fran
changed her instructions for the aligning, or channeling,
procedure. Initially, she instructed students to simply
walk toward and away from the direction of their Vivaxis.
Later, she developed the system of aligning to four directions—toward the Vivaxis; clockwise at right angles to the
Vivaxis; facing the opposite direction to the Vivaxis;
clockwise another ninety degrees; then backward through
the four directions. The head was kept very level during
the procedure, which she called the "four and four"
method of aligning. Fran noted that, depending on
whether the person is situated above or below the elevation of their Vivaxis, the soft body tissues above the waist
absorbs Vivaxis energies when we move in one direction
and the tissues below the waist absorbs Vivaxis energies
when we turn the other way.

After this aligning procedure, students were advised
to bring in other health-giving energies associated with
the Vivaxis by thinking of the Sun and Moon. Fran found
that this rearranged all the Vivaxis energies of the student
so that instead of remaining in a fixed wave to their

---

[9] Nixon *Born to Be Magnetic*, vol. 2, p. 28.

Vivaxis for twenty minutes, the energies rayed out from the person like the spokes of a wheel.[10] You can test this fact that our energies are all in the direction of our Vivaxis for twenty minutes. (See exercise 11.)

One of the problems encountered with the aligning procedure when conducted in company is that anyone within two hundred feet may have their energies temporarily drained for about twenty minutes by the person aligning. This results from the strong alignment of the aligning person to their own Vivaxis, during which period energies in the environment continue to be appropriated. To cut short this effect on others, the aligner can conduct the short form of the neutralizing exercise outlined in exercise 2. They can then move among other persons without draining their energies. This finding underscores the power of recharging ourselves from our Vivaxis. It is not known as yet why this phenomena takes place for about twenty minutes, but perhaps it is related to the energy cycle in our meridian system.

Fran also discovered that anyone watching someone aligning takes in that person's energies through their eyes. It is therefore inadvisable to watch another person during this procedure, even from a considerable distance.

The potency of aligning to our Vivaxis is demonstrated by the fact that before the procedure, an angle wire will turn in the compass direction of our thought, provided that we are clear of any static. For twenty minutes after aligning, the angle wire stays fixed in the direction of our Vivaxis, and no thought can deflect it.[11] Thus, if we think of a direction, say east or west, and our Vivaxis is northeast, the angle wire will not move away from our Vivaxis. Normally, it would move in the direction of our thought. The immune system also appears to be stimulated

---

[10] Frances Nixon, *Vivaxis Manual*, *Part 4* (British Columbia, Canada: Magnetic Publishers, 1975), p. 49.
[11] Nixon, *Born to Be Magnetic*, vol. 2, p. 32.

for twenty minutes as demonstrated by testing our lymph glands via the recording finger (the finger principally used for testing our body energies).

By the time Fran came to Australia, her technique for aligning to the Vivaxis had changed again. After marking the ground in the four directions, the student now turned in the four directions. In each direction, the head was tilted slowly from pointing downward to the chest to full extension of the neck backward. Fran found that this brought in more frequencies, including what she called the universal forces of magenta and gold, which are described below. After the fourth direction, the student completed the exercise a fifth time by facing again toward the Vivaxis. Unlike the earlier instruction, the student did not reverse directions. In the Northern Hemisphere, the direction for turning is clockwise and in the Southern Hemisphere, counterclockwise. With this form of aligning toward the Vivaxis, students no longer think of the Sun and Moon forces, because these frequencies come in during head tilting and then they radiate out from the energy field in all directions.

I found it interesting that on some days when I tilted my head at a particular angle with my eyes shut, a brilliant field of magenta would suddenly appear. This was followed after a few seconds by a field of gold. These are the colors Fran found to be associated with the energies that she named universal forces. At first, I thought this was something to do with looking at the Sun through closed eyelids, but it continued to happen even on cloudy days. Depending on environmental conditions, I found these forces are more active on some days than others. This experience occurred long before I read about Fran's discovery of the universal forces.

The way she discovered these universal forces in 1976 will give the reader a clue to her considerable intuition.[12]

---

[12] Frances Nixon, *Vivaxis Manual, Part 5* (British Columbia, Canada: Magnetic Publishers, 1976), chap. 3.

She was reviewing her findings about the Sun and Moon's lines of force and the fact that we only receive these forces when our heads are tilted at a particular angle during the aligning procedure. Suddenly, she had an intuitive flash of another major force that could be received via our Vivaxis channel if we tilted our heads at yet another angle. She found the particular angle for these forces to be at about twenty degrees from the horizontal and called them universal forces because they were found to be common to the Vivaxis of all persons. Other Vivaxis forces were discovered to be individual for each person.

Fran postulated that the universal forces are related to the North and South Poles. She knew that the South Pole ice was composed of fresh water and that the North Pole water was composed of salt water. She froze a clear plastic container of seawater and one of fresh water and placed them in a line of magnetic north and south with the seawater in the direction of north. They were placed about fourteen inches apart directly on the ground. She found a stream of energy traveling up vertically from between the two containers.

Fran knew that seawater contained metallic gold, and holding a piece of metallic gold cloth in her hand, she found that the recording wire in her other hand was drawn toward the container of seawater placed in the direction of magnetic north. Thus she concluded that the gold is related to the ice at the North Pole. In contrast, a piece of magenta cloth attracted the wire toward the fresh-water ice she had placed at magnetic south. She had previously found that the color magenta was attracted to iron, because when thinking about iron, her recording wire always swung toward magnetic South Pole. In summary, she found that waves from the magenta cloth have a horizontal direction to the South Pole, whereas the gold forces have a horizontal vector to magnetic north.

As a result of this experiment, Fran devised a cloth she called Rose Aura, which had gold threads and magenta color.

For several years, her students placed pieces of this material on points of the body where the energy was disturbed. This was particularly helpful if a person was unable to locate their Vivaxis and draw in the universal forces via their Vivaxis. In other words, the gold and magenta material transmitted the universal forces to parts of the body where disturbed energies were producing discomfort or disease.

Later, when Fran discovered the vertical Vivaxis Force Flows, Rose Aura material was found to be very disturbing if a person was inadvertently standing on a vertical flow of energy. This disturbance was caused by the conflict of energies between the vertical Vivaxis flows and the Rose Aura material. The use of such material therefore was abandoned. This change of emphasis was typical of the evolving nature of Vivaxis work.

Our Individual Vivaxis Colors

As mentioned, Fran found that apart from the universal forces common to all Vivaxes, we have our own individual frequencies, which correspond to the vertical and horizontal flows in our aura and Vivaxis. Before she discovered the mineral correspondences to these frequencies, they were identified in terms of color. Students experimented by shutting their eyes, holding different colored materials, and counting back from fifty as a means to stimulate the brain receptors. These receptors would then receive the information of the prenatal Vivaxis with its individual frequencies at a time before any interference from the environment could distort the frequencies.[13]

When we select the correct two colors of the Vivaxis by trial and error, the other hand or recording wire swings toward the direction of our Vivaxis. One color corresponds to the horizontal wave to our Vivaxis and the

---

[13] *Ibid.*, Chap. 5.

other to the vertical wave. This means that each color is associated with only one hand, and there is no response if this same color is held in the other hand. This finding relates to the fact that the vertical Vivaxis energies flow up the left leg and the horizontal energies out the right hand. Thus we find after testing with many colors that only one color, when held in the left hand, will allow the right hand to swing toward the Vivaxis, and only one color, held in the right hand, will allow the left hand to swing toward the Vivaxis.

Students were advised not to expose themselves excessively to their own color frequencies, but if they experienced energy depletion, they were instructed to absorb their particular colors through the eyes by looking at the selected color for a minute or so. In addition, Fran suggested wearing clothing containing small amounts of the two colors. Later, as you will read, Fran discovered the exact minerals in each Vivaxis that correspond to the color frequencies. Therefore, the use of colored material was forgone.

At this stage of the research in the late 1970s, Fran was teaching students to work with four forces—Vivaxis forces represented by the individual colors, forces from the Sun and Moon, and the universal forces of gold and magenta. All these energies were received through the aligning process, and this process became the central exercise used to restore health.

Electromagnetic Interference to Our Vivaxis

Fran discovered that for accurate testing and good health we should have clear circuits to receive these health-giving energies. Many human-made problems can cause static and energy blocks to these circuits. These factors include X-rays, diathermy, laser treatment, and any machines that form an electrical circuit with the client. Because our energy field has both magnetic and electrical (gravitational) components, external electromagnetic fields can influence the sensitive human field. The electromagnetic aspect of our energy field was demonstrated by Harold Saxton Burr in his work on the "L-fields" from 1938 to 1970, and further elaborated by Robert Becker in the 1970s and 1980s in his work with bone regeneration. Becker found that information for growth and regrowth of bones is transmitted by electromagnetic fields that are actually outside of the nervous system.

In his book, *The Body Electric*, Becker states: "Evidence seems to be quite conclusive that there are steady DC electrical currents flowing outside the neurons proper throughout the body. These are non-ionic in nature and similar to semi-conducting type currents. Perineural cells appear to be the most likely site at which the currents are generated and transmitted." (Perineural means around the main neurons.) Becker further states that this phenomenon constitutes a system of transmission of very basic-type data.[14]

The following case history illustrates the effect of electromagnetic fields from high tension wires on a human Vivaxis and its connections. It concerns a man I helped to make a new Vivaxis.

The Effects of High Tension Wires on a Vivaxis Site

We need to consider the site for a new Vivaxis very carefully, because different weather conditions effect the energies at the site. This fact was forcibly brought home to me after I helped a man with health problems make a new Vivaxis. I selected a site, but my client wanted another place. The site he chose in Melbourne was about three thousand feet from high-tension overhead electrical cables.

---

[14] Robert O. Becker, and Seldon, Gary, *The Body Electric: Electromagnetism and the Foundation of Life.* (New York: William Morrow and Company, 1985).

However, to be sure he would not be affected by the electrical fields, and despite the considerable distance allowed between the power lines and this site, I preferred a site even further away. At the time, my client's site choice seemed clear of electrical disturbance, so after I tested the ion flow and found it to be normal, we went on with the procedure. The weather at the time was very misty, with lots of water vapor in the air.

A few weeks later, the man rang me in great agitation. He felt disturbed and thought the disturbance seemed to be coming from his new Vivaxis. I immediately went out and found the site I had marked. The weather on this day was very clear. To my horror, I found that the Vivaxis site was now affected by the electromagnetic field coming from the power lines. I realized that the misty weather at the time of the procedure had broken down the electromagnetic field closer to the power lines and that in clear weather the field extended much further.

We arranged to destroy this Vivaxis at a particular time. The man was advised to find another suitable location in Sydney on which to stand as I destroyed his Vivaxis in the city of Melbourne by passing the inactivator material over the site. The moment we cancel out our Vivaxis, a new one will automatically form and connect with the nearest energy layer to the person concerned. As the Melbourne area was topographically higher than his location, I was able to test that the Vivaxis had been destroyed by confirming that the vertical wave had disappeared. This meant that his new Vivaxis had formed. I spoke to this man in 1999 and learned he has kept good health and is continuing to work with Vivaxis energies to some extent.

This experience taught me two things. First, check a proposed site more than once and preferably in different weather conditions days before making a new Vivaxis. Second, do not allow another person to override your intuition about how the exercise should be conducted.

The Forces of the Vivaxis

You need to be aware that the use of the terms "gravitational" and "magnetic" in this book do not always correspond with the usual scientific understanding. When Fran talks about gravitational, she sometimes uses the term electric as an alternative, although gravitational obviously also relates to the movement of the tides.

Fran considered that both magnetic and electric (gravitational) forces are among the primary forces in the Vivaxis. As an extension to her finding that the universal forces connected with magnetic north and south, she considered that a vertical component of magnetism is responsible for our relation to the geographical point of our Vivaxis. A further consideration of the Sun and Moon forces resulted in her suggestion that the horizontal wave of the Vivaxis involves the gravitational forces that move the tides.

She put the two components together by suggesting that the daily and monthly tides involve forces that are related to magnetic north and south. When Fran used the terms horizontal and vertical, she presumably meant the direction of the field, and therefore she was saying that the direction of the universal forces are at right angles to those forces she termed "gravitational." Our own energy field, you might remember, also has a horizontal and vertical component in terms of our Vivaxis energies.

Thus I postulate the following model to relate our Vivaxis and electromagnetic field to that of the Earth. Our vertical and magnetic Vivaxis energies received via the left leg relate to the magnetic north and south poles of the planet. Our gravitational/electric, or horizontal, energies that leave the body to travel horizontally back to our Vivaxis relate to the gravitational forces of the Sun and Moon pulling on our planet. The horizontal or gravitational pull will be stronger in the equatorial parts of the planet; in other words, those forces are roughly at right angles to the planetary poles.

Our personal Vivaxis can be described as a recording device for all energy changes taking place in our physical bodies and emotions. It is involved with energy exchange and is a reservoir and receiving station for energies pulsating from the elements deep within the Earth plus biospheric influences from above the Earth.

After Fran established the existence of the Vivaxis and its main directions to and from our bodies, she began to research the various components or elements of the Vivaxis energies. The science of Vivaxis is all about these elements and life-giving frequencies. So, before we go any further with examining Fran's discoveries, we need to look at the meaning of frequencies or energy waves. For instance, as her research developed, the study of mineral frequencies became increasingly prominent. The next chapter explores the concept of frequencies and their use in various areas of natural medicine.

Suggested Reading

Nixon, Frances. *Born to be Magnetic*, Vols 1 and 2. British Columbia, Canada: Magnetic Publishers, 1973.

Nixon, Frances. *Search For Vivaxis, Parts 1 and 2*. British Columbia, Canada: Magnetic Publishers, 1982.

CHAPTER 2

Vibrational Medicine and Frequency

Natural medicine could just as easily be called vibrational medicine, vibration being another name for frequency. Examples of vibrational medicine are homeopathy, flower essences, acupuncture, and color therapy. Fran Nixon discovered the importance of having healthy receptors for the frequencies of all the minerals and trace elements we need for health. If these body receptors or acupuncture points are disturbed, we are unable to take in or absorb the needed frequencies. This discovery therefore may be very basic to acupuncture and to the successful use of herbs, vitamins, and minerals.

In thinking about frequency (see figure 6), it is useful to observe how it has already been applied in natural medicine. Generally, we consider the electromagnetic spectrum as composed of many frequencies of light from infrared to ultraviolet. Our physical senses are only aware of small sections in the electromagnetic range. Conventional

Each of the minerals and vitamins also have their individual wavelength or frequency. Fran's research concerned the mapping and restoring of the body receptors that receive these energies from the Earth via our Vivaxis. Her work is fundamental for the understanding of many natural therapies.

The Electromagnetic Spectrum

					Non-Ionizing Radiation	Ionizing Radiation
Hz = Hertz = cycles per second						
Frequencies (Hz) 30 to 300 Hz	3×10^5 → 3×10^7	3×10^7 → 3×10^{11}	3×10^{11} → 4×10^{14}		7×10^{14} → 3×10^{16}	3×10^{16} and greater
Wavelenths of more than 1KM Extremely Low Frequency (ELF) Household Power 50 Hz—UK 60 Hz—USA Seismic Frequencies	Radio Frequencies	Microwave Radar Microwave Ovens T.V. Transmitters Underground Water Streams	Infrared Rays	Visible Light	U.V. Rays	X-Rays, Gamma Rays Cosmic Rays

Figure 6. The electromagnetic spectrum. Frequency means cycles or waves per second. High frequencies have a short wavelength and low frequencies a long wavelength. This chart indicates that frequencies move from very low on the left hand side to very high in the area of X-rays. It used to be thought that only ionizing radiation was dangerous to human and animal tissue. Controversy now exists as to whether even extremely low frequencies may adversely affect our immune system. Note how small the visible band of the electromagnetic spectrum is.

medicine uses certain sections such as ultraviolet for treating certain skin diseases; X-rays, CT scans, and nuclear magnetic resonance for diagnosis; laser therapy or coherent light for cutting; and diathermy for sealing.

In this chapter, we will explore some of frequencies that have been used in the area of color and sound; we will also see how frequencies are used in homeopathy. Each of the minerals and vitamins also have their individual wavelength or frequency. Fran's research concerned the mapping and restoring of the body receptors that receive these energies from the Earth via our Vivaxis. Her work is fundamental for the understanding of many natural therapies, for if the receptors/acupuncture points are disturbed, we cannot receive the frequencies necessary for healthy life.

Energy generally manifests in waves. Frequency means the number of waves per second counted from the peak of one to the next. The electromagnetic spectrum in our universe is made up of waves of a wide range of frequency and amplitude (height of the wave). They range from the extra-low frequencies (ELF), as for example from power lines, to X-rays and microwaves that have very high frequencies. Our bodies prefer even lower or slower waves, those in the alpha range of about 8-12 cycles or hertz (Hz) per second. This is the same frequency found on the planet in its healthy state, and these background planetary waves are called Schumann waves.

An energy field consists of many waves vibrating at a particular frequency. For instance, you may know that there is an electromagnetic field around a wire carrying electricity. In the United States and Canada, this field has a rate of 60 Hz, and in Australia and Europe it's 50 Hz. This means there is a wave frequency of 50 or 60 cycles per second, an example of a low-frequency field (ELF).

Examples of frequencies are as follows. If we strike the note C on the piano, the associated piano string will vibrate at 256 waves, or cycles, per second. We hear things in a range of 16 to 25,000 Hz, while some animals can hear much higher frequencies. Our visual range of frequencies is different again. Ultrasound, radio frequencies, X-rays, and infrared are all commonly used terms that relate to different frequencies in the electromagnetic spectrum. Our most commonly used frequency is the electromagnetic field of all our household gadgets, which is 50 or 60 cycles per second. This is an important point to remember for our later discussion on the possible damage inflicted on our energy fields by these environmental and household electromagnetic fields.

Human Psychic Frequencies

Everything on our planet is vibrating at particular frequencies, including our organs and tissues. We must also consider the frequencies of our emotions and thoughts. Our inner feelings and thoughts have a conditioning effect on our psychic energy, which in turn is constantly sending out subtle vibrations into the environment and thus affecting other humans, animals, and plants around us.

The range of frequencies of these psychic vibrations is obviously more subtle than the normal electromagnetic spectrum. Psychic fields cannot be measured with physical instruments; however, the effect of changing moods on our electromagnetic field has been observed through high-frequency photography. This type of photography is undertaken by placing a person in a high-frequency field that shows their electromagnetic field on a photographic plate. It is called Kirlian photography after the Russian medical technician who first noticed the effect in 1938.

The emotional aura surrounding a person in an aroused emotional state such as anger often features the color red in this type of photography. Research has established that it is the type of salt in a person's sweat that provides a particular color in the Kirlian photograph. The skin gives off electrons in the presence of the high-frequency field, and these collide with molecules in the air to form the lighted corona, or aura, around the subject in the photo.[15] Clairvoyants also often note that they see red in the aura of an angry person. So, although a Kirlian photograph is only recording our electromagnetic aura, it seems to reflect the more subtle, or astral/emotional, aura as seen by clairvoyants.

When we start to think in terms of frequency or of vibrating or oscillating fields, consider the following hypothetical example. A person with an energy field vibrating at 90,000 Hz will obviously be out of synchronicity with the field of an individual who may be vibrating at between 10,000 and 30,000 Hz. Of course, this is an oversimplification. Our emotional field will be vibrating at a number of different rates, as are all the different organs in our body. But there will be an overall effect that will vary according to whether we are feeling depression, anger, sadness, joy, or creativity.

---

[15] Thelma Moss, *The Body Electric* (Los Angeles: J. P. Tarcher, 1979).

The following practical example is a physical analogy that explains how we affect our environment. Imagine a room in which we place five grandfather clocks with their pendulums all swinging out of sequence. It has been found that, after a certain period of time, the process of entrainment takes place whereby all the pendulums will eventually swing together in simultaneous rhythm.

Translate this to the human kingdom and we have a good explanation for mob psychology. In fact, if we are in a group whose basic energy frequency does not match our own, it is possible our energy field may be overwhelmed (entrained) by the predominant frequency. This may be experienced as either pleasant or unpleasant, according to the prevailing frequency of the mob. When in the company of a person suffering from depression, we easily can absorb their negative mood to some extent. The struggle to maintain our own rhythm may be exhausting. Conversely, a joyful person may lift our spirits. Teachers are well aware of the effect on the class of one disruptive child who may in turn be reflecting turmoil and aggression from home. The various frequencies of our thoughts and emotions have yet to be tabulated.

Diagnosis of Body Frequencies

Practitioners of natural therapies and various schools of esoteric thought have established guidelines for the correct vibratory frequencies for every organ and tissue in the body. Some have gone further and established frequencies for the energy centers in our subtle bodies—the chakras. These are a series of seven major subtle energy centers aligned along the spine from crotch to crown; they are believed to be associated with the endocrine glands. The first group to establish particular rates was the radionic practitioners. The late David Tansley was a well-respected British radionics practitioner who placed this form of diagnosis and treatment into a broad framework that included both science and ancient wisdom.[16]

Instruments such as the spectrophotometer give an indication of elements according to their frequency in the electromagnetic range. More important, we can use our bodies for measuring subtle energies. To measure energy flows and vibratory frequencies, we use the same sense employed by people who practice dowsing, or water divining. This was how Fran started her adventures after learning to become a water diviner.

Although some practitioners using instruments claim they measure frequencies directly, modern electronic instruments can only take indirect measurements of the more subtle fields of the body. By this, I mean we can only infer from such measurements the state of, for instance, the etheric body. Thus, if a person goes to a natural therapist who uses a modern electronic instrument, the reading of the energy in a particular meridian can only be in electromagnetic parameters or frequencies. However, the therapist can infer a disturbance at a more subtle level as a result of the correspondence understood between the etheric body and the changes that can be recorded electromagnetically.

We are beings composed of many subtle and interacting fields. These fields all have their own frequencies. To summarize: there are many approaches and instruments to diagnose frequencies, some perhaps more accurate than others. In the science of Vivaxis as taught by Fran Nixon, we train our body to be the accurate instrument for recording, matching, and measuring frequencies.

Despite the subtle nature of Vivaxis measurements, we can devise and repeat experiments to check our findings with others and thus bring repeatability and cross-referencing into our research. We can even create

---

[16]David Tansley, *Dimensions of Radionics* (Devon, U.K.: Health Science Press, 1977).

experiments where neither the tester nor operator knows the nature of the materials being used—the famous double blind trials of medical science. In other words, we can work in a scientific manner, using our body as an instrument.

Careful discrimination and analysis will enable you to distinguish between etheric and astral, or psychic energies; this is most important because of the interpenetration of these fields. Many people working with subtle energies lose their credibility and reputation because they confuse the etheric body, the more subtle part of the physical body, with the astral body, or psychic energies. Their findings then become confused and conditioned by desires and wishes emanating from their astral nature, which can distort etheric impressions. Etheric energies belong to the more subtle part of the physical realm, while our astral, or psychic, nature is the realm of desire, wishes, and imagination. This is one reason science has found a connection between the observer and the observed in many experiments.

Electromagnetic energies interface between, or are found connecting, the etheric and physical levels of energy. These energies can be measured at the planetary and human level by the normal instruments of physics. We are bathed in the electromagnetic field of the Earth and at any point on the surface we move in a sea of energy existing between the surface of the Earth and the ionosphere, which has an electrical potential of 400 volts per square meter. This is an electrical term meaning the possible electric flow between the ionosphere and the Earth. This potential results from the difference in electrical potential between the surface of the Earth, which is charged negatively, and the lower surface of the ionosphere eighty kilometers above the Earth, which is charged positively.[17] We feel so comfortable in this field that vibrates about 7.5 cycles per second

---

[17] Itzak Bentov, *Stalking the Wild Pendulum* (London: Wildwood House, 1978), p. 39.

(the Schumann waves) that the early astronauts suffered until these waves were generated in their space capsules.

The Human Magnetic Sense

Medical researcher Robert Becker considers that electromagnetic energy has now been returned to a position of prominence for our understanding of both human and geophysical phenomena. Becker points out that the sophistication of modern instruments has revealed that living creatures are intimately related to the Earth's geomagnetic field and derive vital and basic information from it.[18] No statement could better underscore the basis for this book. The science of Vivaxis reveals the profound effect on the human electromagnetic field from human-made electromagnetic sources. On the positive side, the Vivaxis techniques can enhance our electromagnetic field.

Scientists have found that many living creatures with a sense of direction, including bees, pigeons, and fish, have a substance called magnetite imbedded in their heads. Research by the geosciences department at the University of California found that whales and dolphins have similar faculties for their survival and that whale stranding occurs at points of low magnetic field strength in their environment. It appears that whales travel along underwater magnetic troughs that run from north to south. Even small creatures like salamanders have separate magnetic navigational systems.

According to Becker, "The magnetite-containing magnetic organ that is probably present in most life forms, including humans, is closely connected to the brain. It has been shown unequivocally to be a sense organ that informs the organism of the direction of the Earth's mag-

---

[18] Becker, *Cross Currents: The Promise of Electromedicine, the Perils of Electropollution* (Los Angeles: J.P. Tarcher, 1991) chap. 3.

netic field." Becker goes on to say, "It is possible that it (the magnetic organ) is also sensitive to and reports information on the micropulsation frequencies although this aspect has not been studied."[19]

In the light of Fran Nixon's discoveries, Becker's statements are most interesting, for in part 2 of this book, I give exercises to find magnetic north by visualizing the frequency of sodium that relates to the magnetic north pole and by visualizing the frequency of iron that relates to magnetic south. Dr. Robin Baker at the University of Manchester in England has added to our understanding of the magnetic sense by locating a magnetic focus at the back of the nasal passage and just in front of the pituitary gland—the ethmoid sinus. Baker found that humans can sense magnetic north and that this sensing is disturbed for up to two hours after having a bar magnet placed across their forehead for fifteen minutes.[20]

In other words, the bar magnet disturbs the normal orientation of our magnetite crystals. This confirms Fran's experiments on disturbances caused by application of magnets to the body. The pineal gland has also been found to be sensitive to the changing pattern of the Earth's magnetic field and may well be involved in our magnetic sense. Further evidence for our inborn magnetic sense comes from a French scientist, Professor Yves Rocard. He was reported in the journal *Nature* as having found magnetically sensitive points on the body, including the brow ridges and some articulations of the spinal vertebrae. Rocard saw these as crucial receptors of information and energy in the dowsing process.[21]

It therefore appears that our sensing of external fields is mediated through two highly sophisticated internal

---

[19] *Ibid.*, p. 74.
[20] Robin R. Baker, "Human Magnetic Reception for Navigation," in *Electromagnetic Fields and Neuromagnetic Function*, ed. M. E. O'Connor and R. H. Levely (New York: A. R. Liss, 1988).
[21] *Ibid.*

organs. Both these organs—the magnetic organ containing minute crystals of magnetite and the brain's endocrine gland called the pineal, which passes its secretions directly into the blood—are connected to the nervous system. Our magnetic sense is the basis for our dowsing ability, but this ability is perhaps also related to the chakras, or energy centers (which will be discussed in chapter 7). It appears that our magnetic sense is the main factor in sensing the direction of our Vivaxis as well as in the accurate finding of the energy layers discovered by Fran.

As we are basically using our magnetic, or dowsing, sense in our Vivaxis techniques, I will briefly elaborate on dowsing. Most people use some apparatus to help them develop and amplify the dowsing sense. The simplest aid can be a pendulum or two metal rods bent to form a right angle as originally used by Fran in her early work. There are various kinds of dowsing rods made of both organic and metallic materials as well as a sophisticated apparatus that enhances the fine movements of our body to make the perceived vibration more obvious.

The dowser must hold the rods out in front, keeping the horizontal arm of the rod quite parallel to the ground. It is necessary to establish what each movement of the rod means. This will vary from person to person. The rods may swing in one direction for a "yes" response and in another for a "no" response. The dowser then proceeds to ask questions about the subject and to visualize the subject under consideration. Minute reactions in their nervous system in response to the questions are amplified by the pendulum or rods.

It is hard to imagine how this process works with map dowsing, but perhaps the more subtle psychic faculties involving the chakras operate for this purpose. In other words, instead of using their magnetic sense, the dowsers use their psychic senses, which are associated with their astral, rather than etheric, body. Some practitioners use the pendulum to ask questions of a more psychological nature, although as mentioned, once psychic, or astral energy is involved, the accuracy of the reading can be in doubt. The practitioner must have very stable emotions and an unbiased mind or the answer will be conditioned by their own psyche.

Diagnostic Aids for Measuring Frequencies

As there are so many therapists using instruments to measure body frequencies, it is useful to consider how these may work and how this form of diagnosis differs from using Vivaxis. Radionics has already been mentioned and can be described as follows:

Radionics is a system whereby therapists use their dowsing sense, or clairsentience (extrasensory touch), combined with the use of an electrical instrument, to diagnose and treat a patient, often at a distance from that patient. The patient usually sends a "witness," such as a spot of blood or piece of hair, and this is placed on the machine for the purpose of both diagnosis and treatment. The treatment consists of "broadcasting," or sending the remedy in the form of frequencies that will correct the disease pattern in the patient.

From early in the twentieth century, radionic practitioners developed elaborate instruments with dials and wires to measure frequencies. In the early days, these machines often had a rubber diaphragm, and practitioners would move their fingers across it while adjusting the dials to different frequencies as they diagnosed a person or specimen. When they struck the "rate" that corresponded with the vibration of the tissue or organ concerned, they would get a "stick," which meant their fingers would not move so easily over the powdered surface of the rubber. Amusing incidents are described in the literature about how some practitioners obtained the same results irrespective of whether the machine was plugged into the power source. This indicates that the process is basically related to the subjective ability of the practitioner.

The various normal rates or frequencies for healthy organs were established by trial and error over many years. Ruth Drown was a famous radionic practitioner who established a series of "rates" for organs and remedies, for example, 84115 for the elbow and 8491892 for the ankle. These numbers would be dialed into the radionic machine during diagnosis and treatment for elbow or knee problems. A remedy such as a homeopathic medicine or flower essence would be matched to the disease frequency to restore the organ concerned to normal. Refinements to these radionic instruments have been developed over the years, although in each case it is the subjective or subtle response of the practitioner that establishes the diagnosis. Since 1950, a number of electronic instruments for diagnosis have come on the market. One of the most popular in Europe, the United States, and Australia is the Vegatest, which is discussed in an earlier book of mine, *Frontiers of Natural Therapies*.[22]

Most of these diagnostic instruments, such as the Vegatest, measure skin resistance. Some measure minute electrical changes in acupuncture points. The practitioner places various ampoules into the circuitry to establish a number of factors, including chronicity of disease, the most disturbed organs, and the appropriate remedies. The instruments can be used in an open-ended manner for any number of inquiries. However, the assessment is in part dependent on the faculties of the practitioner, and the response of the needle appears to be partially conditioned through a psychokinetic effect from the practitioner. This means the practitioner can affect material objects with the force of their thoughts via their own

---

[22] Jacka, *Frontiers of Natural Therapies*.

electromagnetic field. An example would be bending metal spoons without ever touching them.

Recent diagnostic instruments, known as electrodermal screening devices, are claimed by their manufacturers to measure the frequencies of the patient via skin resistance without subjective input from the therapist. These models usually interface with a computer and give an elaborate printout of the deficient and harmful frequencies in the subject. It is possible that these various instruments can translate etheric energies into electromagnetic frequencies.

However, any measurement whereby the therapist uses electrodes by pressing them on acupuncture points of the client is obviously subject to conditioning by the pressure used by the therapist, and this degree of pressure is perhaps a response from their thoughts. Twentieth-century physics demonstrated that in scientific experiments the results will tend to be influenced to some extent by the researcher. In addition, any device whereby an electrical circuit is made between patient, client, and machine may, according to Vivaxis principles, cause a foreign Vivaxis to be attached to the patient and practitioner.

A clear example of the influence of human beings on empirical data is the anomaly in modern physics that the mass of a particle cannot be measured at the same time as its position or momentum. It is said that as soon as we focus on the particle its wave function collapses.[23] It is almost as if the moment we have the intention to measure or focus on the object, it changes. So we are either measuring it as a wave of energy or as a particle with mass and position. For this reason, it is preferable for people to test their own energies, using their own etheric body as

---

[23] Ervin Laszlo, *The Creative Cosmos: A Unified Science of Matter, Life and Mind* (Edinburgh: Floris Books, 1993).

the instrument rather than an instrument such as the ones I've just described.

When we use our body to measure subtle energies, it is essential that we have serene emotions and a quiet and open mind to achieve accuracy. We need to be able to work in a detached manner and to use the mind as the "common sense." This enables us to overcome the usual situation where the mind is constantly conditioned by past events and by our emotional states. True common sense can develop if the mind is kept open and unconditioned, and thus it can make a valuable synthesis of information received through the senses of sight, hearing, touch, and so forth. In this way, the mind is used as a sense organ. Regular meditation is a great asset to this process.

Although the efforts of natural therapists to assess vibrational frequencies may have a subjective factor, the scientist L.V. De Broglie first established in 1925 that everything has its own specific frequency, or vibration.[24] An instrument called an oscilloscope gives a visual representation of the electrical frequency of elements. This is a consistent procedure and a different approach from the subjective procedure used by natural therapists employing electronic devices to establish frequencies using the dowsing sense. In time, perhaps, a correlation may be found between the two approaches.

Natural Therapies and Vibrational Medicine

In further explaining the role of frequencies in health and medicine, we could say that there are two basic streams of medicine that can work together in a complementary way. Conventional medicine has been

---

[24] John P. Briggs and F. David Peat, *Looking Glass Universe* (London: Fontana Books, 1985).

largely based on Newtonian physics and sees the body as a machine. When a (body) part wears out, it is often fixed or replaced. Specialists dealing with one set of parts do not necessarily have a great understanding or interest in other parts.

This approach pays scant attention to holism. The feelings and thoughts of the person are rarely taken into account in the treatment prescribed unless they become obstructive to the medical procedure. In cases of severe infection, antibiotics or steroids are administered to resolve the crisis. The underlying energies of the body are not acknowledged or addressed except at the cellular level in biochemical activity. Of course, I am generalizing and we all know of dedicated medical people who are very sensitive to the broader situation of their patients; nonetheless, this is the basic approach of conventional medical thinking.

Natural therapy is concerned in particular with enhancing and balancing the energies or vibrational frequencies of the body. It uses vitamins, minerals, herbs, homeopathy, flower essences, color, sound, acupuncture, body work based on the Chinese meridian system, and Earth energies to do this balancing. The significant factor in each therapy is the effect it has on our body energies or energy field. Holism is inherent in the philosophy of natural medicine, because each part of the body is understood to be intimately connected with all other parts through the energy field of the body. In each therapy, natural remedies restore the health, rhythm, vibration, and harmony to some body part that has lost its ease and that has therefore become diseased.

Natural medicine is preventive because it strengthens our natural immunity by enhancing and balancing our basic energies. Skilled natural therapists can observe detrimental changes in body energies before clinical pathology manifests. This was proven by Harold Saxton Burr as early as 1938 with his experiments on the human energy, or Life field (L-field), as he called it. Burr was involved with an experiment whereby the L-fields of 1,000 women were checked. Of the 102 women who showed disturbed energies, 96 were later found to have abnormal or malignant cells.[25]

Conventional medicine and natural therapies are not mutually exclusive. There will always be people who will not work with nature and who push their body to the stage at which emergency measures are needed if life is to be preserved, sometimes at the cost of a limb or organ. Yet natural therapies can help even in these situations to prepare the body for surgery and to aid in the recuperation from surgery or serious infection. Other medical situations such as cardiac conditions and severe infections benefit from a combination of both approaches. There is opportunity for teamwork and there are an increasing number of health centers where natural therapists have referrals from conventional medical doctors.

Perhaps another contrast between conventional medicine and natural therapies is that most natural therapies come from the Earth, although it is true that technology is now used to prepare herbs, flower essences, vitamins, and homeopathic remedies. Generally, manufacturers of these products use technology that does not destroy the life force of the remedy. Unlike pharmaceutical manufacturers, natural preparations contain all the active ingredients of a herb; this approach guards against any negative side effects. For example, traditional Chinese medicine is so Earth-related that it is intimately related to the seasons and cycles of planet Earth. It has five elements that occur in a continuous cycle: spring (wood) gives rise to summer (fire), followed by late summer (earth), and then fall or autumn (metal or air) moves to winter (water). Each ele-

---

[25] Harold Saxton Burr, *Blueprint for Immortality* (London: Neville Spearman, 1972).

ment relates to a main organ system: wood to liver and gallbladder; fire to heart and small intestine; earth to spleen and stomach; metal or air to lungs and colon; and water to kidney and bladder.

In every system of natural medicine, practitioners must deal with energy blocks that cause toxins to accumulate. Removing these blocks improves and balances energies. The more esoteric schools of thought understand that for disease to occur there will be an inner and an outer factor. The inner factor will be disturbed thoughts and emotions that may have old origins going back even to previous lives, or if one prefers the psychological approach of Jung, to the racial unconscious. The philosophies of esotericists such as Alice Bailey describe disease as taking place when there are both inner and outer causes present.[26]

It seems only a matter of time until a system is devised to establish the vibratory rates of all natural therapies that will then be matched to the diagnosed frequency of the disturbed body part. This has already been established to some extent in radionics and homeopathy, where each remedy is carefully matched to the particularities of the diseased state of the individual client. The disadvantage is that it takes many years for a person to accumulate sufficient knowledge to be a successful homeopath and, because of the detail involved in assessing each case, diagnosis can take a long time. Computer programs have alleviated much tedious work in homeopathic case-taking and may be useful in selecting the remedy. The problem of establishing the appropriate potency of the remedy remains. The medicine must be measured against the exact vibratory frequency of each person in the diseased state and the exact potency and dose of the medicine selected.

---

[26] Alice A. Bailey, *Esoteric Healing* (London: Lucis Press, 1953).

One person may require one drop of the homeopathic remedy diluted to three thousand parts in the solution while another person will require a dilution of three
million parts. You can consider these dilutions as representing different frequencies and harmonics of a remedy.
The system of dilution used by homeopathic chemists is
usually based on the decimal or centesimal system. In the
case of the centesimal system, one drop is mixed with one
hundred drops of water and shaken. A further drop of the
subsequent mixture is added and mixed with another
hundred drops of water, and this process is repeated for
as many times as necessary. After the twenty-fifth dilution,
no physical molecules will be left. This was established
mathematically by Amedeo Avogadro (1776-1856), and
hence science talks about Avogadro's number as a particular dilution of a chemical substance in which no physical molecule of the substance remains.

Consider the case of two people needing the snake
poison *Lachesis*. Both of them may have the same symptoms, yet, as their energy fields are understood to condition their physical health, these will oscillate or vibrate at
different frequencies. Over many years, the skilled homeopath learns to discern the sensitivity and susceptibility
of individuals to a remedy according to these differences
in energy.

The dilution of homeopathic remedies appears to
provide the harmonics or overtones to the frequency of
the original remedy in the same way that a note on a
musical instrument will have overtones. Having chosen
the correct remedy, the homeopath practitioner will shatter the disease process in the same way that a singer can
shatter a glass if they sing the exact note corresponding to
the resonance of the glass. In treatment, this process is
called the healing crisis, and it can be accompanied by a
shift and rebalancing of energy that may manifest as fever
and elimination of toxic matter from the normal channels of the body such as skin, bowels, kidneys, and lungs.

This process may take some weeks following the administration of the remedy.

Later, I discuss how the different homeopathic remedies in their low and high potencies are related to the energy layers in the Earth.

The Application of Sound as Healing Frequencies

It appears that the application and use of sound as therapy may also be a very specific way of applying the necessary vibration. This very subtle approach to vibrational therapy brings us closer to our main theme in this book. Sound frequencies, like Vivaxis energies and high potency homeopathic remedies, have no physical form.

In 1992 I visited the clinic of Dr. Peter Guy Manners, who practices in Bretforten, a beautiful little village in the Cotswold country of England. Manners has developed a system of therapy called Cymatics, which is based on the work of Hans Jenny, a Swiss scientist who studied the effect of sound waves and frequencies on inorganic matter. Cymatics comes from the Greek word *kyma*, which means "wave." Hans Jenny found that his experimental substances, under the influence of different frequencies, took on well-known shapes such as sea creatures, human organs, and plant life.[27] It appears that sound has a formative effect and that all life forms on our planet may be precipitated by sound.

Manners set about applying this concept to healing the body. He explained that, with the assistance of acoustic engineers, he "wired up" volunteer medical students to establish the vibratory frequency of all the body organs and tissues in their healthy state. These sounds were then put on tape and played through a special

---

[27] Jonathan Goldman, *Healing Sounds* (Rockport, Mass.: Element Books, 1992).

vibrator that was moved over the skin of the patient. The affected body part was treated for about ten minutes to restore the correct frequency. Manners computerized the system so that the tapes are no longer needed and a modern electronic treatment unit is used. The sound continues to be applied to the body via the vibrator and has a healing effect on the disturbed part.

Further evidence for the healing effect of sound has emerged. At the end of 1994, I attended a seminar called Signature Sound conducted by an American, Sharry Edwards. She told us how she began hearing sounds she could not identify and concluded that she must have tinnitus. Tinnitus is an aggravating condition of the ear that causes hissing or other irritating sounds. On examination, an audiologist found Edwards had a range of hearing beyond any he had encountered. She actually heard sounds that are transmitted by our ears. Edwards's later research demonstrated that each person transmits the frequency *from their ears* that is needed for their own healing. The transmission of the frequency, or note, by the ears is an effort by the body to heal itself.

Sharry Edwards found that the note (or frequency) a particular person needs is usually missing from their voice and that, by receiving this vibration as treatment, their voice eventually produces the healing sound again. The reverse of this finding was established decades ago by the now-famous French physician Alfred Tomatis, who found that the voice could only produce what the ear hears. He found that many people cut out particular sounds from their environment even before birth to avoid psychological pain caused by negative relationships with those close to them.

Tomatis found that usually the missing sounds in the voice were the high-frequency sounds and that these can be restored. He made recordings using an electronic ear to filter out the low frequencies of music that he chose from among classical composers such as Mozart. The filtered music was then applied as therapy through earphones.[28] In time the client is able to "hear" these sounds missed by their ears without the assistance of the tapes.

Through hearing and computerizing sounds, Sharry Edwards has correlated particular notes or frequencies with all the organs and tissues in the body; with all the known elements in nature; and with both pharmaceutical products and natural remedies. With her coworkers, a system of diagnosis has been developed that includes electronic hardware and a software program to chart the voice and to work out the note most relevant for healing. This frequency is then applied by a specially designed unit that is used daily for as long as needed to correct the condition. Edwards described some examples of profound healing, including that of her son following a serious accident.

A practical problem of this therapy is the expense and the time needed by both client and therapist. The client must visit daily for some time and the expensive treatment unit can only be used for a few clients per day. This reminded me of the beauty of the frequency treatment using Vivaxis energies, which is free and requires no expensive equipment.

I was interested that Edwards has worked on the psychological correlates of the needed frequency and that this frequency relates in 80 percent of cases to the birth date and its astrological implications. Other researchers have correlated the Western musical scale to the signs of the zodiac. These people include Ptolemy, Kepler, Heindel, and more recently, Jocelyn Godwin. The most popular arrangement is for the note C to be correlated with Aries; C sharp with Taurus; D with Gemini; and so on through the musical scale and the twelve signs of the zodiac.[29]

---

[28] Alfred Tomatis, *The Conscious Ear* (New York: Station Hill Press, 1991).
[29] Ted Andrews, *Sacred Sounds* (St. Paul, Minn.: Llewellyn Publications, 1992).

These discoveries about sound lead us back to the ancient teachings by Pythagoras that everything in our solar system relates to the musical scale or basic frequencies and that these correspond to the ratios between the planets and their furthest distance from the Sun. We begin to see how subtle energies from our planet like the Vivaxis energies may reflect this "cosmic music" and be used to heal our bodies or to form nature. The Vivaxis flows are vibrations that can be considered as sound or color vibrations/frequencies. Our personal Vivaxis contains those frequencies that can heal if we can learn to align with its energies.

We have looked at the meaning of vibration and frequency with examples of how frequencies can be applied as energy medicine in a variety of treatments. In summary, the aim of all natural medicine is to restore the right vibration and frequency to our bodies and the environment, so that we are in harmony with planet Earth. There are as yet no instruments available that objectively match the correct natural therapy with the exact body frequency needed. The most precise naturally available instrument we can use is our own body, as Fran Nixon discovered.

Fran taught us how to check energy flows through our bodies and how to find energy blocks without the use of any expensive instrumentation and without even a pendulum. She called this approach to diagnosis Testing the Ion Flow. Ion flow is connected with the electromagnetic field of the body and appears to be intimately related to our more subtle etheric body and to the state of our health.

Our Bodies as Instruments for Testing Frequencies

At the Australian seminar in 1980, Fran taught us how to check energy flows through our bodies and how to find energy blocks without the use of any expensive instrumentation and without even a pendulum. She called this approach to diagnosis Testing the Ion Flow.[30] As some readers will know, an ion is the term used for a charged particle. We have positive and negative ions in the atmosphere and in our bodies, and scientists have found that ions are discharged continually from the skin.

An ion is an atom or group of atoms possessing an electric charge. An excess of electrons gives a negative charge, and conversely, a loss of electrons gives a positive charge. In terms of our planetary life, ion flow is associated with magnetic north and south. In times of extreme weather conditions or during earthquakes, the ion flow of the planetary area involving the disturbance is affected. In the Northern Hemisphere, hot winds from the south have been found to make people irritable because they produce an excess of positive ions. In the Southern Hemisphere, the hot north winds have the same effect.

Ion flow is connected with the electromagnetic field of the body and appears to be intimately related to our more subtle etheric body and to the state of our health. Indeed, Fran discovered that a manifestation of a balanced ion flow in the body is a basic need for good health. She found that the ion flow in the body could be measured

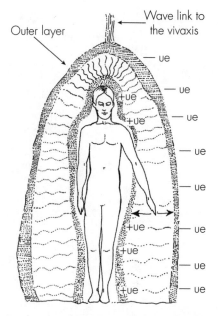

Outer layer — Wave link to the vivaxis

Figure 7. The etheric and electromagnetic fields of our body. The electromagnetic field appears to be a mirror image of the etheric field. The two Vivaxis layers are, first, magnetic, corresponding to Force Flow 3, and, second, gravitational, corresponding to Force Flow 4. If we are above our Vivaxis in terms of altitude, the magnetic is on the outside; if we are below, the outside layer is gravitational. Force Flow 3 emits positive ions, and Force Flow 4 negative ions. When testing ion flow, our recording hand moves back and forth between the two layers at a speed corresponding to our heart beat. If our ion flow is disturbed, our hand cannot record this basic pulsation. Our electromagnetic field is also affected by our environment, including weather, and also human-made electromagnetic factors. If we stand under a power line, we will not find any ion flow in our body as the electromagnetic field of the power line overrides our own.

---

[30] Frances Nixon, *Search for Vivaxis, Part 1* (British Columbia, Canada: Magnetic Publishers, 1982).

through the dowsing sense by using the arm as a recording device. The arm in recording ion flow moves back and forth, first away from and then toward the body at about the same speed as the heart beat, which is about seventy-two beats per minute. We can prove this by exercising vigorously and then noting the subsequent movement of the arm when testing ion flow. The exact technique for doing this is described in part 2. (See figure 7.)

Our bodies require a balance of positive and negative ions for healthy electrical interplay. Pollutants in the environment such as lead, sulfur dioxide, and cadmium prevent normal ion flow and cause a buildup of carbon dioxide so that the oxygenation of our blood is diminished. Excess positive ions are caused by pollution, electrical and electronic machinery, smog, synthetic materials, hot winds, and heaters. Earthquakes, waterfalls, and post thunderstorm conditions produce an excess of negative ions. As the atmosphere becomes disturbed by sunspot activity, earthquakes, volcanic eruptions, and nuclear testing, it is useful to check the environment and our body for ion flow on a regular basis.

It occurred to me that this particular movement of the arm to measure energies is really a pulsation between the electrical and magnetic components of our aura. Later, I will describe the two layers of our aura—one next to the skin and one eighteen inches or so further out. These two layers related to our Vivaxis correspond to what Fran named the magnetic and the gravitational, or electrical, forces. Each Vivaxis layer around our body contains mineral frequencies, and each is connected with either positive or negative ions. These mineral frequencies in our aura will be discussed in detail later. So the movement of our arm is really a pulsation that shows whether there is a balance between these mineral frequencies and between negative and positive ions. Depending on whether we are above or below our Vivaxis, these layers swap positions.

From another viewpoint, Fran found that these energies or fields are at right angles to each other just as they are found to be in all electromagnetic work. If you look again at figure 3 (page 6), you will note that this is probably the reason one wave train comes toward us from our Vivaxis up the left leg in a vertical direction and the other moves out from the right hand in a horizontal direction. However, Fran discovered that when we face our Vivaxis, both fields come into phase and are oriented directly toward the Vivaxis. This would appear to be the rationale behind our ability to take in all the frequencies together when we face our Vivaxis.

In the presence of an energy block or a foreign field, ion flow is very disturbed. Note that we are not here considering blocks associated with heart problems but *stasis of energy* in any part of the body. I have found that some people who have many energy conflicts can appear to record ion flow very easily, but on closer examination, the arm is found to be moving in many directions. The lack of clear rhythm in the energy field of these persons results from an excess of seething energies. These individuals are often practitioners who do meridian body work with many clients and who have not understood how to protect themselves from the energy fields of others. They must spend more time clearing their fields before they can undertake testing for energy flows. A field of conflicting energies and overcharge is as bad as one that is deficient in energies.

When we are in a relaxed state and the brain is in alpha rhythm, the heart becomes a resonating system. The brain and heart are then both resonating to the relaxing frequency of 8-10 cycles per second. This allows the whole body to resonate to the basic planetary frequency of about 8-10 Hz, which is the alpha rhythm.[31]

---

[31] Bentov, *Stalking the Wild Pendulum.*

This is probably the reason the speed of our recording arm, as it tests ion flow, corresponds with the heartbeat. Emotional conflict affects the heart and can cause us to break our connection with the health-giving energies of the Earth. Meditation, psychological counseling, and doing the Vivaxis exercises in this book (explained in parts 2 and 3) restore the healthy alpha frequency and thus restore in us the same rhythm that is natural to our planet.

I have explored the meaning of frequencies and vibrational medicine in some detail so that you will understand that the science of Vivaxis deals with frequencies rather than physical healing methods. The central tenet of this book is that we receive life-giving frequencies from the Earth via our Vivaxis. I have given a number of examples of both commonly known therapies like homeopathy and lesser-known therapies such as the application of sound frequencies, to give an understanding of the application of frequencies for healing. The science of Vivaxis is based on our ability to detect both abnormal and health-giving frequencies and to restore health by learning how to absorb life-giving frequencies via our Vivaxis. The art of dowsing has been explored, because dowsing is the basic technique needed to use our body's magnetic sense for detecting frequencies.

Having described the meaning and application of frequencies as already used in a variety of therapies, we are in a position to move on to another major discovery of Fran Nixon. This is the existence of energy layers throughout the planet that contain both life-giving and detrimental frequencies, or force flows, as Fran called them. Our Vivaxes are connected to these layers and to the associated force flows of many frequencies. Fran made the important discovery that we can use the force flows to enhance our health.

Suggested Reading

Andrews, Ted. *Music Therapy for Non-Musicians.* Batavia, Ohio: Dragonhawk, 1997.

David, William. *The Harmonics of Sound, Color and Vibration.* Marina del Ray, Calif: DeVorss & Company, 1980.

Davidson, John. *Subtle Energy.* Essex, U.K.: C. W. Daniel, 1988.

Gerber, Richard. *Vibrational Medicine.* Sante Fe, N.M.: Bear & Co., 1988.

Mason, Keith. *Medicine for the Twenty-First Century.* Rockport, Mass.: Element, 1992.

CHAPTER 3

The Life-Giving
Earth Frequencies

The following astounding discovery during the late 1970s deepened our understanding about Vivaxis energies and our connection with the Earth. Fran discovered that our Vivaxis is connected to layers of energy on the planet that contain all the frequencies for life.

As with many discoveries, this finding happened by chance. She was working with a trained chemist in her home studio and they were checking the direction for the flow of the chromium frequency from a point on the forehead. They discovered that this chromium flow led to a layer of energies at a level high on the wall of the studio. Later, many other frequencies were discovered, and the two researchers systematically mapped out all the known frequencies for our biochemistry. (See figure 8.)

These layers of energy were found running continuously over the Earth like the skins of an onion. If we placed a huge stake in the ground pointing toward the center of the Earth, the distance between the layers will be eight to twelve feet apart, depending on the location. By tracing the layers over some distance, we find that they are actually in the shape of gentle waves, like most phenomena involving vibration and frequency. When we walk uphill, depending on the gradient, we will cross a new layer every ten to fifteen steps. The layers do not follow the contours of the land but cut through any hill or mountain. Therefore, in many places they will extend into the space on either side of a hill. So, if we mark a layer on a vertical surface such as a tree, the layer will extend in space around the tree. (See figure 9, page 56.) If we start well below the surface of the Earth and move upward into the sky, we will come to a layer that goes right around the Earth every eight to twelve feet.

The Health-Giving Force Flows

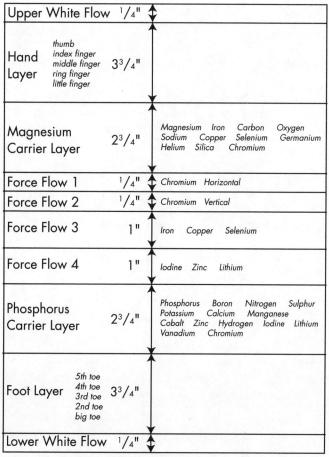

Figure 8. The characteristics of the energy layers. The total depth of the energy layers when marked on a vertical surface, such as a tree, is sixteen inches (forty-one cm). This drawing is not to scale. During major and minor periods when Force Flow 1 and 4 disappear, the layers will contract.

Each complete layer is about sixteen inches deep and consists of a number of force flows.[32] There are four main force flows in each complete layer and a number of other flows that, together with the central four, make ten flows

---

[32] Frances Nixon, and I. Parminter, *Vivaxis Beams* (British Columbia, Canada: Magnetic Publishers, 1980).

Figure 9. The energy layers as marked in our environment

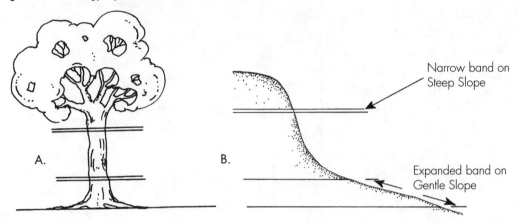

Narrow band on
Steep Slope

A.

B.

Expanded band on
Gentle Slope

9A. Two energy layers depicted on a tree. Each layer is sixteen inches deep when marked on a vertical surface. These layers extend around the tree in all directions in the same plane and thus go right around the Earth. Think of these layers as the skins of an onion, with about eight to twelve feet between each skin of the layer.

9B. This figure illustrates how the layer will be wider on the gentle slope, and this means if we mark the layers on gently sloping ground, we have room to stand on them.

in total. (See figure 8.) Each force flow emits particular frequencies, which are associated with key elements essential for life. The upper and lower boundaries have been named "upper and lower whites," and these flows of energy relate to the brain's pineal gland. The White Flows are only present between 10 A.M. and 2 P.M., when there is maximum light coming from the Sun. Fran called these flows "white," because she associated them with purification of toxins from the body and psyche.

Work with the white layers was the last part of Fran's research in the early 1980s.[33] The upper white layer forms the upper and lower boundaries of the layers between 10 A.M. and 2 P.M. At other times, the hand layer will form the upper boundary and the foot band, the lower boundary. Both the upper and lower white layers are only 0.25 of an

---

[33] Frances Nixon, *Environmental Force Flows Stimulating the Pineal Gland* (British Columbia, Canada: Magnetic Publishers, 1983).

inch wide on a vertical surface. These layers are associated with purification, and in keeping with this concept, garlic has a resonance with upper white and chlorophyll with lower white. The relationship of the pineal gland to these layers may be thought of as purification in a spiritual sense, because the pineal gland is intimately connected with our spiritual development. It is significant that both garlic and chlorophyll are associated with cleansing or detoxifying by natural therapists. Yet Fran had no familiarity with naturopathic medicine when she found these connections with the White Flows; she was simply using her intuition.

Moving down from upper white layer, we find a flow associated with the hand. This flow is about three inches deep. There is a section on this layer for each of the five fingers, and this band can be used for disturbances in the hand, such as static and disturbed receptors, and for medical conditions, such as arthritis, that affect the hands. It should be noted that, as with the previous connections, it was Fran's intuitive sense that found connections between the hands, feet, and particular levels of the energy layers.

The next force flow down is associated with magnesium. Fran called this a carrier band, because it also carries the frequencies of other elements apart from magnesium. Magnesium is an important mineral in the body. In my many years of naturopathic practice, I have used more magnesium compounds for clients than any other. This band is 2.75 inches deep. The magnesium force flow is also associated with negative ions.

Moving further down, we then come to the chromium horizontal flow Fran named Force Flow 1, perhaps because she discovered it first. However, it is also the central flow we mark when locating the energy layers. Force Flow 1 includes frequencies of chromium, oxygen, carbon, cobalt, and calcium. It is one of the two flows that disappear at the low and high tides and for up to eight hours at new and full moons. Therefore, we cannot receive the frequencies of this flow during those times. The associated mineral receptors on the fingers and other parts of the body will therefore be quiet at these times. This flow relates to the Sun's gravitational pull on the Earth and is therefore sometimes called the Sun band. Like the next flow, it is only 0.25 inches deep when charted on a vertical surface.

The chromium vertical flow named Force Flow 2 follows and is considered to be associated with the Earth's wave link to its Vivaxis on the Sun. The associated frequencies are hydrogen, helium, and a vertical flow of chromium. As you will find in chapter 5, we cannot study Vivaxis in isolation from celestial bodies such as the Sun and Moon. Fran, in company with one of her associates who was trained in physics, postulated that just as our human Vivaxis is connected to the Earth, the Earth has an energy connection to our Vivaxis on the Sun. Of course, we are not in a position to do more than speculate on this concept. However, Force Flow 2 does include a flow of the chromium frequency in a vertical direction away from the Earth, whereas all the other Force Flows are horizontal in direction. This flow is actually stronger during the major and minor periods (low and high tides). Its relation to the Sun probably explains why meditation and creative thought appears stronger at this time. It could be that this vertical wave relates to our spiritual alignment with higher planes of being. Remember, in many religions the Sun is a symbol for the highest spiritual being.

Force Flows 1 and 4 disappear at the major and minor periods because of the gravitational effect at these times between the Sun, Moon, and Earth, which causes these force flows to cancel each other out. The receptors on the body associated with the vertical frequency of chromium and Force Flow 2 remain active at all times. Our connection with Force Flow 3, the magnetic layer, also remains at all times. So, despite the disappearance of

Force Flows 1 and 4 at times, we always remain connected to the Earth via Force Flow 3 and with the Sun through Force Flow 2.

Fran called Force Flow 3 the magnetic layer. It contains frequencies for iron, sodium, gold, copper, silver, and selenium; all these elements in their material form can be used to transport an electrical current. Fran called this layer magnetic, because she found it to be connected with magnetic north and south. The saltwater ice of the North Pole and freshwater ice of the South Pole are related to this magnetic factor. Some of Fran's first experiments researched the energy flows associated with ice made from fresh and salt water. Force Flow 3 is associated with negative ions and can be used for increasing the flow of ions in the body; this force flow is one inch deep.

Force Flow 4 is the same depth as Force Flow 3 and includes frequencies of iodine, zinc, and lithium. It is the second flow that disappears at the high and low tides and is connected with the Moon's gravitational pull on the Earth. As these flows are associated with the Sun (Force Flow 1) and the Moon (Force Flow 4), Fran sometimes called them the Sun and Moon flows. Like the elements associated with Force Flow 1, the Force Flow 4 elements cannot be recorded on the body during high and low tides. Force Flow 4 is associated with positive ions.

The next layer is the phosphorus carrier layer, which pairs with that of magnesium and is the same width (two inches). Like the magnesium carrier band, it carries other vibrations and frequencies apart from its main mineral and, together with Force Flow 4, is associated with positive ions. The foot band is below the phosphorus band. It has a section for each toe and is the same width as the hand band. Finally, we have the lower white layer, which like the upper white layer, is associated with the pineal gland and is of the same width of 0.25 inches.

In addition to the elements mentioned, the research chemist working with Fran discovered that between each force flow are frequencies of selenium and germanium that appear to act as one-way switches for energy flow. These two elements are used in modern electronics for a similar purpose. Selenium was found to be involved with the currents or energies moving up through the layers and germanium with the energies moving downward. The reader may be aware that both selenium and germanium are used by natural therapists to enhance the immune system.

Between each force flow are frequencies of selenium and germanium that appear to act as one-way switches for energy flow. These two elements are used in modern electronics for a similar purpose. Selenium was found to be involved with the currents or energies moving up through the layers and germanium with the energies moving downward.

The Detrimental Force Flows

Fran found that, in addition to the health-giving layers, there are detrimental layers of energies found above and mostly below the life-giving layers. The arrangement and position of the life-giving layers remain constant in all geographic locations, but the shape and arrangement of the detrimental flows vary from place to place. The reason may be that these negative energies contain human-made substances such as insecticides, fungicides, pharmaceutical drugs, and other synthetic substances not natural to our planet. The heavy metals such as lead, cadmium, and mercury also feature in these force flows. The frequencies of these detrimental energies are usually found starting four to five inches above and below the "white" frequencies.[34] (See figure 10.) So we realize that just as there are frequencies in a nonmaterial sense associated with life-giving elements, the same applies to toxic elements and compounds.

---

[34] Frances Nixon, *Supplement to Vivaxis Beams: Force Flow* X (British Columbia, Canada: Magnetic Publishers, 1982).

You may wonder how these human-made substances like drugs get into the energy field of the planet. I can only imagine that the frequencies we pick up on the detrimental energy flows are harmonics of the drugs in question, just as the life-giving frequencies are harmonics, or frequencies, related to life-giving elements like iron, sodium, and calcium.

A common arrangement commencing about five inches below the white layer is lead, cadmium, mercury, detrimental electromagnetism, insecticides, ionizing radiation, and aluminum. These will be spread over about fifteen inches if measured on a vertical surface, rather than on sloping ground. A layer of lead is also found a few inches above the upper white band. Obviously, the student is trained to avoid contacting these detrimental flows. However, these flows can be used to monitor the associated frequencies in our bodies, and we can then know when we have eradicated such toxins. An example would be checking a person who has taken measures to remove the effects of the mercury in their amalgam teeth fillings.

Elements such as mercury, lead, cadmium, and aluminum are toxic to the body and may be absorbed through our water, air, or the food chain. Inner-city dwellers are often exposed to high levels of lead from car fumes, and most of us have been exposed to mercury from the gradual breakdown of amalgam fillings in our teeth

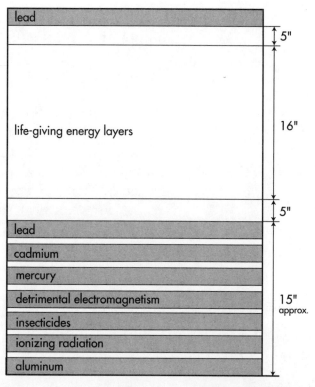

Figure 10. Approximate position of detrimental force flows above and below life-giving force flows, as in figure 9B. The list of detrimental elements is not necessarily complete. (This figure is not to scale.)

and other sources. Many town water systems use aluminum and chlorine in the purification processes.

Finding and Using the Energy Layers

Fran reasoned that, as Force Flow 1 is related to chromium, we could visualize this element to find the force flow. It seems that when we visualize chromium and slowly tilt our head as we face a gentle slope, we will have a back and forth motion in the recording arm when the area in our skull near the pineal gland is in direct alignment with Force Flow 1. (See exercise 7.) You will learn in part 2 to use your arm and the dowsing sense to record all Vivaxis phenomena.

Theoretically, we can also visualize the other elements in Force Flow 1 for the same purpose. But chromium is suggested, because in addition to the above, Fran somehow was inspired to know that singing a tune activates our chromium receptors and we can use that fact to initially locate the correct position for Force Flow 1 and then cross-check by visualizing chromium.[35] The music chosen can be classical, folk, or nursery rhyme, but jazz does not seem to work.

Fran devised many practical exercises for using the energy layers. Techniques to find the energy layers relate closely to our capacity for visualization. She found early in her work that, once our brain has recorded the frequency of a substance through eye contact, the frequency could always be recalled by memory. Some students of Vivaxis think it is adequate to look at a diagram or picture of a substance, but this may not be accurate unless they have previously contacted the substance in question. When visualizing the elements by recalling them to our mind's eye, we seem to use a part of the brain behind the bridge

---

[35] Nixon, *Search For Vivaxis, Part 1*, chap. 3.

of the nose and close to the pineal gland. This skill is probably related to the magnetic sense previously described. Visualization involves memorizing how we saw or perceived something and making a picture in our mind's eye of the object. Thus, if we are visualizing chromium, we think of how we saw the green powder of chromium oxide and recall the look of this powder.

We can align with our Vivaxis in a more powerful sense when standing on particular force flows. The energies can also be used to purify food and water.[36] Water is very sensitive to the imprint of energies. By rolling bottles of water from the top to the bottom of the layers, all the life-giving frequencies can be stored for many weeks, provided the white frequencies are included.

Another discovery Fran made was that individuals who have a particular mineral deficiency should stand on the associated force flow to correct their inability to absorb that particular frequency. For more general purposes, by aligning to our Vivaxis while standing on the energy layers, we enhance our absorption of all minerals and frequencies in our daily food and drink. Fran found that each mineral has a compass direction. Thus the absorption of a particular element is further enhanced by both standing on the appropriate force flow and facing in the correct compass direction.

So there are two basic ways we can bring in healthy frequencies. The first is to align ourselves precisely to the Vivaxis. The second way is to align with a particular element we need, such as iron or calcium, by standing on the correct layer of this element on the ground and also facing in the precise compass direction for the mineral in question. The following case history illustrates the amazing effect the force flows can have on the human system.

---

[36] *Ibid.*, chap. 8.

A *Case of Chronic Fatigue Syndrome*

Some years ago, I treated a young girl who was my first case of chronic fatigue syndrome. The medical syndrome had not officially been established at the time. The girl in question had developed pneumonia following bronchitis, despite naturopathic treatment. After treatment with antibiotics, she started to experience muscle pains and extreme weakness. Her mother had to carry her into my consulting room. I tried every therapy I knew of, but nothing produced much improvement.

In desperation, I explained Fran Nixon's teachings to the girl's mother and invited them both to my home for treatment on the force flows. On scanning the girl's legs, I found they had no ion flow from thighs to toes. As she was too weak to exercise on the energy flows, we carefully laid her on the ground in the position of the marked bands. I found that the energy returned to her legs. She then started to gradually improve, and with further naturopathic treatment, she made a full recovery and finished a university degree in veterinary science.

It appears that the frequencies from the force flows were restored to her body by placing her on the force flows. Without these life-giving frequencies, she did not obtain the full benefit from my naturopathic treatment. Perhaps we could say that, through her profound illness, she developed a "short circuit" in her system, and simply placing her on the energy flows enabled her body to reestablish her Vivaxis energies.

It is a sad thing that we tend to use this pure energy work as a last instead of a first resort, which is the more natural sequence. We experienced the same phenomenon within the history of mainstream natural therapies, for when I first went into practice in 1972, people came to natural healers as a last resort. They had tried drugs and surgery and then, with sick and broken bodies, they were prepared to try vitamins, minerals, and homeopathy. The same back-to-front process is again taking place, with the subtle therapies being requested after mainstream therapies have failed. Eventually, we will work in the *right* sequence and will start by addressing the real underlying causes, which are often energy disturbances from subtle levels of influence.

Other skills using the energy layers pertain to checking yourself and others for mineral deficiencies or toxic elements. You can do this by scanning visually down the layers. (See exercise 7.) For instance, a smoker can be readily identified by the disturbance in oxygen molecules, as witnessed by visualizing that person on Force Flow 1. (See exercise 22.) Disturbances to the hands and feet caused by vibrating tools, such as pneumatic drills and power saws, can be discerned on the hand and foot bands. Another practical use of the force flows relates to treating clothing materials such as polyester and nylon to remove static. This disturbance can be permanently resolved by placing items such as pantyhose, shirts, and dresses on the energy layers as marked on the ground.

After Fran discovered the energy layers, she stopped teaching some of her earlier research, such as work with receptors or acupuncture points. She found working with the force flows to be superior to the visualization techniques she had used earlier. For instance, students no longer visualized the main frequencies of Vivaxis, universal forces, Sun and Moon; the detailed mapping of receptors and their correction was also discontinued. She found that standing on the energy layers, tapping the disturbed areas on the body, and immediately aligning to the Vivaxis in the four directions was the most healing and energizing procedure of all.

Relating Natural Supplements to the Force Flows

All natural remedies, such as herbs, minerals, vitamins, or enzymes, have a matching resonance on the energy layers. This was an area of interest to me because of my many years of clinical naturopathic practice. It is possible to ascertain the frequencies of a range of natural supplements and their location on the energy layers. I have found that all the vitamins register on Force Flow 3. Remember that this force flow is always present; this is significant, as vitamins are so essential for life. We can survive much longer without specific minerals than we can without vitamins, as they are catalysts for many biochemical reactions.

I found the twelve tissue salts (*Ferrum Phosphate, Kali Muriaticum, Natrum Sulfa,* and so forth) and the range of homeopathic remedies in low potencies (12x and lower) on the phosphorus carrier band. These are the dilutions that still contain some chemical molecules of the remedy. Many of the higher potencies (such as the 30th centesimal and 200th centesimal) register on the magnesium carrier band. These are the potencies that theoretically contain no physical molecules, because they have been diluted a number of times.

My findings illustrate that certain frequencies on the energy bands relate to the frequencies of homeopathic remedies. In addition, the higher potencies of these homeopathic remedies correspond to the higher part of the energy band above chromium. For instance, a salt-like iron phosphate is administered by homeopaths in a range of both high and low potencies. It will register on both magnesium and phosphorus carrier bands, but its higher potency will register on the magnesium band and low potencies on the phosphorus band. Another commonly used remedy is *Arnica,* which is given for injuries. In low potencies, it registers on the phosphorus band, and again, the higher potency is found registering on the magnesium carrier band. This correlation does not mean that certain potencies are better than others. Rather, there may be a correlation between the need for acute remedies (low potencies) at times and high potencies at others.

Since the frequencies and potencies of all natural remedies are found on the life-giving part of the energy layers, by regular alignment to our Vivaxis and by standing and exercising on the different layers, the body is provided with whatever frequency it needs. (See exercise 7.) The regular drinking of water energized on the force flows will similarly provide us with the vibrational frequencies needed. For the water to be of optimum use, it needs to include the vertical flows as well as the horizontal flows. (See below.)

The Vertical Flows

During 1981, Fran explored the connections between the horizontal layers. These flows are called the vertical flows for the obvious reason that they go up and down. figure 11 shows the shape and distribution of these flows and lists the elements associated with each. Whereas the horizontal layers are continuous in a horizontal plane, the vertical bands may be considered as thin cords of energy that connect the horizontal bands or flows. This can be verified by visualization and by recording through our feet as we move from one vertical flow to another. This is explained in detail in exercise 9.

The vertical flows are repeated every five and a half inches; they are less stable than the horizontal bands, being affected by pollution to some degree. It is useful

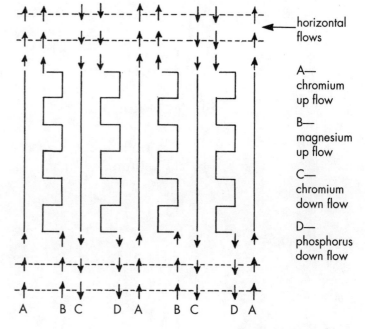

horizontal flows

A— chromium up flow

B— magnesium up flow

C— chromium down flow

D— phosphorus down flow

Figure 11. Vertical connecting bands and their energy flows Note how the energies in some of the vertical flows move in a zigzag fashion. These vertical flows connect between any two layers of the horizontal layers.

Reprinted from *Healing through Earth Energies* by Judy Jacka, 1996.

to include both horizontal and vertical flows when energizing water. This is why we use a bottle at least six inches tall so that, when rolled on its side over the horizontal layers, it will also will contact the vertical flows. There are also occasions when we cannot map or contact the horizontal flows. At these times it is possible to use the vertical flows as they move through the various floors of any building in which we are situated.

We can begin to see and understand the great tapestry of forces that compose the energy field of our planet. We are the microcosm within our planetary field. To further prepare us to understand the connections with our Vivaxis energies the next chapter will focus on our planet as a living being and describe the human energy field in some detail.

Suggested Reading

Nixon, Frances. *Search For Vivaxis, Parts 1 and 2.* British Columbia, Canada: Magnetic Publishers, 1982.

CHAPTER 4

Relating to the Earth as a Living Being

Only recently have many Westerners accepted the idea that we have an energy field that radiates outward from our body, affecting our environment in a positive or negative sense, depending on our psychic state. Extending this concept to our planet provides a thought-provoking model of our possible energy relation to the Earth.

In this chapter, our focus moves from the universal to the particular, and we view the Earth in tandem with our growing understanding of the human. From this model, you will perceive that there may be parallels between the body and consciousness of the macrocosm (Earth) and that of the microcosm (the human). You will also see how our energy field is related to and affected by the Earth's.

Mother Earth as Gaia

The concept of Mother Earth is found in many great religions. In ancient Greece, Mother Earth was known as Gaia, and this name was revived by the British scientist Sir James Lovelock in his useful book *Gaia—A New Look at Life on Earth* in 1979. Lovelock has a scientific background and a visionary sense that has enabled him to present life on Earth in a new framework, with humanity as cocreator.

Like a poet, Lovelock manages to encapsulate a view of Earth from many perspectives in the space of a small book. His book provides a synthesis of science and insight into the self-balancing and self-regulating, or homeostatic, mechanism of our planet. Lovelock shows that this mechanism still works despite the appalling interference by man, but he also warns that this balance could be overturned if humanity does not curb its ecological interference in the future.

Lovelock describes the Earth's living matter, oceans, and land surface as a complex system that can be seen as a single organism with the capacity to sustain our planet as a suitable place for life.[37] The impression he gives is that Earth could indeed be viewed as a *living* being. The Gaia viewpoint suggests that we can see the physical body of our planet in much the same way we see the human physical body. Lovelock sees the possibility of humanity becoming the nervous system of the Earth, as acting almost as an outpost of Gaia's consciousness. Such a concept has interesting ramifications for the practical work in this book as we explore the energy relationships between the human energy field and Earth.

The idea of the Earth as a living being has also come to us through various mystery schools and religions, and it was brought to the West from the Himalayas by writers such as H. P. Blavatsky and Alice Bailey. Their teachings take the Gaia concept further to an understanding that the ecosystems and kingdoms of nature on Earth are simply the physical body of a great living entity in whom we live and move and have our being. According to the Bailey teachings, human beings are considered to be

------

[37] James E. Lovelock, *Gaia—A New Look at Life on Earth* (New York: Oxford Press, 1979).

living "cells" in the body of this greater Being in both a physical and spiritual sense.[38]

The association of this consciousness with planet Earth is a rational explanation for a Being who is both a transcendent and immanent God and who is evolving toward ever-greater perfection. The perennial wisdom is concerned with the big picture of how all the kingdoms in nature interact and evolve on our planet. In this view, all kingdoms gradually evolve toward perfection. There is a natural hierarchy of being and an orderly interaction of ecosystems forming the physical vehicles for many ascending levels of consciousness.

We tend to reject the idea of hierarchy, because we project onto this concept our fear of being controlled by those "above" us. However, in the ancient wisdom tradition, the term hierarchy is understood to be the result of the natural movement of spirit toward matter and its return to the source of all being, bearing the rewards and qualities developed in the long journey through millions of years. From this viewpoint, the individual human sense of awareness and consciousness is never lost but continually grows and expands on its journey back to the source. Once we move beyond the human kingdom, hierarchy becomes Hierarchy and directs those Beings who help to direct life on planet Earth.

A Model for Planetary and Human Evolution

We can summarize this teaching as a basic progression: spirit + matter ➤ consciousness. Spirit chooses to further its expansion by incarnating in planetary substance to redeem or reveal the light at the center of every atom of matter. Human spirits have their origin as sparks of individual life within those great Beings who use the

---

[38] Alice A. Bailey, *Treatise on Cosmic Fire* (London: Lucis Press, 1952).

various planetary spheres in a way corresponding to how we use a physical body as a means of living on the physical plane. The role of our Sun assumes both a spiritual and a physical position around which the planets in our system revolve. In this sense, the physical Sun is the physical body for a great Being. This gives meaning to why in many religions the Sun is the symbol for the highest spiritual Being. The planets that revolve around the Sun are likewise the physical bodies of great Intelligences. This concept fits with the speculation that the Earth has its own Vivaxis on the Sun.

The ancient wisdom teachings state that our spirit gradually moves in an involutional phase through matter through different levels or planes of being during millions of years and then gradually evolves via the mineral, plant, and animal kingdoms in nature. Finally, in the human kingdom we develop self-consciousness and, later, spiritual consciousness. It is at the stage of self-consciousness that our truly human journey begins. Thus far science has only documented the most recent one million years of our human development, although this development may have started *much* earlier.

There are writers in the Western world outside the esoteric tradition who have also developed comprehensive models of the unfolding of the kingdoms on planet Earth. Ken Wilber, for example, has developed a similar view of evolution, drawing on anthropology, psychology, mythology, and religion in his acclaimed book, *A Brief History of Everything.*[39]

The perennial wisdom has emerged through many religions and schools of thought. It views humanity as part of a vast hierarchy stretching from the atom to the Godhead. The teaching encompasses a concept of energy

---

[39] K. Wilbur, *A Brief History of Everything* (Melbourne: Hill of Content, 1996).

fields that interact at different levels of consciousness. Modern physics has supported this concept at the physical level by recognizing the energetic relationships between all atoms and forms on our planet. Our planetary manifestation is seen by some thinkers as a vast "thought-form," or hologram, rather than as a machine with separate parts. There is an emphasis on energy fields at both the macrocosmic or microcosmic levels. It is important to be able to place the science of Vivaxis, with its emphasis on energy fields and flows, into this backdrop of both philosophy and physics.

We can again review the Earth as a living body with an energy field interpenetrating every kingdom in nature. The etheric and electromagnetic field of the planet therefore conditions our energies as human beings. We have also explored the idea that each individual has an energy or etheric body that interfaces with the physical body via an electromagnetic field and that this field can be measured to some degree by physical instruments. It seems logical, therefore, that there may be a connection between our personal energy field and that of the Earth—the Vivaxis of Fran Nixon. From our model, we can perceive that there may be similarities in both energy and consciousness between the macrocosm (Earth) and the microcosm (human).

This is a major theme in this book—the relation between the human energy field and that of the Earth. In fact, the Vivaxis energies appear to be those etheric and electromagnetic forces that connect us with the Earth in a two-way circuit. One wave train of this circuit flows into the left side of the body from the Vivaxis via the left foot and the other flows back to the Vivaxis out the right side of the body. (See figure 3, page 6.) This flowing energy between our bodies and the Earth is in stark contrast to the scientific view of our planet in nineteenth-century Newtonian physics.

In the Vivaxis model, we view the planet and its various kingdoms as a system in which each level flows into the next throughout all the kingdoms in nature. The view of scientists who followed Newton was that the universe is like a giant machine, with fixed laws and rules that govern all the processes on the planet. Until very recently, most scientists in medicine and psychology have reflected this viewpoint in their assessment of the human being, but now that is starting to change.

This is a major theme in this book—the relation between the human energy field and that of the Earth. In fact, the Vivaxis energies appear to be those etheric and electromagnetic forces that connect us with the Earth in a two-way circuit. One wave train of this circuit flows into the left side of the body from the Vivaxis via the left foot and the other flows back to the Vivaxis out the right side of the body.

The Newtonian view of the body as a machine gave rise to the emphasis on specialization in various branches of medicine and psychology. The term "psyche" means soul, but until the recent development of transpersonal psychology, psyche had nothing to do with the soul. So, even in the area of psychology, holism was not practiced in terms of including the soul. The development of natural medicine recognizes the importance of holism, which means treating the whole person. By "whole person," we mean not just the whole body, but also the psyche as it embraces both psychological functioning and spiritual direction. The natural medicine trend of holism has been helped or underscored by developments in modern physics, where it has been determined that everything in the universe is connected through fields.

Twentieth-century physicists discovered that the minute particles that form the basis of our universe exist both as waves and particles. This dual manifestation gave rise to the particle/wave dichotomy in physics and placed a new emphasis on energy and energy fields in the macrocosm and microcosm. This quantum paradox was born through the research of two scientists, Max Planck and

Albert Einstein, early in the twentieth century. The basic finding of modern science is that light and other particles have this dual personality—at times behaving as particles and at other times as waves.[40] It is the wave aspect of particles that relates modern science to the findings of Vivaxis, and indeed to many natural therapies.

The universe is no longer viewed as being reduced to ultimate particles that can be moved around to form different arrangements like parts of a machine. It is now acceptable for scientists to focus on energy and energy fields. The evolving model of interaction between the universe and human beings allows for a new viewpoint on the complexity of human life. Our different levels of consciousness can now be envisaged as being expressed through increasingly subtle energy fields associated with planet Earth. Modern science has only started to explore the most obvious subtle energy fields.

The Human Constitution

There is a well-known saying from the ancient wisdom tradition: "As above, so below." It means that the cosmos is mirrored in humanity and the microcosm and that humans on Earth are affected by the various frequencies of the planet. As individuals, we also have our own frequencies, which can be enhanced or deteriorated by those of the Earth, depending on both the natural and humanized environment in which we work and live.

There has been a shift in consciousness in relation to how we view the human being. We no longer see ourselves as a collection of atoms and molecules grouped together to form organs and tissues with, we would hope, something like a soul floating above us. Modern science suggests the possibility that the universe, and by inference,

---

[40] Briggs and Peate, *Looking Glass Universe.*

humanity, consists of interpenetrating energy fields with different frequencies that extend beyond our physical body.[41] (See figure 12.)

We can view our different levels of consciousness as belonging to a number of energy fields that connect with and interpenetrate one another. Compare this scenario with how solids, liquids, and gases all interpenetrate in a mixture of sand, water, and air. Each has its separate characteristic and yet interacts with the others. Thus we are aware of sensations, feelings, and thoughts from our different levels of functioning as being distinct experiences, but ones that also overlap. For example, touching a hot object gives us pain (physical body), which may lead to a feeling of fear (emotional body), to which our mind (mental body) responds by thinking about taking more care in the future.

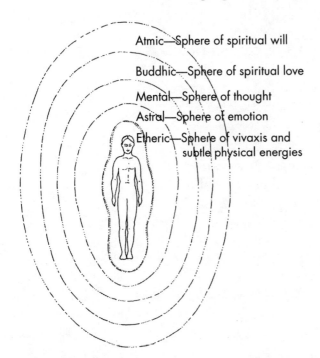

Atmic—Sphere of spiritual will

Buddhic—Sphere of spiritual love

Mental—Sphere of thought

Astral—Sphere of emotion

Etheric—Sphere of vivaxis and subtle physical energies

Figure 12. Our five bodies, or vehicles. The physical human body exists within a series of shells, or "coats," each with its own quality of energy and consciousness.

Reprinted from *Meditation, the Most Natural Therapy* by Judy Jacka, 1990.

In esoteric teachings, there are seven layers of consciousness and seven vehicles for this consciousness. The physical body is only the outer "coat," and the first "vehicle" of significance is understood to be the energy field that underlies all physical organs and tissues. In the West, this energy body is often termed the etheric body. Most of the Vivaxis techniques described in this book deal with electromagnetic and etheric energy. The purpose of this etheric body is threefold:

---

[41] Laszlo, *The Creative Cosmos.*

1. To provide the pattern for all physical growth and regrowth, the blueprint described by Burr in his research on the L-fields.

2. To receive energy from the Sun and to transport it to every part of the physical body.

3. To act as a mediator between the higher states of consciousness and the brain and nervous system.[42]

The physical interface between the etheric body and the physical appears to be our electromagnetic field. Robert Becker clearly established that this field transmits information for growth within the body. His research explains what is presently inexplicable in embryology, that is, why does an ear grow on the head and not on the toe? It is the etheric body that provides the blueprint for where the ear should be, and this information is then transmitted by the electromagnetic field to the cells. (Details of the scientific basis for the etheric body have been explored in a previous book of mine entitled *Frontiers of Natural Therapy*.[43]) The work of medical scientists Harold Burr, Robert Becker, Rupert Sheldrake, and Australian medical scientist Bevan Reid all point to the concept that there are energy fields underlying the physical body that provide the pattern for growth and regrowth. Their work also highlights the effects of chemical and electronic pollution in modifying these fields in a detrimental manner. The research of Burr and Becker focused on the electromagnetic fields as being able to transmit information for growth.

In our Vivaxis studies, we also focus on the electromagnetic and etheric fields as being the area of all Vivaxis

---

[42] Bailey, *Esoteric Healing.*
[43] Jacka, *Frontiers of Natural Therapy.*

phenomena, and therefore we can use the research just cited to understand these subtle fields more fully.

For example, Kirlian photography highlights the electromagnetic field of the human body and how it changes before observable disease takes place. The object or subject to be photographed is placed in a high-frequency field that causes an acceleration of electrons to be given off from the skin. These electrons then collide with molecules in the air, which creates light that manifests as an aura on the film without any external light source being necessary for the photo. The scientific name for this effect is coronal discharge.

It is understandable, following the indications of Kirlian photography, that the etheric vehicle is often called the light body. Science has established that excited electrons can become light particles or photons that have movement but no mass. The human body has been found to emit light particles all the time, and a number of scientists attracted to the leading edge of medicine have researched how to record this light body.

One of the leaders in this area is Harry Oldfield in England. He designed a video camera and software program that capture the light body on a computer screen, thus allowing colored prints to be made without the need for a high-frequency field. Blocks of color on the images received are interpreted as blockages of energy, and they have been found to coincide with physical problems in the subject. To date, no detailed published material exists on his technology or research, but some background to his work is featured in his *The Dark Side of the Brain*.[44] This research helps us to further understand the significance of the subtle energies of the body that are the sphere of the Vivaxis connection.

---

[44] Harry Oldfield and R. Cogwheel, *The Dark Side of the Brain* (Dorset, U.K.: Element Books, 1988).

We need always to be careful to distinguish the electromagnetic field around the body from the etheric body, which is probably beyond the range of the electromagnetic spectrum. However, the etheric body appears to interpenetrate and express itself through the electromagnetic field, and thus high-frequency photography and Oldfield's more refined technique may give us indirect but important information about both electromagnetic and etheric energies of a person, and in turn, help to clarify our model of the Vivaxis.

In Fran's research, our physical body appears to have two enclosing layers, or spheres, beyond the skin corresponding with the frequencies of Force Flows 3 and 4 and with negative and positive ions respectively. That appears to explain why when we test ion flow on our body, there is a movement of the arm back and forth between these two layers, except when we are facing directly toward our Vivaxis. In addition, these layers are related to the corresponding layers and force flows on the planet. Healthy people have a free two-way energy flow back and forth from this envelope around the body to the Vivaxis. The fact that this double-layered envelope is related to positive and negative ions seems to indicate that our Vivaxis energies are intimately related to an electromagnetic field.

We often receive interference to this electrical envelope around our body from human-made technology. This detrimental effect occurs because our electromagnetic field is weak compared to the much stronger fields associated with modern technology. It is not surprising that Fran found the Vivaxis connection to be disturbed in many people. Medical researchers have now established a close link between the nervous and immune systems. As a link also exists between the electromagnetic field of the human and the nervous system, it is understandable that the immune system could be severely compromised by electromagnetic interference.

Because the etheric field is conditioned by more subtle fields of emotion and thought, it is essential to reflect on the more subtle fields beyond the etheric. Many health problems of the etheric body have their cause in emotional problems, and this model needs to be explored before we look at the details of how to restore Vivaxis energies.

The energy fields in the human being include the physical brain consciousness, the etheric field underlying the physical, our astral or feeling consciousness, our mental consciousness, plus more subtle states loosely called the soul and spiritual consciousness. (Refer again to figure 12.) In our daily living, these states overlap, although, as individuals, we often choose to focus on one or more levels in preference to others. These levels of energy and consciousness can all interpenetrate each other.

Each part of our being or energy level will have its own resonance or vibratory frequency and each part exists within the many vibratory possibilities on planet Earth. In this sense, there is no definite line of demarcation between our energy fields and those of another person or between the Earth and our own energy field. A constant interaction will also exist between all lives on our planet and between the various kingdoms in nature. This is why Fran was so particular about not allowing students of the Vivaxis science to invade the energy field of another person while testing or correcting disturbances. Her precise investigations proved the effects of such interaction.

Consider the implications of this concept in family and work life. Each family member can have a profound psychological or physical effect on the family health, both individually and collectively. Psychologists work with this scenario every day as they seek to free their clients from the conditioning effects of family life. Although this psychological conditioning is accepted by the average person, the close interaction of energy fields is not generally considered to be the cause of such conditioning. Yet we all have the experience of wanting to get away and walk or sit by ourselves after a busy time at work, or after confinement with people in a small space.

The energizing field of Earth can be experienced when we walk in a forest or parkland and experience how our energies get recharged. We do not always attribute this healing effect to the health-giving resonance that flows into our energy field from the magnetic field of Earth. We are more likely to think, "I'm exhausted after all that talking and arguing and I just need to get away from everyone for a while."

The many exercises described in part 2 deal with that level of energy we sense when we walk in the forest or by the sea. This energy comes from the etheric body of the Earth and is linked to our own etheric body—the first subtle layer beyond the physical body. It is the basic energy that we acknowledge when we say that we are either weak or vital—the *chi* of Chinese medicine, the bioplasma of the Russians, the orgone of Wilhelm Reich. These are all concepts about etheric energy. Vivaxis is not exactly the same as saying etheric or chi or orgone; rather, the Vivaxis is a sphere of energy that is *associated with* etheric energy.

I understand the science of Vivaxis energies in terms both of this relationship between the etheric body of Earth and our own energy field and of the free flow of energy between the two. Fran said this about our energy relationship with Earth: "The world behaves as one large magnet and we as individuals are an integral part of the magnetic whole. We not only have a wave link characteristic of a given magnetic point, but we also are able to receive and link circuits with other waves in the same band of wave links that are also magnetically linked with the world's magnetism. This gives us a gigantic communication system, linking all life that is part of the same magnetic whole."[45]

In summary, our planet consists of many overlapping and connecting energy fields in which Vivaxis energies form a part. The area of Vivaxis research concerns the first

---

[45] Nixon, *Born to Be Magnetic*, vol. 1, p.13.

two subtle fields beyond the physical body of living beings and the planet—the electromagnetic and etheric. Our human constitution also consists of interpenetrating fields and is linked by our Vivaxis to the planetary system. The science of Vivaxis is thus an expression of some of the electromagnetic and etheric fields on our planet.

Modern science, with its emphasis on connecting fields, has provided a framework whereby we can place the Vivaxis force flows and associated phenomena such as our personal Vivaxis into a larger framework. This model also accounts for the "weavers" of that tapestry depicted here as an ascending Hierarchy of intelligent Beings, who guide our planetary life. We can view our planet, Gaia, as related to the intelligent consciousness of our planetary life.

Suggested Reading

Devereaux, Paul. *Re-Visioning the Earth—A Guide to Opening the Healing Channels between Mind and Nature.* New York: Simon and Schuster, 1996.

Jacka, Judy. *Meditation, the Most Natural Therapy.* Melbourne: Lothian, 1990.

Russell, Peter. *The Awakening Earth—Our Next Evolutionary Leap.* London: Routledge and Kegan Paul, 1982.

Sheldrake, Rupert. *The Re-birth of Nature—the Greening of Science and God.* London: Century, 1990.

CHAPTER 5

Planetary Cycles
and Influences

The central theme of this book is Earth energies. However, we cannot separate our planet from its interaction with other heavenly bodies and the electromagnetic effect they exert on our planet, just as we cannot separate our body's energy field from that of the planet. The gravitational effect of the Sun and Moon produces the tides in our oceans, and these profoundly effect the force flows and mineral frequencies of our Vivaxis connection.

The physical light from the Sun and Moon is received from different angles by our planet, and this phenomenon featured strongly in Fran's research. I found this subject to be one of the most significant studies in relation to our body energies. In particular, Fran researched the changing vectors (or directions) of light as the Earth turns on its axis in relation to the Moon and also during its yearly passage around the Sun. (See figure 13.)

In chapter 1, we explored absorption of forces from both the Sun and Moon in a general sense. In this chapter, we'll look at the effect of the *angular* relationship between the Sun, Moon, and Earth as received by our body. This includes discoveries made about light as a carrier wave for

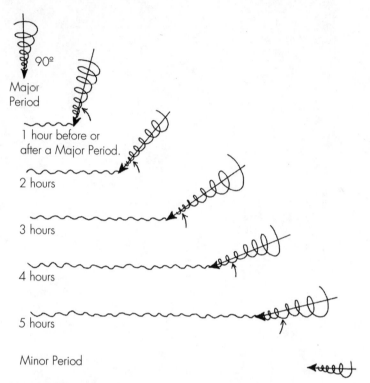

90°

Major
Period

1 hour before or
after a Major Period.

2 hours

3 hours

4 hours

5 hours

Minor Period

Figure 13. The changing angles of light between major and minor periods. As the Earth turns in relation to the Sun and Moon, various angular relationships are formed between them. These angles are reflected in our spinal fluid, allowing us to chart the angular relationship between Sun, Moon, and Earth on our bodies. The spirals represent energy as it spirals downward. Energy rarely moves in straight lines in nature.

forces from the north and south of our planet and for particular mineral frequencies that are present in our Vivaxis and in the energy layers on our planet.

Effects of the Sun and Moon on Our Energies

Each day as the Earth turns on its axis, a cycle involving the alignment between Sun, Moon, and Earth causes the daily tides. There are roughly two high tides and two low tides each twenty-four hours. The high tides occur when the Moon is directly over a particular place and also when it is on the opposite side of the Earth, both conditions being caused by the daily rotation of the Earth. At the time of the two daily low tides, the Moon is at right angles to its previous position and is therefore found on the eastern or western horizon of the place in question.

Extra-high tides (called spring tides) occur at the full and new moons. Extra-low tides (called neap tides) occur when the Sun and Moon are at right angles to each other, which is the same condition as the low daily tides mentioned above. The difference between the daily and monthly tides is that the former are caused by the rotation of the Earth in relation to the Moon and the latter by the passage of the Moon around the Earth. (See figure 14.) In Vivaxis work, we need to know the position of the

Sun and Moon to undertake the Vivaxis exercises. (See exercise 5.)

Over a thirty-year period, Yale University medical scientist Harold Saxon Burr conducted an experiment on the effect of this planetary relationship on the vegetable kingdom. He attached electrodes to the living layer (cambium) of tree trunks on his property in Connecticut. His research was designed to show the effects of planetary rhythms on the life fields (L-fields).[46] Burr established that both the turning of the Earth on its axis, new and full moons, and the seasons as the Earth circled the Sun had a definite effect on the electromagnetic or L-field of his trees. The L-field fluctuated in intensity with these planetary movements. Burr found that there was a pattern between the lunar cycle, sunspot activity, and the seasons that was reflected in the voltage gradients of his trees as

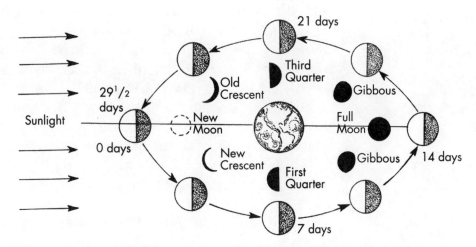

Figure 14. The phases of the Moon. During the phase of the full moon, the Sun, Earth, and Moon are all aligned to each other. Consequently, there are two opposing gravitational pulls on the Earth from the Moon on one side and from the Sun on the opposite side, as indicated by the long black lines and arrows in the figure. Reprinted from *Vivaxis Manual* by Frances Nixon, 1974.

---

[46] Harold Saxton Burr, *Blueprint for Immortality* (London: Neville Spearman, 1972).

recorded over the thirty-year period. He postulated electromagnetic connections between the cosmos and all living things.

In terms of quantifying his results, we are talking about millivolts, or tiny and subtle fluctuations, although we also know that the extra sunspot activity that occurs every eleven years can have profound effects on the planetary human-made electrical power grids. In the late 1980s, the electrical power in Quebec, Canada, was "blown out" for a few days as a result of sunspot activity. Epidemics affecting humanity have also been noted to feature strongly at these times. It would be difficult to wire up humans in such a continuous way, but if one kingdom in nature is affected in this way, the inference is that all kingdoms of nature would show effects from the Moon cycle.

Scientists studying oysters established another example of this effect on living creatures. Oysters were taken from their oceanic home and transported thousands of miles away. After a few weeks in their new watery habitat, they changed the opening times of their shells to coincide with their new position.[47] In other words, they had become adjusted at their new location to the alignment between Sun, Moon, and Earth. This demonstrates the gravitational effect of the Moon on living creatures even when far away from their usual geographic position and not subject to the movement of the tides.

Planetary Effects on Mineral Frequencies

Fran discovered that during certain angular alignments between the Sun, Earth, and Moon such as high and low tides (named major and minor periods), the

---

[47] F. A. Brown, "Persistent Activity Rhythms in the Oyster," *American Journal of Physiology* 178 (1954): 510.

frequencies that correspond to the Sun and the Moon cancel each other out. As mentioned, these frequencies compose those layers of energy named Force Flows 1 and 4. Fran developed techniques to teach the Vivaxis student how to chart the angular relationship of Sun, Earth, and Moon on the body so that use can be made of the Vivaxis energies at times when all the frequencies are present. During the major and minor periods, the mineral frequencies in these force flows of our Vivaxis and in the receptors on the body are missing.

Fran developed techniques to teach the Vivaxis student how to chart the angular relationship of Sun, Earth, and Moon on the body so that use can be made of the Vivaxis energies at times when all the frequencies are present.

The time period between major and minor periods is known as the sol-unar flow, a period that lasts for approximately six hours. It is during this period that we can safely undertake all the Vivaxis exercises, because all the energies are then present. Tide positions have always been used by fishermen to determine when fish are most likely to bite. They are apparently hungrier at high and low tides. I found that it is a fairly simple procedure during holidays by the sea to check the technique for finding solunar flows as developed by Fran with the tables for tides that are in most local papers. (See exercise 5.)

When we are by the sea, we may observe that the tide seems low for a long time even though this minor period lasts for only about twenty minutes. The major period corresponds with high tide and lasts for over an hour, although the tide may look high for longer than this. These anomalies result from the fact that a body of water takes some time to respond to planetary movements. However, the energy changes are immediate, and this is why we will continue to use the terms major and minor period instead of high and low tide.

These rhythms can be accurately discerned on the body no matter how far away we are from the ocean. It is the angle of light as our spine receives it that enables us to chart these planetary alignments on the body. At the major period, the vectors of light come into our spine in a vertical direction and at the minor period at right angles. (See figure 13.) Fran found that people with spinal trouble sometimes had trouble discerning the tides until these disorders were corrected. The reception of this planetary information by our spine is not dependent on whether we face toward or away from the Sun.

At the full and new moon, I find that the same planetary phenomenon as in the major and minor period takes place but for a longer period of about four hours before and after the peak of the Moon activity. For this reason, we do not practice any of the Vivaxis skills during the full or new moons for three days. There was, however, one exercise Fran showed us to undertake during the minor period. At this time, the element selenium is enhanced in its frequency. This mineral is needed for good immunity, and it is a powerful antioxidant, or destroyer, of free radicals (toxins) in the body. We stand on the force flow containing selenium and find and align to the direction for selenium during the middle part of the twenty-minute minor period.

Astronomical Research on Planetary Effects

The celestial bodies and their effect on us have inspired the work not only of astrologers but also of poets, musicians, and philosophers throughout the ages. Even the conventional physicist Isaac Newton was a keen advocate of not only the laws pertaining to astronomy, but also to those of its interpretation, namely astrology.

Although Fran's research did not extend to the farther planets in our solar system, it is possible that the whole basis of astrology relates to light from these bodies acting as carrier waves for many subtle influences. Thus our Vivaxis may include influences from all the planets in our solar system. The traditional horoscope consists of the angular relationship between all the planets in the solar system at the time of our first breath. (See figure 15.) It is not unreasonable to think that these planetary energies may contribute to our Vivaxis energies and account for the individuality of our mineral patterns. The planets have always been associated with particular minerals such as Mars with iron, Venus with copper, and so on. The most interesting research in this area was undertaken by the students of Rudolf Steiner. They measured the ash of plants grown under certain stellar influences. They also

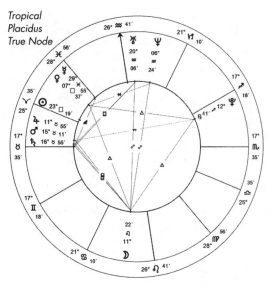

Figure 15. Mary East natal chart. This is a hypothetical horoscope showing the planets (see symbols) and their degrees of longitude in the signs on the zodiac; the houses of the chart, shown here as twelve divisions; and the aspects or angles between the planets, shown as the connecting lines between each of the symbols. The point on the eastern horizon (center left) is known as the ascendant (asc), meaning the point of the zodiac rising over the eastern horizon at the time of birth. The houses are counted counterclockwise around the chart from this point. At the beginning of each house is a sign of the zodiac marked with its symbol and degree of longitude. Every birth chart forms a different pattern, which is as individual as our fingerprints. In this chart, you can see that the planets tend to be clumped together in several places.

Compliments of *Solar Fire*, developed by Esoteric Technologies

experimented with chromatography, where certain metallic salts were used to bring out characteristics of the herbs they were evaluating.

Astrology is sometimes considered a poor cousin to astronomy, but scientific research is changing this perception. In the 1970s, the French psychologist Michel Gauquelin and his wife investigated the birth charts of many thousands of individuals and established that particular planets were related to the prominent points, or "angles," of the birth chart in relation to both temperament and a successful profession or pursuit. The groups surveyed included the following associations between prominent planets and particular activities: athletes with Mars; scientists with Saturn; medical people with Saturn and Mars; poets and writers with the Moon; and successful actors, politicians, and diplomats with Jupiter.[48]

In relation to our subject of Earth energies, the conditioning influences of these planets are mainly focused through the point of the zodiac on the eastern horizon at the time of birth—the traditional ascendant—and also at the point on the zodiac that is the highest point in the sky at the birth time. This is traditionally called the midheaven, and except at the equator, it is never directly overhead. The angle of the equator to the ecliptic (the path traveled by the Earth around the Sun) accounts for the twenty-four hours of darkness or light at certain times in extreme latitudes.

As the Earth moves around the Sun, different angular relationships are formed with each of the other planets as they pursue their orbital paths. Myriad patterns are formed that influence life on Earth. In the area of astronomy, scientific research has discovered that particular angular relationships between Mars, Saturn, and Jupiter correspond with sunspot activity and epidemics.[49]

In addition to the angular relationships between the planets, such as 90 degrees, 180 degrees, and 120 degrees, there are the ratios between one planet and another. From the time of Pythagoras, mathematical ratios between the planets have been noted and their significance debated. From this phenomenon comes the beautiful idea of the

---

[48] Michel Gauquelin, *Cosmic Influences on Human Behavior* (New York: ASI Publishers, 1978).
[49] Michel Gauquelin, *Birth Times—A Scientific Investigation of the Secrets of Astrology* (New York: Hill and Yang, 1983).

"music of the spheres." Pythagoras taught that the Western musical scale has a mathematical connection to the distances between the planets. For instance, the distance between the orbit of Venus and that of Mars may be slightly less than that between Mars and Jupiter. These varying intervals are thought to coincide with our musical notes. This is often termed the "harmony (or music) of the spheres."

Earth Rotation and Daily Rhythms

The turning of the Earth on its axis over twenty-four hours creates various bodily rhythms known as the circadian rhythms. These rhythms affect our sleeping, eating, and glandular functions. Traveling long distances in a short time by air can profoundly affect these rhythms. At our new destination, we want to sleep during the day and we then often lie sleepless for hours at night. In addition, we may wish to eat at strange times, and our digestion can be impaired. Many women suffer menstrual irregularities when they travel. In summary, the body clock becomes very disturbed with the effect of jet lag.

The brain's pineal gland is one of the main timekeepers in the body. It also is the director of the endocrine system. This means that the pineal regulates the other glands, including the pituitary, thyroid, thymus, pancreas, adrenals, and gonads. The pineal gland, a tiny pinecone-shaped organ in the center of the brain, secretes a hormone called melatonin. The production of this hormone is stimulated by periods of light and darkness and, of course, when we travel across time zones, its usual patterns are disturbed. Melatonin production peaks between 2 A.M. and 4 A.M., normally the darkest time during the twenty-four hour cycle. The health of the pineal gland is very important for Vivaxis research, as it is connected to our magnetic sense.

Early in her research, Fran demonstrated how central the pineal gland is in our energy relations with the planets. She discovered that if the top of the head and the forehead are covered in black cloth during testing at the full moon, the energy patterns of body organs revert to those at other times of the month. It may be that light from the Sun and Moon acts as a carrier wave for electromagnetic and more subtle energies from the planets.[50] We know that the pineal gland in the head is affected by light. Perhaps light from the Sun and Moon is sensed by the pineal gland more strongly at the full moon and the use of the black cloth to cover the head stops the pineal from receiving light. This finding may be related to the fact that we usually can only find the vector for light with our eyes open. But at the full moon, Fran found that light could be tested with eyes shut, which indicates that the light is more powerful at those times. Our bodies, therefore, appear to be very sensitive to changes in light from the Sun and Moon, and our body rhythms appear to be influenced correspondingly.

Some people are very sensitive to changes in light intensity, and they become severely depressed in winter. This problem is called Seasonal Affective Disorder (SAD). It can be alleviated by exposing the person to a strong full-spectrum light each morning for an hour or so.[51] Clinical trials have been conducted using medication with the hormone melatonin. One of the first discoveries about melatonin was its polarity with the gonadal hormones. Women with fertility problems were found to conceive if they slept in a lighted room during the time of ovulation. In other words, if there is an oversecretion of melatonin during the hours of darkness, the function of the ovaries will be suppressed and light can be used to help resolve the problem. It would be interesting to know if these women also suffered from depression.

---

[50] Frances Nixon, *Vivaxis Manual, Part 3* (British Columbia, Canada: Magnetic Publishers, 1974). p.22

[51] R. Sandyk, et al., "Magnetic Fields and Seasonality of Affective Illness: Implications for Therapy," *International Journal of Neuroscience* 58, no. 3-4 (June 1991): 261-7.

The pineal gland also secretes a hormone called sero-tonin, which is needed for relaxation. Perhaps this is one reason that traveling during the night can lead to trouble sleeping on subsequent nights.

The White Force Flows on the Earth (as described in chapter 2) correspond to the pineal gland frequency. These layers are active when the Sun is near its meridian, that is, between the hours of 10 A.M. and 2 P.M. This may vary a little according to the latitude of the place on the planet. Particular techniques are described in part 2 for using the frequencies from these energy bands to improve the health of the pineal gland. (See exercise 14.)

As the pineal gland appears to be related to the reception of both physical and spiritual light, its health is important in many respects. Not only is it affected by the cycle of day and night, but it also possibly reacts to the relationship between the Sun, Moon, and Earth that man-ifests as the major and minor periods and as the Moon phases each month.

The daily turning of the Earth brings in etheric ener-gies that teachers of spiritual practices and meditation have known about for a long time. We have always been advised to meditate *early* in the morning, as close to dawn as possible. A special energy apparently flows toward us as the Sun rises in the east. This subtle energy is quite dif-ferent from the energy that comes from the heat of the Sun when it is at the highest point in the sky. Many med-itators have found three points of the day to be significant for meditation: dawn, midday, and sunset. Different types of energies are available at each of these periods.

In summarizing these thoughts, the planetary rhythms related to their positions and relationships are reflected in our human health and rhythms. The pineal gland appears to be a sensitive instrument for receiving light and, in turn, regulates our glandular cycles. The "White Flows" of the ener-gy layers discovered by Fran reflect the daily position of the Sun and can be used to restore health to our pineal gland.

Eclipses of the Sun and Moon

Another planetary rhythm or phenomenon occurs during eclipses. Such times have always been regarded as significant in human lives.

The Moon is the closest celestial body to our planet and exerts on Earth the greatest gravitational effect, manifesting as the ocean tides several times each twenty-four hours. New and full moons occur when the Moon, Earth, and Sun form a straight line in terms of celestial longitude. Occasionally, the Moon, Earth, and Sun will also be in the same latitude, and this causes the Moon to block out the light of the Sun, or the Earth to overshadow the Moon at that place on the planet where an exact alignment occurs. These phenomena are called eclipses of the Sun or Moon. An eclipse of the Sun occurs when the Moon comes between the Earth and the Sun at one of the new moons.

This temporary disappearance of light from the Earth has always been seen by the superstitious as a bad omen. It is understandable that the physical disappearance of light can come to symbolize the disappearance of spiritual light. It is interesting that there was an eclipse of the Sun close to the beginning of the U. S. engagement in the Gulf War in the beginning of 1991. This war was possibly the first war of aggression on our planet when almost all nations across the globe condemned a single aggressor, Iraq.

The world's reaction to the Gulf War could be considered as a milestone in a spiritual sense, despite mixed motives in relation to oil supplies in the Middle East. Although the eclipse may have signified a disaster from one point of view, humanity behaved as a global village for the first time in recorded history. It is interesting that shortly after a very strong eclipse in August 1999, a major crisis developed in East Timor (a territory claimed by Indonesia but seeking independence) and involved peacekeepers from many nations. At the same time, war erupted again between Russia and Chechnya.

If we analyze what takes place during an alignment between Sun, Moon, and Earth, we come to the following consideration: at the time of the new moon, the Moon is between the Earth and the Sun. At these times, the effect of the Moon on the Earth would be expected to be the most powerful in terms of its gravitational effect. In most religions and cultures, the Sun symbolizes spiritual light, and therefore the new moon could be interpreted as temporarily blocking out spiritual light on the planet. Thus in some cultures it is the traditional time each month when evil tendencies are thought to be strengthened. During an eclipse of the Sun, this effect from the Moon is further enhanced.

With respect to more individual effects from the Moon, medical research has established that hemorrhage from surgery is far more likely to occur at the time of the full moon.[52] Perhaps the Moon may have some extragravitational effect at these times on bodily fluids such as on blood circulation. This effect has not yet become understood by science, but medical procedures are adequate these days to cope with any unexpected hemorrhaging tendency.

Another type of eclipse occurs when the Earth comes between the Sun and the Moon at one of the full moons. The Moon is then on the opposite side of the Earth from the Sun, and the Earth blocks the light of the Sun from shining on the Moon. Again, this is caused by alignment in both longitude and latitude of the Sun, Moon, and Earth. As this phenomenon does not cause any disappearance of sunlight, an eclipse is viewed as a time for enhancement of spiritual practices.

In relation to Vivaxis work, we need to know about all of these stellar positions because they profoundly

---

[52] L. Watson, *Supernature* (London: Coronet Books, 1973).

affect the availability of mineral frequencies. Whenever the Moon and Sun are in strong alignment, they correspondingly cancel out the Force Flow 1 and Force Flow 4 energies.

Enhancing Our Meditation Practice

Indeed, over the period of the full moon each month, we can experience a deeper and greater spiritual alignment. This provides an opportunity to access energies from the particular constellation behind the Sun for the healing of ourselves, the planet, and the kingdoms of nature. In this planetary alignment, the Moon can fully reflect back to the Earth energies from the Sun and whichever constellation is behind the Sun. So, at the full moon of Cancer, the constellation of Cancer is behind the Sun, and at the full moon of Leo, the constellation Leo is behind the Sun. These alignments are considered to enhance our spiritual practices.

During the year, we have an opportunity to receive energy from each of the twelve signs of the zodiac as the Earth moves around the Sun. These energies are experienced more fully when we meditate as a group, thereby providing a greater means for transmission of energies. The other advantage of a group meditation is to protect the individual from the powerful energies contacted. Many individuals and groups throughout the world celebrate the full moon each month as a spiritual festival. I have found over the years that individuals who have learned to focus their minds by meditation can easily visualize the mineral elements in Vivaxis work. They are also accurate in measuring the Vivaxis layers. It is not essential to meditate for Vivaxis work, but it is very helpful.

Buddhism celebrates the Wesak festival at the full moon of May, often called the full moon of Taurus because that is the constellation in line with the Sun at that time. This festival is also the high point for many people who gather with the aim of transmitting spiritual energies into our planet. Alice Bailey is one writer who has written extensively on this full moon approach as a means to align with the spiritual hierarchy or inner teachers in the subjective planetary realms.[53]

In Celtic cultures, May Day was held as a special time when the fertility of the Earth was celebrated by a pagan rite during which large numbers of people joyfully copulated for that purpose. The aim was to transmit this human expression of fertility into the Earth for the promotion of life-giving crops. Perhaps there originally was a more spiritual impulse of this Celtic expression that was lost over the centuries. The full moon effect is yet another example of planetary and stellar rhythms that can profoundly affect our daily lives. I see the Vivaxis connection as part of this larger picture when we have a constant ebb and flow of subtle electromagnetic and etheric energies. It matters not whether we use the term "spiritual" for the deeper meaning of the full moons; the energies are there by whatever term we use.

The smaller cycle of the daily tides can be used for spiritual purposes and for meditation. Meditators have always experienced sunrise and sunset as powerful times for meditation. I have found that when the Moon is also on the horizon at low tide (minor period), meditation is again more powerful, aiding alignment and spiritual penetration. Unfortunately, the tides occur one hour later each day, which means that we cannot meditate with the low tide at the same time each day. However, every twelve days or so, the low tide will correspond with sunrise or sunset, and this is especially powerful, because the Sun and Moon are then in an alignment on our planetary horizon. The main application for Vivaxis work here is our ability to become increasingly aware of the major and

---

[53] Alice A. Bailey, *Esoteric Psychology* (London: Lucis Press, 1942).

minor periods. It is often easier to do Vivaxis work with the clarity of mind that meditation brings.

My work with Fran Nixon taught me a practical reason these planetary movements may have an effect on our consciousness. Fran found that creative thought is stimulated by the receptors on the body that are associated with the vertical vector, or direction, for chromium. We don't know why the element chromium is particularly associated with creative thoughts. We have found that creative thoughts are inhibited if the brain receptors associated with chromium are disturbed. You may remember that the chromium receptors are stimulated by singing. There are horizontal and vertical vectors for most of the elements in our bodies. The word "vector" is used, because, in addition to meaning a direction, it denotes force and velocity. For that matter, in this book the terms "force flow," "wave link," or "direction" are terms often used interchangeably instead of the term vector.

As I stated, at the new and full moons and also at high and low tides, many of the receptors for elements on the body become quiescent.[54] However, the vertical chromium receptors are more powerful at high and low tides. Perhaps they provide the subtle physical means whereby our connection with higher levels of manifestation is increased. Eventually, it may be discovered that every mineral frequency has both a physical and metaphysical significance in the body. Perhaps this will eventually become a new basis for astrology and take us back to the relations of the elements with particular planets.

Fran's work with light vectors in relation to both the human body and the planet is an extraordinary discovery. It is significant that our etheric or energy body is often called the light body and it appears that our energies are closely conditioned by the direction of light flow from

[54] Nixon, *Search For Vivaxis*, Part 1.

the Sun and Moon to the Earth. The angular relationship between the Sun, Moon, and Earth, as reflected in the spinal canal, can be related to the Eastern teaching about the spinal channels.

In Eastern spiritual teachings, the subtle channels associated with the spine are considered to house energy flows that are directly related to our spiritual growth and practice. Three channels are described in Eastern philosophy: *ida, pingala,* and *sushumna.* One is masculine, one feminine, and the central channel, *sushumna,* is a synthesis of the two. *Ida* is usually considered as the feminine, or Moon, channel, and *pingala* as the masculine, or Sun, channel. These channels are connected with the energy centers (chakras) and are discussed in chapter 7.

As the energy centers become active and purified, the energies in the spinal channels rise upward toward the head. These subtle spinal canals and currents connect with the endocrine glands in the head via the two head chakras at the brow and at the top of the head. The pituitary gland is connected with the *ida* channel, which in turn connects with the two chakras concerned with our creative life and the sacral and throat chakras. The *pingala* channel responds to two other chakras, the solar plexus and heart, and relates to the pineal gland. The central channel is related to the base and crown chakras, the last pair to become active.

The "third eye," or brow chakra, develops from the union of the magnetic fields around the pituitary and pineal glands, according to the esoteric teachings of Alice Bailey. This relation of the pituitary gland to the pineal takes place at a stage in our spiritual life when the energies are able to travel freely up the spinal channels. Here we are talking about an energy relation between the two glands. It coincides with an opening and alignment among all the chakras. In a psychospiritual sense it also relates to the alignment between our integrated personality and our soul, or inner essence. In mystical philosophy, this is termed the "marriage in heaven" and allows us to experience Heaven on Earth. As we grow spiritually, we experience integration on many different levels. The integration of the personality refers to a balance and integration between our physical body, our emotional or astral nature, and our mind or mental body. Later, we can experience an integration or blending with our soul.

This excursion into metaphysics is relevant here because at the major and minor periods, and at the new and full moons, the gravitational influence of the Sun and Moon possibly affects the fluid in our spine and the more subtle energy currents in our spinal channels. Perhaps this is why meditation seems more powerful at low tide (minor period). I usually check the relationship between Sun and Moon as registered on the spine after meditation so as not to condition my expectations beforehand. (See exercise 5.) Remember, the tides occur one hour later each day, so we cannot always keep these special times. However, it is very useful to understand these gravitational effects.

The importance of working with these factors will be realized more fully later when we look at the various types of mineral and energy flows on the body in exercise 6. Because many of the mineral frequencies disappear at the major and minor periods and at the new and full moon, a few people feel very unbalanced at these times. This phenomena may explain why mental institutions have always found disturbances in the inmates at the full moon. These individuals could be deficient in the minerals that coincide with frequencies that temporarily disappear during these key moments in the Moon cycle.

Another example of celestial influences on body physiology in the general population relates to chromium, which regulates blood sugar by the pancreas. It is possible that those deficient in chromium are more likely to suffer hypoglycemia, or low blood sugar, when the chromium, or Sun flow, is canceled out by the Moon flow.

The zinc and silica frequencies are on the Moon layer and could also be implicated in this way, meaning that deficiency symptoms from these elements may be worse at these times. Homeopaths have consistently noticed that people with an imbalance of the element silica are worse at the new moon. This means that all their bodily symptoms and fears are exacerbated at this time.

In summary, knowledge about the position of the Sun, Moon, and Earth as reflected in our body is useful for *practical* issues, including the best times to absorb mineral frequencies necessary for good health. We have looked also at connections with the other planets, and how the patterns in the heavens may be reflected on both our planet via the energy layers discovered by Fran and in our bodily rhythms and glandular patterns. At the metaphysical level, we can note the effect of the stellar pattern between Sun, Moon, and Earth on our meditation practices. There appears to be an overall relationship between the planets, including the Sun and Moon, Vivaxis energy layers, ocean tides, human glandular systems, and the mineral balance in our bodies. You see how the Vivaxis connection seems to involve the solar system, and not just the body and Earth.

We now turn to the specific points on the body, which can receive each of the various frequencies. Fran started her research with the Vivaxis and the energy circuit between the Vivaxis and the body. She named these points "receptors," and in most instances they correspond to acupuncture points. The sequence of influences flowing toward our body can be visualized as follows:

Earth frequencies (as on the energy layers) and force flows ➤

There appears to be an overall relationship between the planets, including the Sun and Moon, Vivaxis energy layers, ocean tides, human glandular systems, and the mineral balance in our bodies. You see how the Vivaxis connection seems to involve the solar system, and not just the body and Earth.

our Vivaxis ➤ connecting links between our Vivaxis and the energy field immediately surrounding our body ➤ body receptors that receive the many frequencies of the force flows on the Earth in the energy layers.

I will now discuss the body receptors and their frequencies as part of the central key to the Vivaxis connection.

Suggested Reading

Oken, Alan. *Alan Oken's Complete Astrology*. New York: Bantam, 1980.

Seymour, Percy. *Astrology—The Evidence of Science*. London: Arkana, 1990.

CHAPTER 6

Our Body Receptors for Life-Giving Energies

We can see an emerging pattern from the life science based on the Vivaxis connection. We can enhance all the frequencies necessary for a healthy life from the Earth via our Vivaxis and the energy layers. A horizontal flow moves up one foot to the hand on one side of the body and out the other hand and foot back toward the Vivaxis. The frequencies of these energy flows that come from the energy layers are received by hundreds of receptors on the body, commonly called acupuncture points. Disturbances to these receptors interfere with our receiving the health-supporting energies from the Earth via the Vivaxis.

A large portion of the research undertaken by Fran, starting in 1970, involved the body receptors. She spent months mapping the receptors responsible for transporting wave messages from the brain to the limbs and organs. She found techniques to remove static and interferences; she developed skills to enhance receptor functioning; and she discovered the associated mineral frequencies. In addition to those receptors involved with body movements and organs, Fran found others related to communication, and still other receptors associated with memory. Each receptor carries a particular frequency into our energy field and from there to the physical body.

The receptors correspond exactly to the acupuncture points on the body, according to research Fran accomplished with scientists.[55] The reader might wonder how Fran first discovered the qualities and processes associated with the receptors. In all her research, she was an exceedingly intuitive thinker, always looking for connections. Some people would call her "right-brained," but she was at the same time very meticulous and logical—qualities generally associated with the left side of the brain. In addition, Fran often seemed to wake in the morning with a solution to a problem. Most significant, all her research was replicated by many of her students and instructors, and their findings appeared to be very consistent with hers.

The frequencies of the elements in the Periodic Table have been established by science with spectrophotometry, where the wavelength or frequency of each element is measured in terms of light. Each element emits a certain frequency, which is linked to the atomic weight of that element. Our bodies contain all those elements in the Periodic Table that are essential for health and life, such as hydrogen, oxygen, nitrogen, carbon, calcium, sodium, magnesium, sulfur, potassium, chlorine, fluorine, phosphorus, and so on. Some elements on our planet are also harmful in any but minute quantities, such as lead, cadmium, and mercury. The frequencies for these elements are found on the detrimental energy layers described earlier in chapter 3.

Also in chapter 3, I discussed the leading edge of medicine in terms of the vibratory frequencies important for life. I presented a model of health based on the restoration of the correct frequencies to different parts of the body, and I suggested that eventually we will know exactly what sound, color, mineral, herb, homeopathic, or

---

[55] Nixon, *Vivaxis Manual, Part 1*, p. 19.

flower essence is needed to rebalance our body frequencies. The appropriate remedy will completely disrupt or change the disease frequency and will therefore help restore the individual to health and harmony. The correct frequency not only may be the cure, but it also may be the essential nature of all remedies and substances.

Fran discovered that many of the key receptors for the life-giving elements are on our fingers, toes, and around the eyes and head. She also charted the receptors that are concerned with transmitting energy for movement of all body parts. In every case of paralysis or impediment to normal movements, for example, she found disturbed receptors on the head, fingers, and toes.

The Receptors or Acupuncture Points

Thousands of years ago Chinese medicine established that our body energies associated with each organ run in circuits called meridians. (See figure 16.) There are twelve primary meridians and many other subsidiary meridians that have recently been the subject of research. Acupuncture points on each meridian have a lower electrical resistance than the surrounding skin area as charted by instruments that measure skin resistance. The points are used by acupuncturists to link one meridian with another for the purpose of balancing the energies of the body. For example, if the liver is found to have too much energy (acupuncturists call it *chi*), acupuncture needles will be placed to shift the excess liver energy to another organ that may be depleted.

Remember that we are connected to our Vivaxis by both vertical and horizontal energies. Fran added to this discovery by finding that each acupuncture point or receptor has both a horizontal and vertical wave flow linking it with our Vivaxis.[56] She also identified the minerals associated

---

[56] Nixon, *Vivaxis Manual, Part 2*, p. 30.

with the receptors by trial and error, using her dowsing sense. This discovery is not surprising, because minerals are necessary to carry an electrical current—even the tiny currents associated with the physical body. Some individuals respond better to acupuncture than others, and I consider this to be partly related to the mineral status in their body. If their mineral status is low, the tiny electrical currents (as discovered by Burr, Becker, and other medical scientists) may not be carried from one part of the body to another via the meridians.

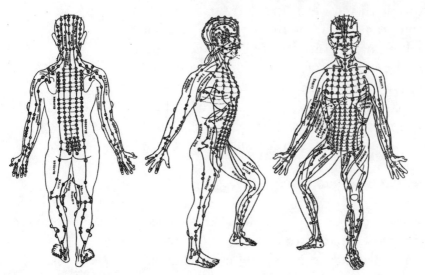

Figure 16 A, B & C. Acupuncture points. Numerous acupuncture points are found on the body's twelve main energy circuits, or meridians.

The body can only absorb minerals if they are in a very assimilable form, either through the plant kingdom—the correct food and medicine for humanity—or through colloidal preparation in which the minerals are in a very fine suspension. As minerals are the basic building blocks of the cells, their presence in the body in the correct balance and frequency is very important for health. We can also obtain corresponding mineral frequencies directly from the force flows in the energy layers, and when we do this, it helps us to assimilate those elements in our food.

The Elements on the Fingertips

The receptors on our fingertips are associated with the key minerals in our Vivaxis and also with the energy layers of the Earth. Fran taught how to visualize the elements and then to find which fingers resonated to each element. The position for the key points on each finger pad is in the center of the finger whorl or loop and, correspondingly, on the center of the fingernail. If you look at your finger pad under a good light, you will see this loop or whorl. Everyone has horizontal and vertical pairs of elements on both hands, although the position of each element varies from person to person. We are connected to our Vivaxis via these receptors on our fingers. (See figure 17 and exercise 6.)

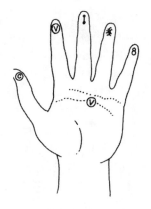 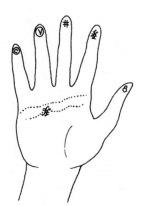

© copper
Ⓥ gravitational group
⚡ vertical chromium

♏ magnetic group
♋ selenium
horizontal chromium

Figure 17. Groups of elements in the center of the finger pads. You can see by this figure that the Vivaxis flow fingers are those with the gravitational and magnetic groups. They are the fingers carrying the mineral frequencies that correspond to the two layers of our Vivaxis field. The gravitational group has zinc or iodine as its central frequency, and the magnetic group has iron as its central frequency.

Reprinted from *Healing through Earth Energies* by Judy Jacka, 1996.

The elements chromium, iron, copper, and selenium are common to all persons tested, but two different elements seem to divide us into groups. These elements are zinc and iodine. Some people have iodine featuring on a fingertip of each hand and others have zinc; the "zinc" people compose the larger group. As yet, the reason for this difference is unknown; however, I have a theory that it is associated with our expression through a particular chakra. We know that iodine is associated with the thyroid and consequently the throat chakra, while zinc is associated with the gonads (ovaries and prostate glands) and therefore with the sacral chakra. Both of these chakras are represented on Force Flow 4—the gravitational band. The throat and sacral chakra form a pair, as you will see in chapter 7.

There are interesting reversals in the positioning of the elements on the hands. Thus, if we have iron on the first finger of one hand, it will feature on the fourth finger of the other hand. If we have copper on the thumb of the right hand, it will feature on the little finger of the left hand, while the position of selenium will feature on the other thumb and little finger. In addition, one side of the hand will have the vertical flows and the other the horizontal flows of the main Vivaxis minerals. Visualizing the elements is one of the easiest ways to become familiar with the frequencies of the Vivaxis connection.

In addition to the central element associated with the center of each fingertip, four other elements cluster around the central one, and these are individual for each person. This individual group is probably related to the individual colors for each person, as described in chapter 1. For instance, in her book, *Mysteries of Memory Unfold*, Fran listed the group of elements surrounding her iron receptor as calcium with the element carbon found opposite, and phosphorous found opposite sodium.[57] (See figure 18.) So we have a general pattern of elements for everyone, apart from the zinc and iodine groups of persons, and a more individual pattern of elements around the central element of each fingertip. As yet, there has not been much research on the latter.

A physicist pointed out that the atomic numbers of each pair around the central element on the fingertip added to twenty-six which is the atomic number of the central element—iron. In each case examined, the same pattern was discerned—the atomic numbers of the pairs of elements added to the atomic number of that element in the center.

If you look at figure 18A, you will note that around the central element iron there is carbon (6) and calcium (20), and these add to the atomic number for iron (26). The other elements are phosphorus (15) and sodium (11), and this also adds the central element of iron (26).

This is one of those patterns in nature we do not understand completely, but it does indicate perhaps the profound pattern of atomic energies in our physical bodies.

---

[57] Frances Nixon, *Mysteries of Memory Unfold* (British Columbia, Canada: Magnetic Publishers, 1978), chap. 4.

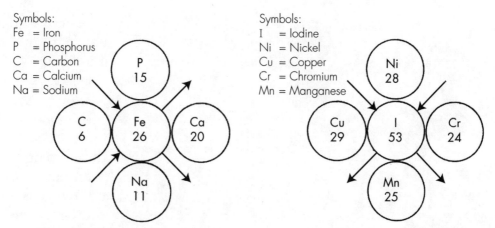

Symbols:
Fe = Iron
P = Phosphorus
C = Carbon
Ca = Calcium
Na = Sodium
P 15
C 6
Fe 26
Ca 20
Na 11

Figure 18A. Example of a magnetic group on first fingertip

Symbols:
I = Iodine
Ni = Nickel
Cu = Copper
Cr = Chromium
Mn = Manganese
Ni 28
Cu 29
I 53
Cr 24
Mn 25

Figure 18B. Example of a gravitational group on fourth fingertip

Reprinted, with slight alterations, from *Mysteries of Memory Unfold* by Frances Nixon, 1978.

The Triple Vivaxis Groups

All receptors in these groups are imprinted with the frequency of a particular element. For instance, on either side of the chromium group on the forehead is a line relating to the other elements on the fingers—iron and zinc, or iron and iodine.[58] Not all these receptors are known as acupuncture points.

The elements on the fingertips are part of a triple mineral group system that is found throughout the cranium and skeleton. The groups are arranged in columns an inch or so apart down the torso and legs. Each group consists in turn of three lines of receptors close together. The middle line contains receptors that resonate to chromium with a horizontal and vertical wave alternating down the line. The lines on either side have receptors alternating between the magnetic group (iron) and gravitational group (zinc or iodine), depending on the personal frequency. Between each receptor are frequencies for selenium,

[58] Nixon, *Search for Vivaxis, Part 2*, chap. 3.

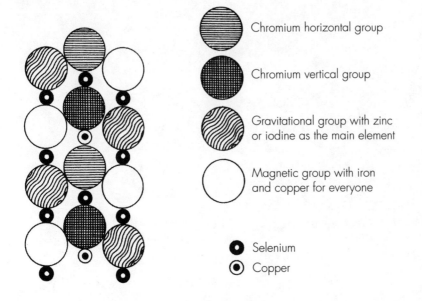

Chromium horizontal group

Chromium vertical group

Gravitational group with zinc or iodine as the main element

Magnetic group with iron and copper for everyone

⚫ Selenium

◉ Copper

Figure 19. The triple Vivaxis groups. These groups run vertically up and down the surface of the body, and each triple line is about half an inch from the next triple line. So there are about six rows of triple groups on each side of our midline front and back. It is interesting to compare this to the standard meridian lines (see figure 18) when there are only three lines of pairs—either side of the midline.

Reprinted, with slight alterations, from *Healing through Earth Energies* by Judy Jacka, 1996)

copper, germanium, and lithium. (See figure 19.) The magnetic and gravitational groups correspond to the force flows of those names as described in chapter 3, that is, magnetic group (Force Flow 3) and gravitational group (Force Flow 4).

Germanium and selenium work in the same way as they do in electronics: they assist the passage of energies in one direction only. The selenium receptors are concerned with energies moving vertically up through the energy layers, and the germanium group is concerned with energies moving vertically down through the energy layers. Again, we can be amazed at how Fran found the passage of energy in our etheric field to be organized in a way familiar to physical scientists, yet totally unknown to date by medicine.

Each magnetic group (iron) and gravitational group (iodine or zinc) will have horizontal waves on the front of the body and vertical waves on the back, or the reverse, depending on whether we are above or below the Vivaxis. This arrangement corresponds to the location of the vertical and horizontal waves on the fingers. The rows of triple groups are all connected to our Vivaxis.

In addition, the receptors have alternating left- and right-hand spin as we test down the line of groups. Spin means that the energy flowing through the receptors moves clockwise or counterclockwise. Fran found that the normal energy flow in our electromagnetic field has two vertical directions—one up and one down—representing the clockwise and counterclockwise spin on our receptors. She thought this spin was connected to the rotation of the Earth and concluded this was why our receptors become disrupted during earthquakes and other planetary disturbances.[59]

An electrical polarity appears to be manifesting through all the Vivaxis work. I think the opposite spin found in adjacent receptors is probably related to centrifugal (outflowing) and centripetal (inflowing) currents that probably flow in opposite directions throughout the body. In the polarity therapy founded by Randolph Stone, centrifugal and centripetal currents of energy are described as manifesting widely in nature. This phenomenon also relates to the yin and yang of traditional Chinese medicine. In fact, the ancient wisdom, or perennial philosophy, describes such currents that move in opposite directions as underlying all physical forms in the vegetable, animal, and human kingdoms.

Many of Fran's discoveries seem related to known theories of physics, but as yet the connections between even the known laws of physics and the human body have not been elaborated. This matter of spin in our receptors falls in this category. The main point to grasp is that Fran found this spin in the receptors to be disturbed when ill health manifests, and this usually happens when an energy outside our own electromagnetic field interferes with our energies. This interference can be emotional, chemical, or electromagnetic. You will learn to test for this spin associated with receptors in exercise 6.

The groups of receptors discussed so far, those on the fingertips and the triple groups, are all connected to our Vivaxis. These include receptors that respond to the

---

[59] Frances Nixon, *Magnetically Yours* (British Columbia, Canada: Magnetic Publishers, date unknown), p. 22.

frequencies of chromium, iron, copper, selenium, zinc, and iodine. Fran sometimes called these involuntary receptors because of their permanent wave activity to organs and to our Vivaxis. This means that in health these receptors have a permanent energy link to our organs and also receive a continual flow of energy to recharge our body from our Vivaxis.

The receptors have alternating left- and right-hand spin as we test down the line of groups. Fran found this spin in the receptors to be disturbed when ill health manifests, and this usually happens when an energy outside our own electromagnetic field interferes with our energies. This interference can be emotional, chemical, or electromagnetic.

The Brain Receptors

Fran found that brain receptors are strategically placed where they can influence and control the various Vivaxis links in the body. A brain receptor is always sandwiched between two other receptors placed about one quarter of an inch apart from each other. In keeping with the receptors previously described, the energy in one receptor has a clockwise motion and in the other a counterclockwise motion. The brain receptors are in two basic groups—lower and higher. (See figure 20.) It is significant that the chromium frequency is present at the center of all our brain receptors and no doubt this accounts for why we can find the chromium layers on the planet when visualizing chromium. Our visualization creates a resonance between the chromium of our brain receptor and the same frequency in the environment. The central brain receptors in these groups all respond to mathematical-type thought, but there are other differences between the higher and lower groups as described below.[60]

Lower-brain receptors are primarily located on the head below the hairline. They consist of twenty-four

---

[60] Nixon, *Born to Be Magnetic*, vol. 1, p. 112.

groups, each comprised of three receptors.[61] The central receptor in each group responds to mathematical thought and is linked to the Vivaxis with horizontal and vertical waves. Some of these central receptors have been identified by acupuncturists as known acupuncture points. A receptor is located on either side of the central brain receptor. They can be described as follows:

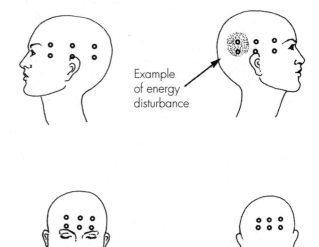

Example of energy disturbance

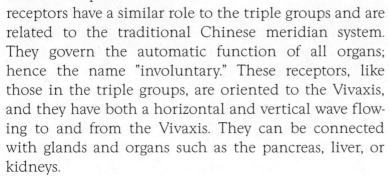

Figure 20A. Lower-brain receptor groups

1. An *involuntary* receptor is located immediately to one side of the central brain receptor. These receptors have a similar role to the triple groups and are related to the traditional Chinese meridian system. They govern the automatic function of all organs; hence the name "involuntary." These receptors, like those in the triple groups, are oriented to the Vivaxis, and they have both a horizontal and vertical wave flowing to and from the Vivaxis. They can be connected with glands and organs such as the pancreas, liver, or kidneys.

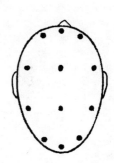

Figure 20B. Higher-brain receptor groups as seen from the top of the head

Reprinted, with slight alterations, from *Healing through Earth Energies* by Judy Jacka, 1996).

2. A *voluntary* receptor is located at the same distance on the other side of the central brain receptor. These receptors are associated with body movement and with communication in our environment. They have a horizontal wave that is associated with the object in our environment

---

[61] Nixon, *Vivaxis Manual, Part 2*, chap. 5.

under consideration and a vertical wave that only extends down to the level of our feet. These receptors are not connected with our Vivaxis. They were sometimes called flexible receptors. These receptors can become inadvertently connected to another person's Vivaxis because of their capacity for communicating with the environment. (See figures 21 and 22.)

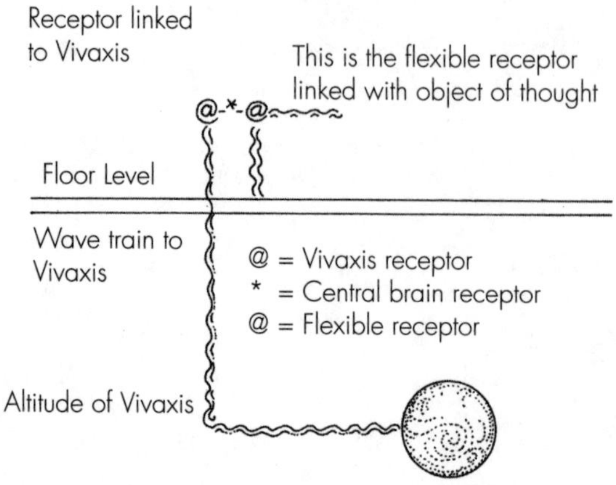

The receptors on either side of the central brain receptors swap their function, depending on our position in relation to our Vivaxis. This switching mechanism reminds us of the receptors in the triple groups, which also switch their wave directions, depending on our position in relation to our Vivaxis. The switching mechanism appears to be one of the electromagnetic functions of our body.

There are twelve groups of higher-brain receptors, and, apart from being stimulated by mental exercises, they are associated with memory, creative thought patterns, and energies from the Sun and Moon.[62] These receptors are located on the crown of the head above the hairline. On one side of the central higher-brain receptor is a Sun receptor and on the other side a Moon receptor. As with the lower-brain pairs, these swap their position, depending on our relation to our Vivaxis.

The central higher-brain receptor in this group is imprinted with the Vivaxis frequencies, and like other Vivaxis receptors, it is linked to it both horizontally and vertically. This central receptor is stimulated by mental exercises, by recalling a past incident, or by thinking of

Receptor linked to Vivaxis

This is the flexible receptor linked with object of thought

Floor Level

Wave train to Vivaxis

@ = Vivaxis receptor
* = Central brain receptor
@ = Flexible receptor

Altitude of Vivaxis

Figure 21. The wave flows from the receptors on either side of a communication brain receptor. The flexible receptor has a vertical wave train flowing to the floor and back and the possibility to link horizontally toward an object of thought. Under certain conditions, the horizontal wave is permanently attached, and a foreign field is formed. The other receptor has a wave train to the Vivaxis and back.

---

[62] Nixon, *Vivaxis Manual, Part 4,* p. 20.

the Vivaxis. This is illustrated when the tester activates the brain receptors with mathematical thought, and his hand moves in an alternating movement toward the Vivaxis and back.

If, however, we think of moving a limb, we activate the voluntary receptors for movement and the wave movement will flow toward a track of receptors associated with the limb in question. Fran devised checks to test that the brain groups are in good working order and to test limb movement. These simple tests are outlined in part 2, exercise 16.

If we are free of static, our brain receptors are able to direct a recording angle wire held in our hand to rotate in the direction of thought. If we are static, the wire refuses to follow the brain's command because of the disruption of the key receptors. (See figure 23.)

The following two case histories illustrate how easily interference to our brain receptors may occur. It is hard to know exactly the number of contributing factors to these disturbances. In the first case (Naomi), the disturbance appeared to relate to electromagnetic interference; in the second case (Davine), it may have resulted from the hypnotic effect of another person.

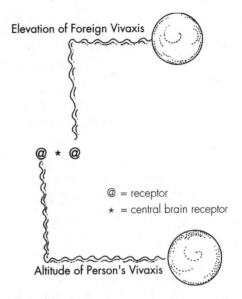

Figure 22. Vertical wave flow of a flexible receptor linked to a foreign Vivaxis. Note that here each side receptor is wave linked to a separate Vivaxis. The two lack resonance and teamwork. The entire meridian would also have the same conflicting energy streams. Note the difference between this scenario and that in figure 21, where there is no link to a foreign Vivaxis.

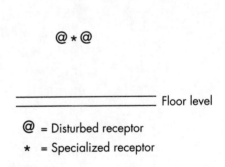

Figure 23. Disturbed and malfunctioning receptors. There are no vertical or horizontal wave vectors linked to a Vivaxis, because this is a disturbed receptor. It therefore is in a static condition. When wave links to a Vivaxis are interfered, the entire meridian to which the receptors belong will be affected. This is analogous to the missing link in a chain.

Disturbed Brain Receptors: Two Cases

Naomi's mother had taken my Vivaxis course and sent her daughter to me for treatment. Naomi was doing university studies and was exhausted with headaches and had very poor concentration. When anyone says they have very poor memory or concentration, I always test the brain receptors. I found Naomi's were all disturbed, and I took her outside for work on the energy layers. She exercised on each force flow, and after we applied water energized on all the layers to her head, she immediately felt clearer in the head.

In the course of examining Naomi's lifestyle, I discovered she slept with a digital clock near her head. This could have been a major contributing factor to the disturbed receptors. One month later she reported a big improvement in her concentration, and I found that her brain receptors had stayed in a normal state. She remained in good health throughout the rest of her year at university. Some time later, I heard from her mother that Naomi had not relapsed and was keeping in good health and able to undertake her studies.

Davine, a woman in her early sixties, was another client who came to me with disturbed brain receptors. She was doing university studies and finding it nearly impossible to study and write. A complication in her case was her impression that a previous romantic partner still had an hypnotic effect on her. As you will remember, hypnosis can cause a foreign field, so I had Davine undertake the neutralizing exercise on several successive days. I applied treated water to all parts of her head and she felt relief immediately. On testing her brain receptors one month later, I found they had remained in working order. It is now many months since the initial treatment and Davine remains well.

The brain receptors will respond less during major or minor periods, because Force Flows 1 and 4 (the Vivaxis/ Sun and Moon flows) cancel each other out. These are the times when the angular position between Sun, Moon, and

Earth cause the high and low tides. Vertical chromium flows, which are associated with higher or abstract and creative thought, will be more active, while other types of thought tend to be less active during these periods.

There are two other types of receptors based on Fran's work:

1. H points: These are another classification of receptors itemized early in Fran's work. (See figure 24.) Fran said that these points involved signals from the brain's hypothalamus, and hence she called them H points. In addition to the four points marked, there is one on the soft palate that is always disturbed by dental work. There are terminal locations for the central H points at the center of each hand and center of each instep, and on the side of both hands and feet. Fran found it very important to check these points for possible connections with foreign Vivaxes and to correct these points before reinstating Vivaxis energies into our bones through aligning to our Vivaxis.[63]

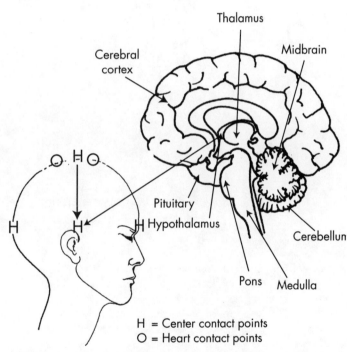

H = Center contact points
O = Heart contact points

Figure 24. H points—Hypothalamus connections. The hypothalamus, one of the most vital organs of the body, is located in the lower central portion of the brain, where its position provides maximum protection from physical injury. It has one of the richest blood supplies of any part of the body. Despite its importance, it is quite small.   From *Vivaxis Manual* by Frances Nixon, 1974.

---

[63] *Ibid.,* p. 43.

2. Specialized receptors: This type of receptor is associated with particular organs such as eye, ear, tongue, pancreas, and so on. These specialized receptors are found not only near the organ concerned but also on other parts of the body. For instance, there are adrenal receptors at the end of each eyebrow. A number of organs have associated receptors on the ends of the fingers and toes corresponding with the traditional Chinese meridian system, where there are end points for each organ system on the digits.

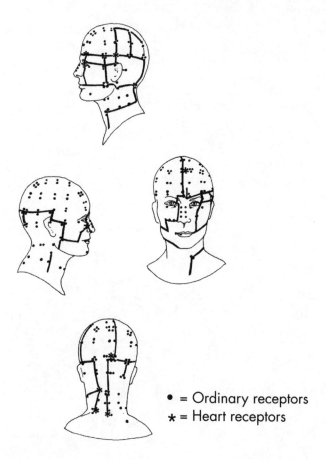

• = Ordinary receptors
★ = Heart receptors

Figure 25. Early chart of communication centers. The groups of receptors with a heart receptor are communication centers. A brain and eye receptor is included in each communication center group. The heavy black lines are communication pathways that become wave stimulated when a person projects their thoughts into objects or others in their outside environment. These are not pathways connecting wave messages from brain to limb. Note how the communication pathways on the left side both are strongly concentrated around the temple and ear and lead over to the left side of the lip.

Special Communication Centers

Fran discovered special groups of receptors that she named "communication centers."[64] Each group includes a brain receptor, eye receptor, heart receptor, and a group of less specialized receptors. (See figure 25.) Communication brain receptors have links to terminal points in the center of both thumb whorls. Fran

[64] Nixon, *Born to Be Magnetic*, vol. 1, p. 134.

also found that the left index finger is intimately related to the communication center on the left temple. This is the receiving finger for when we are situated above our Vivaxis. This receptor site is also interesting, because the speech center is in the left temporal part of the brain.

The communication center on the left temple area is connected to lymph glands under the left arm. Linking too strongly to another person through fear or worry can cause these lymph glands to be permanently and energetically linked to the energy field of another person. The immune system will then be at risk, a factor that may account for diseases such as cancer manifesting after a person has linked negatively with another person for some time. We hear of cases where a person nurses a dying spouse for many months and then later also succumbs to cancer. Perhaps this only happens in the presence of continuing grief or anger over the death of a loved one. The point to remember is the effect on our lymphatic system when we link negatively with another person. Obviously there are other contributing factors in cases of cancer.

Linking too strongly to another person through fear or worry can cause these lymph glands to be permanently and energetically linked to the energy field of another person. The immune system will then be at risk, a factor that may account for diseases such as cancer manifesting after a person has linked negatively with another person for some time.

A special communication center between the thumb and forefinger is involved with leg movement and bladder control. Fran made this discovery when working with a young man who had previously suffered a bullet wound to that part of his body. She corrected the disturbed receptors in the area, and he regained the use of his legs and bladder. Another important communication center is found between the thyroid gland and thymus where the two breast bones meet.

A very significant communication center is located at the center point on top of the head. The receptor on the left of this center has an ear receptor in front. The receptor on the right has an eye receptor in front. At the center point itself is a respiratory receptor with a brain receptor located front and back of this receptor.[65] A corresponding center is located just beyond the back of the hard palate on the roof of the mouth. These are important points to test for people who have diseases like multiple sclerosis or Menieres's disease. So we need to establish whether those receptors are disturbed in such persons and to correct those disturbances as explained in exercise 15. This communication center is in line with the hypothalamus, which is the organ controlling the nervous system.

During the major period, or high tide, the receptors on top of the head become stimulated during daylight by the light flowing vertically down on them. This, in turn, stimulates the receptor associated with appetite for food and especially influences the digestion of protein. Even fish apparently look for their protein food during high tide, and for this reason fishermen prefer to fish at this time when the fish are most likely to take their bait.

Disturbed Receptors and the Origins of Illness

The network of receptors covers the entire head, neck, and body. If the voluntary receptors for movement are disturbed, wave messages to limbs and reflexes are also disrupted. If the involuntary receptors associated with organs are disturbed, there is a physiological disturbance to organ function, and so on. When any receptors are disturbed, the associated physiology and organ function suffers, and this scenario eventually leads to disease.

---

[65] *Ibid.*, p. 121.

Perhaps at this point we should step back and review the significance of the receptors. They are the crucial link between the Earth energies and our body. They are like tiny electrical transformers and transmitters for the energies necessary to drive our cells. They have an electrical current going toward our Vivaxis, with its connection to the Earth, and a current flowing from the Earth and our Vivaxis toward us. They carry the frequencies of all the elements necessary for a healthy physical body. If they are disturbed, we cannot absorb certain minerals adequately from our food. They are connected with the functioning of all organs and with all body movement. Finally, the brain receptors are concerned with the expression of our thoughts.

Receptors act like tiny transformers for moving energy throughout the body. Normal receptors have a fixed wave toward our Vivaxis. A disturbed receptor has lost both its horizontal and vertical wave and therefore it is in a static condition. That is why our recording hand just circulates around and around when we test a disturbed receptor. The chemistry associated with a particular part of the body produces a specific characteristic that is reflected in the wave pattern of its associated receptors. These wave frequencies have not yet been identified by medical science. A disturbed receptor is an energy contact point whose group of elements have developed an imbalance in part of their atomic structure, which, in turn, affects the electromagnetic field. It is a receptor with a static electrical potential and lacking an organized arrangement necessary for any wave motion.[66] This produces the chaotic, circulating energy flow in the recording hand when the testing finger is placed over the receptor.

Fran found that the brain receptors must be in good working order before we can effectively use the brain to test Vivaxis energies. Dysfunction can be caused by

---

[66] *Ibid.*, p. 117

earthquakes; electric storms; magnetic disturbances; electrical equipment, including diagnostic instruments in hospitals and clinics; computer terminals; fluorescent lights; and many other sources that emit electromagnetic frequencies. Mental frustration and prolonged negative thoughts can also disturb our receptors.

Five particular brain receptors give distress signals in response to these causes. Two of these are positioned in the center points of the ears, two more are at that level on the bridge of the nose and back of the head and one is on top of the head. Distress in these points can be easily tested, as shown in figure 26.

The Effect of a Foreign Field on Receptors

Disturbances to receptors can also occur from foreign fields. For instance, the voluntary receptors make connections with the environment. They emit a horizontal wave, which flows in the direction of the object, place, or person on whom we concentrate at a particular time. These receptors respond to the command of our brain or to the command of another brain, if we are under hypnosis. Normally, when our thought ceases, the horizontal wave no longer communicates with the subject under consideration. However, it can become linked permanently with another Vivaxis, which then manifests as foreign waves. In such a case, the whole meridian to which this receptor is linked will be affected.

This damaging link can occur through contact with magnets, hypnotism, or diagnostic and treatment machines with a pulsed wave, and sometimes through body work, where a therapist holds bilateral meridians for more than a few seconds. Hypnotism disturbs receptors located in the center of the forehead and also corresponding points at the back of the head.

It is easy to understand how our memory, personal relations, and communication from brain to limbs will be

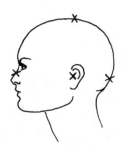

Figure 26. Brain receptors affected by static. Brain receptors at these points can register static, which is evidenced by a circulating motion in the recording hand. Our Vivaxis channel will then usually appear at right angles to its normal position until we have corrected the energy in these points.

Reprinted from *Healing through Earth Energies* by Judy Jacka, 1996.

profoundly disturbed if a foreign Vivaxis is connected to receptors in our communication centers. It appears that in health we have considerable immunity to outside energy fields but through accident, infection, stress, negative thoughts, and feelings, or through biochemical disturbances, we are vulnerable to other sources of energy being introduced in our circuits. This may relate to "catching" an infection from another person or being more vulnerable to the source of infection. If a foreign wave from another person or an electromagnetic source links to our communication center, some of its receptors will stay connected to the foreign Vivaxis and others will stay linked to our Vivaxis. Perhaps this is the mechanics for how some people experience the discomfort of another person. However, a foreign Vivaxis is usually a more permanent problem.

The use of magnets to remove pain works, because the flexible receptors of the area concerned are connected to the Vivaxis of the magnet. It is the flexible receptors that relay pain messages to the brain so that when they become fixed to a foreign Vivaxis, the person no longer feels pain. However, the long-term effect of having foreign Vivaxes in our energy circuit is a *confusion* of energies, and this leads to long-term problems such as exhaustion and inability to concentrate or memorize. Surely it is important to find the cause of pain rather than simply to mask it.

The meridian system is understood by many natural therapists to be connected to the larger energy system known as the chakras. Fran did not research or teach about this level of function. She was very wary of New Age interests and preferred to focus on the practicalities of Earth studies. She was certainly a religious person in her reverence for life and its creator.

However, from my perspective and experience, there is a chain of phenomena related to health that could be listed as follows from the Earth upward toward the higher principles of our constitution:

Earth frequencies ➤ Vivaxis ➤ receptors and meridian system ➤ endocrine glands ➤ blood and tissues ➤ nervous system ➤ minor chakras ➤ major chakras.

In this chain, we are connected with the mechanism for carrying consciousness itself. Disease can result from an interruption to the life energy at any point in this chain. For instance, Fran found that states of consciousness such as negative emotions profoundly effect the body receptors and Vivaxis flows. But she was not interested in the wider picture of our inner constitution involving the chakras.

From my viewpoint, the subtle body includes the receptors or acupuncture points, meridian system, and the chakras. The chakras are often the conditioning factors of the receptors, factors that Fran admitted can come from our emotions and thoughts. The major chakras are related to our various levels of consciousness, and therefore the state of the chakras have a profound effect on our Vivaxis work. The next chapter explains the main qualities of each chakra in terms of consciousness.

I have worked with balancing the chakras in my clients for many years. I find that their emotional and mental states significantly affect their chakras. This, in turn, affects their biochemistry and body receptors for all the Vivaxis energies. I have also found when teaching Vivaxis that if a person is stressed or in an emotional state, they find it very difficult to monitor the etheric and electromagnetic energies of Vivaxis work with any accuracy. This finding leads me to state that we cannot research Vivaxis energies in isolation from an understanding of the deeper mechanics of our subtle constitution. We need to include and understand the chakras so as to place the science of Vivaxis in the larger picture.

The chakras register on the Vivaxis Flows 1 through 4 and can be monitored. (See exercise 10.) We will trace the relationships of the chakras to the energy layers in the next chapter. The subject of chakras is also a further adventure in understanding the electrical aspects of our constitution, as they are large transmitters and transformers of energy from one plane of consciousness to another. The tiny receptors or acupuncture points already discussed reflect this process in their transmission of energy within the electromagnetic field of our bodies. We therefore cannot ignore the chakras, because they are the higher counterpart of the meridian system with its thousands of receptors for energy. They are yet another component of the Vivaxis connection.

Suggested Reading

Kaptchuk, Ted. *The Web That Has No Weaver.* Chicago: Congdon & Weed, 1983.

CHAPTER 7

The Chakras, Glands, and Earth Energies

This chapter explores the relationships between the chakras and our various states of consciousness, and how their balance or imbalance profoundly affects the meridian system and, in turn, the Vivaxis energies.

The body receptors receive and are transmitters for mineral frequencies that come from the Earth via our Vivaxis. The health of our endocrine glands depend, in part, on these mineral flows. The balance or imbalance of the glands then feeds back into the associated chakras. Conversely, imbalance in the chakras may also affect the glands.

We have seven endocrine glands: the adrenals, pancreas, gonads, thyroid, thymus, pituitary, and pineal. An endocrine gland produces a hormonal secretion that goes directly into the bloodstream. Some glands, such as the pancreas, produce both exocrine and endocrine substances. The exocrine secretion of the pancreas is pancreatic juice, which flows into the digestive tract; insulin is the endocrine production, which is secreted into the bloodstream to keep sugar levels balanced. Each endocrine gland therefore performs a vital physical function.

Many minerals and vitamins are important for the health of the endocrine glands. Over the years of her research, Fran often found receptor disturbances related to the endocrine glands. For healthy glands, we need a good flow of mineral frequencies from the Earth via our Vivaxis to all the receptors on our body. In my clinical practice, I have also found many glandular disturbances in my clients. Some of these disturbances come, in turn, from a chakra imbalance caused by negative emotions and crystallized thought patterns. Thus

Crown Center

Ajna Center

Throat Center

Heart Center

Solar Plexus

Sacral Center

Base Center

Pineal gland, upper brain, right eye

Pituitary gland, lower brain, left eye, ears and sinuses

Thyroid gland, upper respiratory system, lymphatic system

Thymus gland, circulatory system, lungs and breasts

Pancreas, digestive system

Reproductive system, ovaries and testes

Adrenals, kidneys and spine

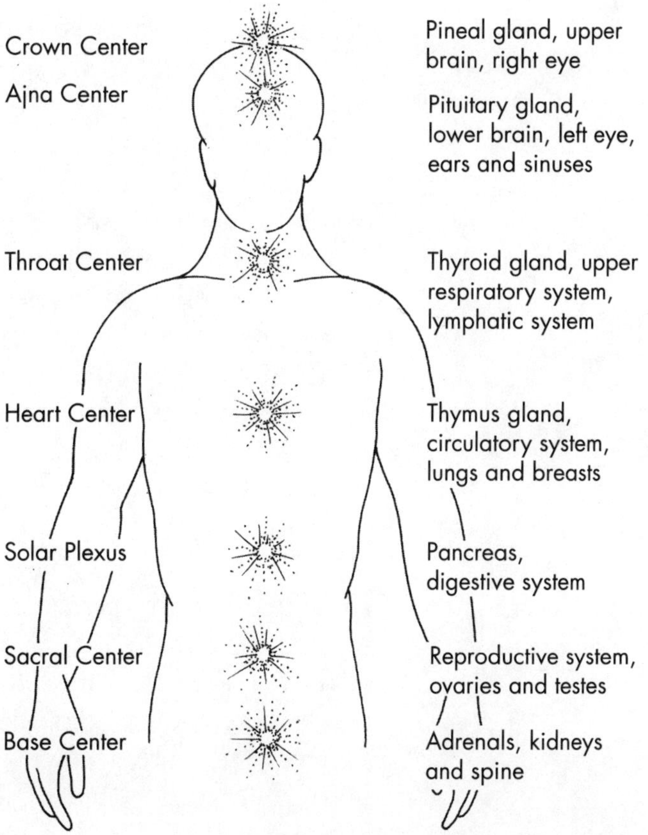

Figure 27. The chakras and main body connections

Reprinted from *Meditation, The More Natural Therapy* by Judy Jacka, 1990.

there is a two-way flow between our glands and chakras just as there is between our Vivaxis and energy field. The chakras and their health can influence the gland, and these influences are mainly related to our thoughts and emotions. Alternatively, the glands may be disturbed from mineral imbalance and thus may feed back disturbance into the chakras. (See figure 27.)

The seven main endocrine glands are each connected with a chakra in the ancient wisdom teachings. In some teachings, each gland and chakra is also connected with a planet, as for instance, the solar plexus with Mars and the throat chakra with Saturn. Negative emotions that affect the chakras may be fear, anger, jealousy, resentment, and depression. At the mental level, persistent negative or crystallized thought can lodge in a chakra, and these thoughts are often amplified and energized by our emotions.

The chakras are the mechanism for transmitting our spiritual impulses, thoughts, and emotions to our physical-brain mechanisms. They are, in a sense, electrical transformers and transmitters for states of consciousness beyond the physical in the same way the tiny receptors are also transmitters for the mineral frequencies to our bodies from the Earth. In the case of the chakras, they transduce, or change, subtle energies into a suitable form for reception by the glands and nervous system. The energies received by the body will vary according to our states of consciousness.[67]

The chakras manifest at the three levels of our personal expression—physical/etheric, astral (emotional), and mental. Perhaps it is worth mentioning here the analogy of how sand, water, and air can interpenetrate as an example of how the chakras interpenetrate at the three levels and yet retain their own substantial existence in subtle matter. Of course the analogy is not perfect because the chakras at their three levels are all in subtle substance of various degrees.

In summary so far, we can make a flow chart of the various levels of our being. This chain could be depicted as:

Soul ➤ mind/mental chakras ➤ emotions/astral chakras ➤ etheric chakras ➤ meridians ➤ Vivaxis/ receptors ➤ nerve plexi ➤ blood ➤ tissues.

Breaks or blocks or disturbances can occur at any level that will affect our health. For instance, an inherited condition may affect our glands such as occurs in some cases of diabetes or thyroid problems. A block to creativity may affect the throat chakra and indirectly the thyroid. I remember one client who wanted to be a creative writer

---

[67] Bailey, *Esoteric Healing*.

but kept allowing her life to be overtaken by various activities. Blood tests revealed an underactive thyroid for which the physician wished to give her thyroid hormone. After some discussion on the situation and balancing of the chakras, the next blood test on this woman was normal. This is an example where the uptake of iodine and other minerals needed by the receptors for the thyroid had been blocked at the level of emotions and thought.

Another interference in this chain of health could be a very poor diet, whereby even if the receptors for the mineral frequencies are in good order, there is no crude material coming into the body in a nutritional sense. As a natural therapist, I have seen many of my clients over the years fall into this category. Increasingly, however, I am finding the need to work with the more subtle factors of the chakras. If the chakras are in balance, then the individual will tend to choose both a healthy nutritional lifestyle and outdoor activities that tend to promote health in terms of their Vivaxis energies.

The exciting work conducted on psychoneuroimmunology (PNI) is another example that indicates that the nervous system, immune system, and hormonal activity are profoundly affected by our mental and emotional life.[68] In our Vivaxis work, we are mainly concerned with the lower end of the flow chart (provided above), which is the relation between the Vivaxis/receptors and our etheric field. However, it is the profound affect that the chakras can have on the functioning of the Vivaxis receptors that concerns us in this chapter.

We must always consider the conditioning effect of the emotions and mind on the etheric field. In working with people using Vivaxis techniques, it has become apparent to me that an emotional disturbance immediately affects both

---

[68] R. S. Hall, et al., "Transformation of the Personality and the Immune System," *Advances* 10, no. 4 (1994): 7–15.

the energy field and one's ability to accurately repair and measure Vivaxis energies.

I have stated that the main seven chakras are each related to a level of consciousness. This is depicted in figure 28. The chakras tend to function in three pairs, and indeed, I find them to be represented on the energy layers in *pairs*. First, we will look at the sacral and throat pair.

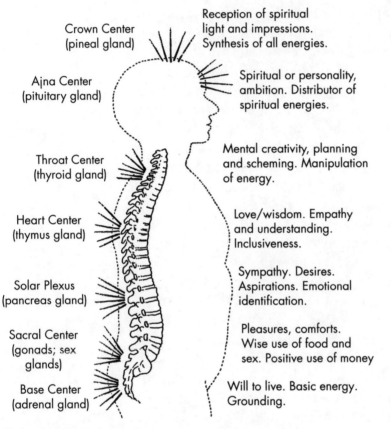

Crown Center (pineal gland)

Reception of spiritual light and impressions. Synthesis of all energies.

Ajna Center (pituitary gland)

Spiritual or personality, ambition. Distributor of spiritual energies.

Throat Center (thyroid gland)

Mental creativity, planning and scheming. Manipulation of energy.

Heart Center (thymus gland)

Love/wisdom. Empathy and understanding. Inclusiveness.

Solar Plexus (pancreas gland)

Sympathy. Desires. Aspirations. Emotional identification.

Sacral Center (gonads; sex glands)

Pleasures, comforts. Wise use of food and sex. Positive use of money

Base Center (adrenal gland)

Will to live. Basic energy. Grounding.

Figure 28. Positive qualities expressed by the chakras

Reprinted from *Meditation, the Most Natural Therapy* by Judy Jacka, 1990.

The Sacral Chakra

The gonads (ovaries and testes) are related to the sacral chakra, which together with its higher counterparts, the throat chakra and thyroid gland, is linked with Force Flow 4. Some of the key minerals associated with these glands are zinc and iodine. As would be expected, these mineral frequencies are contained in this force flow.

Iodine is the main mineral required by the thyroid for healthy functioning. Zinc is a key element needed by the gonads. The link between the gonads and zinc was established many decades ago after clinical trials with this mineral produced secondary sexual characteristics in male dwarfs. Zinc is also an important supplement for infertility as a result of low sperm count.[69] When we are assessing whether minerals are disturbed in the body, we can monitor the person on the energy flows at the level where the minerals occur. In relation to the sacral and throat chakras, we will monitor zinc, iodine, and other associated minerals.

The sacral chakra is concerned mainly with our appetite for food, sex, and other physical comforts. It was obviously very active in primitive mankind, who experienced little more in life than a focus in these areas. There are very few humans today who function solely through this level of consciousness, but we can see a definite correlation in domestic animals, which are happy and content if adequately fed, housed, and comforted. To inhibit the expression of their sexual instincts, we often have them neutered, because this makes them even more domesticated and manageable.

Television advertisements feature the function of the sacral chakra very strongly. This chakra is the target of most manufacturers, with advertisements placing an emphasis on the body beautiful, on food, and on products to increase our comfort. Providing ourselves with the most comfortable existence possible requires money, and therefore the handling of money is intimately related to the balance of the sacral chakra. From an esoteric perspective, money is related to energy and is considered to be crystallized *prana*, or etheric energy. Hence the sacral chakra is generally associated with the handling of energy and with our etheric body.

The sacral chakra is the psychic organ that is linked with our etheric body and, by extension, to the etheric body of the planet. Consequently, all work with natural therapies that involves improving and balancing energies

---

[69] Judy Jacka, *A-Z of Natural Therapies* (Melbourne: Lothian, 1987).

in plants, animals, and humans is related to etheric energies and the sacral chakra. In particular, Vivaxis energies are involved with the etheric level and therefore indirectly with the planetary and human sacral chakras. The base and spleen chakras are also intimately involved with physical and etheric energy. The spleen chakra is mainly responsible for receiving prana from the Sun and is discussed in the next chapter.

People who are unable to handle money may have an imbalance at this sacral level. Health problems associated with the sacral chakra affect the gonads, the reproductive system in general, and the associated tissues. These problems may include ovarian cysts and tumors, uterine fibroids and menstrual difficulties, infertility in both sexes, prostatitis and enlarged prostate in the male, cystitis, and cancer of any part of the reproductive system in either sex. Psychological sexual problems are also part of the functioning of the sacral chakra. From an esoteric perspective, our health problems are caused by an imbalance of energy, and that means either overstimulation or understimulation of the chakras. This imbalance may be influenced by our psyche; our environment, including our heredity; and the relationship between the sacral center and its higher counterpart, the throat chakra.

The planet itself has a gross sacral imbalance. This can be inferred from the fact that the sacral center is concerned with handling etheric and physical energies. So this is represented on the planet by distribution of prana, and this can manifest as changes in weather, temperature, fertility of one region as compared with another, and so on. Thus an area like the Sahara and also the Australian central deserts have become deficient in those energies that lead to rainfall and fertility of the region. There are, of course, many factors related here, such as wind patterns, temperature, interference by humanity with the soils and forests. In this latter factor, we have the needs and often greed of the human sacral center overlapping with the effect on the planetary sacral center. So the handling of money (crystallized prana) and planetary resources are intimately interwoven.

The general lack of balance in the planetary etheric body manifests as abundance of rain in some parts or even floods to famine in other parts. It is interesting that in the last years of the 1990s we had excessive imbalance in terms of planetary weather patterns with the worst floods and droughts ever experienced. Again, it is interesting to consider the interaction between humanity and the planet. Weather scientists have stated that the more dramatic manifestation of the El Niño and La Niña effects results in part from our *interference* with the planetary ecosystems.

When the planetary sacral chakra is balanced, it will coincide with a redistribution of wealth and planetary resources and lead to an improvement in health and housing for all the Earth's inhabitants. It is a process I hope has begun already, as indicated by the increased responsibility we take for people who are in need—the starving, homeless, and uneducated persons in each country. Examples of this global focus are the various agencies of the United Nations as well as hundreds of nongovernment organizations (NGOs) and large private corporations that are endeavoring to help rebalance planetary resources. This development is an aspect of our developing global village and illustrates Gaia as a self-balancing entity.

The Throat Chakra

The throat chakra is related to the expression of our thoughts and creativity. It became very active in the twentieth century, and the great interest we had and still have in continuing education in all areas of life is evidence of this fact. The knowledge explosion was concurrent with the growth of radio, television, satellite, computers, and the Internet. These technological developments made it possible to accelerate learning in every sphere of life. Thus the throat chakra expresses the developing mind within humanity and is now very active globally.

As the psychic organ for creativity, our throat chakra is involved with planning and producing creative work whether through writing, painting, building, gardening, or other creative pursuits. It corresponds to the development of mental power and is therefore much associated with design, or more unfortunately, with manipulation.

The throat chakra's associated endocrine gland is the thyroid, which largely controls our metabolism. An overactive concrete mind will overstimulate our throat chakra, and this, in turn, stimulates the thyroid. We can then become a person who is too speedy in every way. In extreme cases, individuals may suffer from hyperthyroidism (overactive thyroid). The concrete mind is that aspect of our psyche that is concerned with our mundane, as distinct from our higher creative, activities.

The condition of hyperthyroidism, or overstimulation of the metabolic processes, leads to conditions of weight loss, nervousness and irritability, and tachycardia (fast heartbeat) and may eventually cause a strain on the heart. Conversely, if the throat chakra is too sluggish (hypothyroidism), we may experience symptoms such as weight gain, slow and dull expression of thoughts, dry hair and skin, and a general slowing down of all the metabolic processes, leading to tiredness and depression.

In my clinical practice, I often treat people for a subtle imbalance of the throat chakra, although their blood tests may not show an imbalance in the thyroid. Their symptoms of depression, exhaustion, and mental sluggishness often disappear after herbal and homeopathic treatment balances the thyroid. Sometimes, low-grade hypothyroidism is completely overlooked by medical doctors. There are other organs and tissues associated with the throat chakra, including the bronchials and upper lobes of the lungs, the shoulders and arms, and the lymphatic system. All lymphatic and catarrhal conditions such as bronchitis and asthma are associated with this energy center, or chakra. (The lower lungs are associated with the heart chakra.)

As the throat chakra becomes active and creative thought is stimulated, energy is drawn up from the sacral center and a balance between the two centers is established. This gives us the capacity to control our appetites and energy in many ways. If this balance is not adequate, we may find an individual who has wild and interesting creative schemes but no way of grounding them in a practical sense. The sacral energy should be used to manifest the creative schemes of the throat center providing the energy and resources (money) for the enterprise.

To ensure that our creative works are altruistic and not produced simply to satisfy our ego along with the need for fame and fortune, the energies from the sacral center should pass through the heart center on their way to the throat. We all tend to move through a stage of selfish creation. Many artists fall into this category, although their works are often uplifting because of their sheer beauty. Artists may write, paint, or compose for their own needs, but the results can be uplifting for all. The most spiritual type of creativity answers a need, and this often will not fall into the category of art. For instance, it may be a new surgical procedure or apparatus that will give health to thousands. Other examples on a larger scale may be

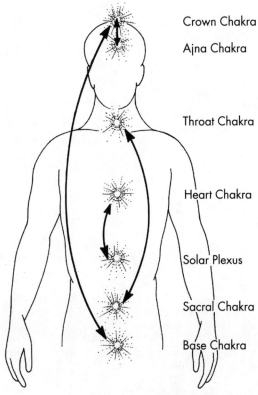

Crown Chakra

Ajna Chakra

Throat Chakra

Heart Chakra

Solar Plexus

Sacral Chakra

Base Chakra

Figure 29. The three pairs of chakras. The three pairs involve sacral and throat, solar plexus and heart, and base and crown. Although not shown, the energies of the first pair should (metaphorically) pass through the heart so that the creative activity of the throat takes place for unselfish purposes. The magnetic relationship between the ajna and crown chakras is also shown.

processes that purify the air or water in our environment or new processes that assist farming and food production.

The Heart and Solar Plexus Chakras

Both the heart chakra and the solar plexus chakra are linked with Force Flow 3—the magnetic band. You may remember that this band contains all those elements that conduct electricity—copper, iron, selenium, nickel, gold, silver, and sodium. The associated endocrine glands are the thymus gland (heart) and the pancreas (solar plexus). There is no obvious connection between the minerals and the glands here, and I have pondered on the relationship.

It is interesting that this layer of energy remains constant during both major and minor periods and at all times during the year. Perhaps this reflects the central and important position the heart and its chakra have in our lives, for if the heart stops beating, our life soon ends. In addition, consider the associated tissues and functions of the heart: copper and iron are both essential ingredients of the blood, while selenium is needed for good immunity and thus relates to the thymus gland (behind the sternum). Further, gold is the element that has always been linked with the heart in terms of alchemy. We even have a colloquial saying: "She has a heart of gold."

Silver is associated with the Moon, which has always been linked to our emotional life; it has its main gateway through the solar plexus chakra. Sodium is alkaline in effect and is related to the pancreatic fluid, which must neutralize the acid secretion of the stomach. Both silver and sodium frequencies are emitted by Force Flow 3. We therefore can see that there are some logical connections between the elements on Force Flow 3, the pancreas and thymus glands and the associated chakras.

The solar plexus is the psychic organ for the expression of energy from that plane or level of consciousness called the astral plane. In the individual, it is the gateway to our astral body. It relates to our moods, feelings, desires, emotions and, in its highest aspect, our aspirations. This chakra and its gland, the pancreas, governs all our digestive organs and processes. From an esoteric perspective, the many health disturbances in this area suffered by mankind result from understimulation or overstimulation of this chakra. We may find health problems include dyspepsia; stomach, duodenum and bowel ulcers; constipation; diarrhea, gallstones; appendicitis; diverticulitis; pancreatitis; diabetes; and cancer or tumors of any of these parts. Considering the number of these problems, we realize how active our solar plexus life continues to be.

In the mass of humanity, the energy from this chakra is combined with the energy of the sacral and base chakras. In other words, our desires are often related to our appetites for sex, comfort, and money. The positive attribute we call sympathy expresses itself through the solar plexus, but it is often combined with attachment to other people in a possessive way. Many family relationships are based on a possessive type of love. We tend to feel discomfort in this region when we have concern about the health or well-being of a loved one. Much of modern psychological practice is designed to work on our emotions and to remove blocks of solar plexus energy. People are also coping with negative energies from the solar plexus through individual and group therapy. The aim is to be free of negative emotions and to freely acknowledge feelings and emotions.

As we grow and develop, the heart chakra opens and provides us with a more universal and unconditional love. We can see much evidence in the world of heart unfoldment through the many thousands of individuals and groups that serve the planet in many ways.[70] Before

---

[70] C. McLaughlin and G. Davidson, *Spiritual Politics* (New York: Ballantyne Books, 1994).

the Second World War, there were relatively few charitable groups like the Salvation Army, St. Vincent de Paul, and the Red Cross, which provide service to those in need. The stimulation of the heart chakra enables the more self-centered love of the solar plexus and personality to be drawn upward. This process gives us gradual control of an unruly solar plexus, which for most people is thrown into movement with every passing astral current or desire.

Problems with understimulation or overstimulation of the heart chakra can cause various circulatory problems and lead to coronary artery disease, which causes heart attacks. Lower lungs and the breasts are also conditioned by the heart chakra. I have observed that many of my breast cancer patients have had a psychological trauma over "heart" concerns. Possibly the great increase of heart disease and lung and breast cancer at this time in our planetary history is related to blocks of heart chakra energy as our consciousness begins to focus through that center.

Just as there needs to be a balance between the sacral and throat centers, a balance is gradually created between the solar plexus and the heart. Wisdom and understanding are two outstanding qualities of heart consciousness that relate to the buddhic, or fourth, plane, the central of the seven planes of consciousness. The buddhic plane is traditionally associated in esoteric teaching with inclusive love and atonement and is understood to be the final and true home for humanity. Being the fourth plane of the seven, there are three planes above and three below. Therefore, the buddhic plane is the central plane. It is significant that the heart chakra, which is always associated with the buddhic plane, is found correlated with the central Vivaxis flow—Force Flow 3. The heart is situated in the center of the diaphragm in our body and is therefore anatomically central. In an esoteric sense, the heart is a "magnetic organ," meaning that it has drawing power and can radiate inclusive love. Appropriately, therefore, this chakra is found linked with what Fran called the "magnetic force flow," a flow that never disappears from the energy layers as do Force Flows 1 and 4.

The Base Chakra

The base center and the associated glands, the adrenals, are also linked with Force Flow 3. This relationship is understandable insofar as certain iron pigments are found in the adrenal glands, together with large amounts of vitamin C. The frequencies of iron and vitamin C are emitted by Force Flow 3. The frequency for sodium on this force flow has been mentioned in connection with digestion. Sodium is also involved with water balance, and one of the functions of the adrenal hormones (hydrocorticoids) is fluid balance in the body. The adrenal glands help us to survive in life-threatening situations, and it seems appropriate that they should be connected with that force flow, which never disappears.

The base center is related to the will to live and to be and it is no coincidence, therefore, that the adrenal glands react to stress and are involved with the fight-and-flight response. Hormones both from the medulla and cortex of the adrenal glands condition the sympathetic nervous system, which is closely related to our astral body and therefore to our emotional life. Our nervous system is in several parts: the central nervous system, which includes the brain; the peripheral nervous system; and the autonomic nervous system, which includes those functions not under the control of the will such as heartbeat, blood pressure, and glandular secretions. In addition, the autonomic nervous system has two parts: the parasympathetic and the sympathetic sections. They are like the yin, or feminine (parasympathetic), and yang, or masculine (sympathetic). The sympathetic part of the autonomic nervous system is related to fight-and-flight. It is closely related to the adrenal glands, which secrete adrenaline and cortisone, preparing us to metaphorically fight an enemy whether outside or inside the body.

You can see how there is a close relationship between the sympathetic nervous system, the adrenal glands, and the astral body, because the astral body is that part of us that tends generally to react to situations very strongly. Thus any fearful or angry emotion causes adrenaline from the medulla, or internal part, of the adrenal glands to rush throughout body. The adverse effect on our immune system of this adrenal response to constant stress has already been established by medical scientists.

The adrenal cortex secretes cortisone, sex hormones, or androgens and other hormones, which are associated with glucose and water balance. Cortisone is used to treat many life-threatening diseases that involve inflammation, swelling, or incompetence of the immune system as occurs in autoimmune disease. Conditions such as asthma, certain forms of arthritis, lupus, and ulcerative colitis are temporarily helped by cortisone treatment. Unfortunately, the administration of any supplementary hormones causes a further shutdown or suppression of those hormone secretions in the body. In the case of cortisone, there are many side effects such as fluid retention, weight gain, and the masking of infections as a result of the suppression of the inflammatory response.

For all hormone medications, there are natural remedies that can replace the need for hormone therapy in the long term, although it obviously may be necessary in the short term for crisis conditions. There are also cases where it is necessary to prescribe hormones as a life-long medication. For instance, it is essential to give thyroxin (a thyroid hormone) if the thyroid gland has been removed. Fortunately, there are not many side effects from thyroxin, and it is used less frequently than cortisone.

It should be obvious that balancing our glands with natural remedies and Vivaxis techniques is the preferred approach. I have explained how we have receptors for the minerals associated with each endocrine gland, and these are always disturbed with any imbalance of the glands. Therefore, the Vivaxis techniques in exercises 15 through 17 are basic to the correction of glandular problems. The general aligning to the Vivaxis in exercise 12 is the regular way to keep all our receptors in good functioning order. Regular meditation will keep our mind and emotions balanced, thus preventing disturbance to our glands from inner causes.

The organs and body sections associated with the base chakra are the kidneys, ureters, bladder, and spine. The external genitalia are usually considered to be related to the base center. Health problems associated with this chakra involve all disorders of the adrenal glands, kidneys, bladder, and spine. These conditions will include nephritis, tumors of the kidneys, spinal problems, and cystitis. More subtle problems involving the energy flow through the base center affect both the basic level of our physical energy and our will to live and survive.

High and low blood pressure can be related to imbalanced flow of energy through the base center. Some forms of high blood pressure are caused by blocked arteries, and in this case, the heart chakra is involved. In the case of blood pressure being related to the base, high blood pressure relates to excess energy flowing through the base center and stimulating the adrenal glands. Low blood pressure is often associated with a deficient energy flow through the base center. This is why the medical profession gives beta-blockers to suppress the sympathetic part of the autonomic nervous system in cases of high blood pressure. For long-term results, blood pressure can be treated by teaching people to meditate. This stimulates the part of our autonomic nervous system called the parasympathetic, or the vagus, nerve. In health, we have a balance between the two parts of the autonomic nervous system, the parasympathetic and the sympathetic. Our current "busyness" tends to make our sympathetic nervous system dominant, and this results in all stress-related disorders as was first discovered by the well-known physiologist Hans Seyle.[71]

The following case history indicates the relationships between the chakras and the receptors for particular organs. In recent years, I have been amazed at how many people have disturbed adrenal glands. The adrenal receptors at the ends of the eyebrows are usually also affected at the same time. (See part 2, exercise 17.)

Isobel is a young mother of two children and feels that she is constantly battling to create sufficient space for relaxation. She came to me for basic naturopathic treatment, and as part of that treatment, I always check the balance of the chakras as well as the organs for normal ion flow. (See exercise 4.) Checking all the organs for ion flow has been a standard part of my naturopathic practice for many years and enables me to immediately know which organs are under stress. I usually find a correspondence in the chakras to this stress. It is impossible to completely separate disturbed receptors of an organ from the chakra related to that organ.

In the case of Isobel, I found that the ion flow in her adrenal glands and receptors was corrected after performing the chakra balancing in her energy field. I include this case to indicate that you can sometimes correct the receptors using other methods, although, since I was checking for ion flow, I was still using my Vivaxis skills to monitor the process.

An opposite condition produces low blood pressure. This occurs when insufficient energy is flowing through the base chakra. It is almost as if a person in this situation is not fully incarnated in the physical body.

---

[71] J. Moynihan, "Stress-induced Modulation of Immunity: Animal Models and Human Implications," *Advances: Journal of Mind-Body Health* 10, no. 4 (Fall 1994).

So, in terms of base center malfunctioning, there are two problems. First, there are stressed people who are not able to relax and recharge themselves. Usually, they don't find the time to do a physical activity, such as walking, which would enable them to tap into the energy currents of the Earth. Lifestyle issues such as wearing synthetic clothing, poor diet, and lack of sleep can affect energy reception. Second, some people have no energy because they are just not focused in their physical body. Young men and women who give the impression of being very vague and dreamy are examples of the need for "grounding." The base chakra is associated with the physical plane, and together with the sacral chakra, it involves focusing energy at the physical level. Both sacral and base chakras are associated with earthing and grounding—that is, establishing an energy connection between your body (its base center) and the planet.

In a global sense, there is less to say about the base chakra. It will become active at a later stage in human development. At our present stage, the more negative aspects of the base chakra relate to aggression, as for example in terrorist activity. Thus the "will to be" is manifesting in a destructive way through groups that force their will on others. Eventually, the will for the good of the whole will manifest.

In a highly developed and spiritual person, the base chakra is linked with what is called the kundalini energy and with the manifestation of spiritual will. This takes place when the base chakra relates to the crown chakra (at the top of the head) after the latter draws up the energies from the base chakra through the unfoldment of spiritual attributes. A life of meditation and service to humanity or the other kingdoms in nature can be the precursor for this transformation of energy.

The techniques described in this book have a profound effect on the base chakra because it has a powerful connection with the Earth. To cope with strong energies, we need to be grounded, and many people today are not sufficiently connected to the Earth, or grounded. Our lifestyle often tends to interfere with our link to the Earth, such as through the shoes we wear. Think of how many shoes we have with acrylic soles. Acrylic molecules block life-giving energy. Therefore, if we habitually wear shoes with synthetic soles, Earth energy cannot flow up through our feet and legs during walking or running. Most "jogging" shoes have synthetic rather than rubber soles.

> *Our lifestyle often tends to interfere with our link to the Earth, such as through the shoes we wear. Think of how many shoes we have with acrylic soles. Acrylic molecules block life-giving energy. Therefore, if we habitually wear shoes with synthetic soles, Earth energy cannot flow up through our feet and legs during walking or running.*

To properly ground ourselves, we need to be barefoot or to use shoes with soles made of natural substances such as leather or rubber. Both fashion and sports shoes can be found with appropriate materials if we take the time and energy to search for them. The more we support such manufacturers, the more likely they are to survive the synthetic explosion. Some synthetic materials are not as impervious to energy flows as acrylic and can be changed by exposure to the energy flows. Nylon and polyester are in this category, and although they cause static on the body, they can be inactivated by exposure to the force flows of the energy layers.

People with chronic disease or long-standing exhaustion always have low energy in their base center. Is it any wonder that, in these times of stress, our energies are low when we have no means of recharging ourselves, because we even prevent the healing energies from the Earth from flowing through our feet.

The chakra corresponding with the base chakra is the crown center, which is situated just above the head. It is associated with the pineal gland. This gland is the conductor of the endocrine "orchestra" in many ways. It is concerned with the "white energy flows," discussed in the next chapter. The other head chakras, the ajna and its associated gland, the pituitary, and the alta major center (back of the neck), with its mysterious gland sometimes called the carotid, are also represented on the white layers.

Summarizing the ideas in this chapter, I remind the reader we have looked at the five chakras associated with the spine. They are all connected to particular levels of consciousness. These chakras condition our etheric body (or energy field), endocrine glands, meridians, and receptors and, indirectly, all physical organs and tissues, and they are linked to the various Vivaxis energy layers on our planet.

The energies flowing through us can be blocked at many levels. We can disturb our chakras with negative emotions and crystallized thoughts and this, in turn, imbalances our glands and Vivaxis receptors. This then means we cannot receive the mineral frequencies from the energy layers and therefore absorb the minerals adequately from our food. Alternatively, poor diet and lifestyle and electromagnetic interference from our environment can work inward by affecting the Vivaxis receptors, glands, and finally, the chakras. We need to consider all these factors and perhaps to realize that in this stage of technological development on our planet, the area of Vivaxis in relation to our receptors is of paramount importance. This is because there are so many electromagnetic and chemical factors in the environment that interfere with these body energies to the extent that even our chakras are eventually affected.

In the next chapter we will study the remaining chakras that are associated with the White Flows and that have a positive and purificatory effect on psychic, chemical, and electromagnetic pollution as mentioned above. These chakras include those on the head and the spleen, and they can have a powerful effect of our Vivaxis skills.

Suggested Reading

Karagulla, Shafica, and Dora van Gelder Kunz. *The Chakras and the Human Energy Fields—Correlations between Medical Science and Clairvoyant Observation.* Wheaton, Ill.: Quest Books, 1989.

Landsowne, Zachary. *The Chakras & Esoteric Healing.* Maine: Samuel Weiser, York Beach: 1986.

Tiller, William. *Science and Human Transformation—Subtle Energies, Intentionanility, and Consciousness.* Walnut Creek, Calif: Pavior, 1997.

CHAPTER 8

The Chakras and the White Layers

We have looked at the five main chakras up the spine and their associated glands and Vivaxis connections. The chakras on the head and that of the spleen need a separate chapter because they are so important. The three head chakras are like a trinity that eventually oversees all the other chakras. They only become strongly active when we have made an effort to develop ourselves in a spiritual sense. It is most significant to me that we find these chakras represented on what Fran called the White Force Flows, since "white" in most languages symbolizes lack of color or the condition of purity. You will remember that the White Flows define the boundaries of the energy layer and are only present when the Sun is near its meridian each day—between 10 A.M. and 2 P.M.

It is logical that the chakras associated with spiritual development will find their reflection on the "white" layers. These chakras are the crown, ajna, and alta major, which all are found in the head area. The spleen is also found associated with this force flow; as it is part of our immune system, this is not surprising. The immune system purifies the body of unwanted bacterial and viral invaders. White has come to represent cleansing and purification; throughout the ages, religious groups have worn white clothing to symbolize purity. White is associated with spiritual light, and in the science of color mixing, it results from a perfect blend of all colors.

Two substances traditionally associated with cleansing and enhanced immunity are associated with the White Flows: garlic with the upper White Flow and chlorophyll with the lower White Flow. Garlic contains selenium and germanium, which both play significant roles in our immune system. These substances are commonly used by natural therapists for detoxifying the body and enhancing immunity. I have mentioned that selenium and germanium are involved in transmitting energy between one layer and another of the energy flows. This may give a clue as to the importance of these flows that form the top and bottom layers of the energy flows. The White Flows carry the frequencies of many substances essential for life. This subject in connection with the pineal gland was the last area explored by Fran before she died at the age of seventy-five in 1985.

The Spleen Chakra

All of the chakras discussed thus far are psychic organs for different levels of consciousness. The spleen chakra deals with energy, which is received directly from the Sun in a physical sense and is not associated with any state of consciousness. This chakra is the subtle counterpart of the spleen organ and is located in that position of the body—left of the midline and under the left ribs. I have found it to be partially blocked in cases of chronic fatigue syndrome. The spleen chakra functions best when there is some direct exposure of the central part of the body to the Sun. This chakra, together with two other minor chakras on the torso, form the "pranic triangle."[72]

---

[72] Bailey, *A Treatise on Cosmic Fire*, p. 98.

The term "pranic triangle" is explained by Alice Bailey in her work, *Treatise on Cosmic Fire*. (See figure 30.) Prana is another name for energy, and the pranic triangle in the human body receives energy, or prana, from the Sun and circulates it to all parts of the body. The points of the triangle are the spleen and two minor centers, one above the heart and one near the diaphragm. Bailey suggests that centuries of clothing style have prevented these centers from receiving sufficient sunlight for our energy needs. She wrote this before the decades of excessive Sun exposure that led in part to an increase in skin cancers, especially in Australia.

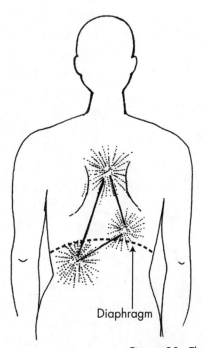

Figure 30. The pranic triangle. It consists of an energy center above the heart, near the diaphragm, and near the spleen.

Although it is important to avoid excess Sun exposure, taking a sensible position on the subject of sunbathing is also necessary. The most appropriate time to sunbathe in tropical countries and areas is when the Sun is *not* near midday, especially during summer months. In most parts of America, the Sun is not so strong as in equatorial regions, and such care is not needed. Winter, when sunlight is weak, is not a concern, and we should take the opportunity whenever the temperature is warm enough, and the situation is suitable, to expose our pranic triangle to sunlight. In tropical countries, precautions must always be taken against overexposure. When we expose our pranic triangle to the Sun, energy is circulated around it and is distributed to all parts of the etheric body and then to the nervous system, organs, and tissues.

We also gain energy from the Sun via the Earth. This energy has already been processed by the Earth and radiates outward through its energy layers. How this works is the central theme of this book. As there are parts of the planet that always receive energy directly from the Sun, we can receive some energy from the planet regardless of our local weather. However, just as there are blockages in the human energy body, there will be places on the planet where energy is received more easily than others. These are the planetary chakras, meridians, and energy layers, and these may or may not be in a healthy state at any particular point in time.

Alice Bailey was the first to write about planetary chakras, which she did in the first half of the twentieth century. She explained how the five chakras up the spine corresponded on a planetary level to London, Geneva, New York, Darjeeling (in India), and Tokyo. Other, more recent New Age writers have talked about various sacred sites such as Uluru in Central Australia, Mt. Shasta in California, and Glastonbury in England. There is a general discussion among persons researching Earth energies that the planet has a network of energy centers and pathways as does the human body, although writers do not always agree on the same sites.

In relation to energy flows, it is interesting to find that the spleen chakra registers on the White Flows, which relate to the pineal gland and therefore to those hours with the most sunlight. Sunlight has always been considered to have a purifying effect and to be capable of killing germs. There is a significant relationship between the spleen as part of the pranic triangle receiving purifying energy from the Sun and the White Flows, which manifest when the Sun is at its highest point in the day. It is also significant that the two elements that Fran associated with the White Flows in terms of frequencies are garlic and chlorophyll, as both agents are used for purifying the body of toxins.

The Ajna Chakra and Pituitary Gland

I found that the ajna and crown chakras are represented on the upper White Flow. In our body, the ajna chakra is situated between the eyebrows. Its function is to gather up all the forces of the personality, which means the energies from all the chakras except those in the head. The ajna is related to the pituitary gland, which secretes hormones that stimulate all the other endocrine glands. A feedback mechanism exists between the pituitary and the other glands so that a balance between the glands is maintained. A parallel situation exists between the ajna and the other chakras, with the ajna expressing a synthesis of the whole personality life.

The feedback mechanism can be seen in the relationship between the pituitary and the ovaries, such as when the ovarian secretion falls below a certain level. The anterior part of the pituitary then produces the follicular stimulating hormone (FSH), which causes more estrogen to be produced in the ovary. The ovaries then take over and the pituitary secretion is reduced. At menopause, the ovaries can no longer respond and the pituitary produces larger amounts of FSH, because there is no further input from the ovaries. Temporary side effects from this process are hot flashes, insomnia, and general nervous upsets in many women. The contraceptive pill also interferes with this natural feedback mechanism in women of childbearing ages by suppressing ovulation, because it floods the bloodstream with synthetic estrogen or progesterone, or both.

Other hormones from the anterior pituitary stimulate the thyroid, pancreas, and adrenal glands. There is a delicate hormonal balance between all the glands. The nervous system is linked to the pituitary through an important structure in the head called the hypothalamus, an organ situated just above the pituitary gland and intimately related to hormonal and nervous function.

Apart from the pituitary, the tissues associated with the ajna center are the lower part of the brain, left eye, sinuses, and ears. Health problems arising from a disturbed ajna center include migraines, sinus headaches, eye and ear trouble, and general nervousness caused by overstimulation of the nervous system. Brain tumors occur occasionally in connection with this chakra. Living in a state of chronic tension may temporarily produce some of the problems mentioned here.

The esoteric function of the ajna chakra is to receive spiritual impressions and ideas. These impressions are then worked into a pattern or plan by the level of consciousness expressed through the throat chakra. The ajna center eventually becomes the distribution organ for spiritual energy that can be used for healing and other spiritual purposes. The center can also formulate a spiritual intention from ideas received from divine levels of consciousness. Gradually, as we develop spiritually, the two head chakras, ajna and crown, establish an interplay of energies. At this stage, the personality becomes the servant or transmitter of spiritual and soul energies.

The Pineal Gland

The pineal gland is a small pinecone-shaped structure about one-third of an inch long sitting in the center of the brain just behind the third ventricle. (There are four ventricles in the brain.) It is only recently that this gland has been subjected to extensive research. This apparent delay is in keeping with the tendency for humanity to make discoveries that correlate with human and planetary unfoldment. There is more to say about this gland than the others, because it has so much to do with our sensing and magnetic skills in Vivaxis work.

The pineal gland has an indirect connection with our eyes and is related to both the nervous system and other endocrine glands. It is responsive to light through photoreceptor cells in the retina. This pathway, plus stimulation from the hormone noradrenaline transported by the sympathetic nervous system, results in the secretion of the pineal hormone melatonin. The pineal gland also secretes other hormones called serotonin and dopamine. The gland is associated with light in both a physical and spiritual sense. Perhaps there is significance in the fact that it also has the highest physical position of any gland in the body.

The history of the pineal gland is very interesting. From 300 B.C. to A.D. 1200, leading thinkers thought it was a "valve" in the brain. In the seventeenth century, the French philosopher Rene Descartes spoke of it as the "seat of the soul." Modern research of this gland began in the 1950s and established that it contains many minerals, including calcium, magnesium, iron, phosphorus, zinc, copper, and manganese; other substances since discovered include vitamin C, sulfur-based amino acids, glycerides, phospholipids, tryptophan, and histidine.[73] This gland has the capacity to sense many frequencies, possibly because it contains small amounts of numerous elements.

The production of melatonin, which normally peaks between 2 and 4 A.M. each morning, is responsible for the circadian, or daily, rhythms of the body. All the endocrine glands are interrelated, but there is a particular relationship between the pineal gland and the ovaries and possibly with the testes. Secretion of melatonin tends to suppress ovarian function, and thus it has been found that ovulation can be enhanced in infertile women if they sleep in a lighted room during their ovulation time. By so doing, they suppress the pineal secretion. This fact may account for why some women suffer menstrual irregularities when they travel long distances quickly, thus disturbing their pineal function.

Our body rhythms are disturbed following long air flights, because the functioning of the pineal gland is interrupted and this contributes to jet lag. As melatonin is now considered to be the precursor of serotonin, the

---

[73] Becker, *Cross Currents*, p. 76.

inhibition of melatonin by long flights may be related to the inability to sleep after long flights because serotonin is needed for relaxation.

The pineal gland exhibits a degree of calcification (or crystallization) from the second decade of life onward. From a medical point of view, it is not known why this occurs. It has been speculated that the amount of calcification may depend on the level of serotonin secreted by the pineal gland. Fran was particularly concerned to discover ways of preventing and reversing the aging or calcification of this gland. She noted that when the energies associated with the pineal gland were strong, such persons had excellent memories and were inclined to be creative individuals. She also noted an ability to resist levels of radiation that would seriously disturb the average person. Fran made these discoveries by testing the pineal frequencies of her students.

An article in the *International Journal of Neuroscience* discussing the magnetic sense in humans and its relation to the magnetic field of the Earth found strong indication that the pineal gland is a magnetosensitive system and that changes in the Earth's magnetic field affect melatonin secretion and circadian rhythms.[74] The diminishing of the magnetic field's strength in winter may account for Seasonal Affective Disorder (SAD), which occurs in 5 percent of the population and which is usually blamed on light deficiency. The article suggested that treatment for people with SAD may be improved by applying magnetic fields as well as light therapy. Apparently, the application of magnetic fields resembles strong exposure to light with respect to how it inhibits melatonin secretion.

This relation of the pineal gland to magnetic fields was anticipated by Fran's early discoveries. Medical researcher Robert Becker described research on the

---

[74] Sandyk, et al., "Magnetic Fields and Seasonality of Affective Fields," *International Journal of Neuroscience* 58 (3-4) 1991. pp. 261-7.

homing instinct of birds, animals, and humans in relation to the magnetic sense for direction, and as I said earlier, found that minute crystals of magnetite were embedded near the pineal gland to give us a homing instinct like that of pigeons. However, Fran's focus on our capacity for finding our direction predates by many decades the magnetic sense described in the scientific literature.

We need to examine whether calcification of the pineal gland prevents sensitivity to magnetic currents. Do the people who suffer most when the magnetic field of the Earth weakens during winter have significant calcification of this gland? Do these people also lose their sense of direction? This possibility would seem a logical explanation, because calcification would surely diminish our capacity to respond to weak magnetic fields.

Recent research reported in an article about "the immunoneuroendocrine role" of melatonin shows that a tight physiological link between the pineal gland and the immune system exists, based on a series of experimental studies.[75] Experiments that inhibit melatonin synthesis have induced a state of immunodepression, which is counteracted by administration of melatonin. A link between melatonin and the thymus gland has been established, and we know that the thymus is intimately associated with immunity through the production of white blood cells called T-lymphocytes. This illustrates again the vital links between the various endocrine glands and how crucial it is to balance their energies.

The Crown Center

The crown chakra sits just above the head. This chakra, associated with the pineal gland, forms a pair

---

[75] G. J. Maestroni, "The Immunoneuroendocrine Role of Melatonin," *Journal of Pineal Research* 14, no. 1 (January 1993): 1–10.

with the base chakra and is finally unfolded and vitalized in response to spiritual will. In a fully developed person, energies are drawn up the three spinal channels (*ida, pingala,* and *sushumna*) from the base center by the unfoldment of the head, heart, and throat centers. This happens in a natural sequence alongside the development of the higher, or reflective, mind (through the throat and ajna centers), unconditional love (through the heart center), and the spiritual will that accompanies the unfoldment of the higher centers.[76]

The tissues associated with the crown chakra, apart from the pineal gland, are the right eye and upper brain. Health problems directly related to the crown chakra involve disorders of the pineal gland, including tumors, right eye problems, and imbalances between the pineal gland and the pituitary. These imbalances can result in some types of migraines and in nervous problems. When a magnetic field is finally established between the pineal and the pituitary glands, a light around the head, or halo, is often seen by sensitive people. This stage of illumination indicates that the energies of the chakras above the diaphragm control the chakras below it. It means that there is free passage for energy traveling up the three etheric spinal channels and that a relationship exists among the three head centers. This brings us to a short discussion on the alta major center, a chakra less understood than the others.

The Alta Major Center

The alta major center is situated near the junction between the top of the spine and the base of the brain—in other words, at the nape of the neck. It is therefore very close to the cerebellum, or "old brain," the more primitive part of the human brain. The associated gland is the

---

[76] Jacka, *Meditation, the Most Natural Therapy.*

carotid, which is rarely referred to in physiological texts. Students of metaphysical teachings have speculated that this gland may be related to the *corpus cerulius*, a small body that is found in the fourth ventricle of the brain situated very near to the brain stem. Recent research shows that nerve fibers connect the *corpus cerulius* to both the pineal and pituitary glands. This finding concurs with the esoteric concept that the three glands in the head and their associated chakras are all closely related.

The alta major center, the lowest of the three head chakras, is the head chakra most directly related to the physical body. Energies flowing up the spine from all the other chakras pass through the throat chakra and alta major before passing into the head proper. This chakra is therefore also similar to the throat chakra anatomically and in terms of some of its functions. It links up with minor chakras below the ears and is involved in conditions of vertigo or dizziness and also in cases of deafness. Other health problems may involve the cerebellum and brain stem. The precise function of the associated gland, the *corpus cerulius*, is unknown at this point.

The ajna and crown chakras register on the upper White Force Flow and the alta major is situated on the lower White Flow. The White Flows are active between 10 A.M. and 2 P.M. and at this point of time we can only speculate as to their full effect on the chakras.

To summarize the relationship between the White Flows and the head chakras, I suggest the following relationships: The White Flows correspond in frequency or vibration with two well-known agents for purifying the body of toxins—garlic and chlorophyll. The head centers, or head chakras, only develop fully when we are on the spiritual path, and when they become active, the body is purified of negative psychic energy and also from physical impurities. It seems logical that the crown, ajna, and alta major centers would be found resonating to the frequencies of these energy flows.

By using water treated on these White Flows, we have a remedy that can help purify the body and enhance the health of the endocrine glands (pituitary and pineal) associated with the head chakras. I find it interesting that the first natural therapists used water extensively in their treatment plans and that we have come full circle, using water again in a more specialized way. The fact that the energy from the White Flows only operates between 10 A.M. and 2 P.M., when the Sun is at its highest position, reminds us that the Sun is known to have a physical purificatory effect. It may also symbolize more subtle purification as a result of its relationship with the functioning of the pineal gland, which has always been related to the crown chakra and spiritual development.

Suggested Reading

Bailey, Alice. *Esoteric Healing.* London: Lucis Press, 1953.

CHAPTER 9

Clearing Disturbances from Our Circuits

All types of holistic therapy provide a major emphasis on the removal of toxins. Many of the discoveries and skills taught by Fran relate to removing chemical and electromagnetic disturbances from our energy field. She found that modern living interferes with our Vivaxis channels and energy fields and she searched almost desperately to find techniques to restore harmony and balance in the human, animal, and environmental systems. No matter how far we travel from our Vivaxis, we remain connected and can be recharged via its connection to the Earth. However, we have already mentioned the many forces—electromagnetic, chemical, and psychic—that can interfere with our Vivaxis channel, and it is important to be able to diagnose and clear ourselves of these disturbances.

Electromagnetic Disturbances to Your Vivaxis

Robert Becker's medical research related to the effect of human-made electromagnetic fields on the human body and showed that our delicate electrical nature is easily overpowered by the fields associated with power lines, television screens, and transformers. Electromagnetic interference of a much higher frequency is encountered from the microwave transmitters now scattered all over the Earth. Becker researched how electromagnetic fields from household appliances such as refrigerators, hairdryers, computer terminals, electric blankets, and cellular phones have detrimental effects on the body.[77] He also commented on the negative effect we receive from the type of electrical circuits used in medical and natural therapy procedures. Examples of these circuits are diathermy, electrocardiographs, and some of the electronic diagnostic devices used by natural therapists. Since Fran first made her discoveries, our exposure to many of these fields has greatly increased.

Methods to Clear Your Energy Field

Over the years, Fran developed various methods for clearing energy blocks and static energy from the Vivaxis circuits. These included techniques that neutralize or carry away excess electrical energy, particularly in the form of static. This problem is constantly increasing with our bombardment from electromagnetic sources from computer screens and from microwave sources, such as leaking microwave ovens and cellular phones and towers. She also researched how to remove connections to a foreign Vivaxis.

Early techniques for removing general static included standing in a wire hoop, the hot shower spray, and the soda and salt bath. Static could be defined as a condition on the body very similar to static on a radio. When a radio is not correctly tuned, we hear a very discordant sound. When the body has static, it cannot be tuned to the frequency of our Vivaxis, and chaotic energies affect

---

[77] Becker, *Cross Currents*, p. 276.

our well-being. When we test for ion flow on a part of the body affected by static, we find a chaotic circulating energy instead of a healthy pulsation. (See exercise 4.) These methods are detailed in part 2, exercises 3 and 7. The following method was her final and favorite choice and one that she taught at the Australian seminar where I learned my Vivaxis skills.

Exercising on the Energy Layers

Exercising on the layers where the various force flows are located is the most successful method for removing energy blocks and reenergizing the body with all the frequencies needed for a healthy life. The person exercises on each of the force flows (as described in exercise 7), with feet firmly on the ground, while jarring each part of their body in turn with closed fists. The jarring to body parts stirs up negative-energy patterns in the bones, and these energies are replaced with the life-giving energies of the force flows. We also twist the body in different directions while standing on each force flow, because each life-giving element is connected to a different direction in space.

Exercising in this manner on the energy layers enables us to pick up frequencies through our feet from the layer on which we stand. In addition, as we face various directions with the twisting movements, we receive frequencies from different compass directions. (For the exact compass direction for each element, see figure 40, page 219.) About two minutes of exercise on each band is sufficient.

Clearing X-rays with Carbon

A common problem with the electromagnetic, or energy field of our body involves the residual effect of X-rays. Most of us have had X-rays of some kind, whether for broken limbs, chiropractic treatment, or dentistry. Fran

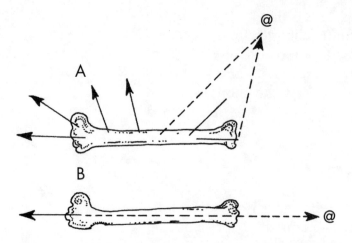

Figure 31. Vivaxis energy field in normal bone. **A. Bone not aligned to its Vivaxis:** When not aligned, the center point and one end of the bone will have strong wave vectors to the bone's Vivaxis. Vectors recorded from other points along the bone will fan out in different directions relative to each other.

B. Bone aligned to its Vivaxis: When the bone is aligned longitudinally, facing the direction of its Vivaxis, each point along the length of the bone records a direction of flow channeled toward its Vivaxis; with the exception of the extreme opposite end of the bone. This end has a wave vector in the opposite direction.

Reprinted, with slight alterations, from *Vivaxis Manual* by Frances Nixon, 1974.

found that after our body receives an X-ray, the carbon atoms in our bones take on a disturbed direction that does not disappear with the passage of time. Normally, the carbon and calcium atoms of our bones have wave or energy directions toward both our Vivaxis and true north and south on our planet.[78] (See figure 31.)

Fran's first realization of the ability of our elements to orient to specific force flows came when she was scanning and recording the waves in her husband's energy field. She was surprised to find a wave emanating from his bone structure when he concentrated on carbon. Testing the orientation of the carbon, she found it had a vector to true north and that the carbon was absorbing energies from true north. Later, when teaching students, Fran found that those with X-rayed bones lacked this energy flow to true north. She then discovered that calcium had a vector toward true south and that these two elements—carbon and calcium—are a pair. (She did not mention why she chose to test calcium, but presumably it was because of its traditional association with bones.) Fran found that there are pairs of elements with

[78] Nixon, *Search for Vivaxis, Part 1,* chap. 12.

attracting frequencies that stimulate waves traveling in the same channel but in opposite directions.[79] You may recall that both these elements feature in Force Flow 1.

Over the years, Fran found that when there is a disturbance to the carbon atoms, especially in the back, backaches, disc trouble, and muscle problems are prevalent. Once we develop the technique of recording our body energies, we can test the profoundly harmful effect X-rays have on the body. Usually, this effect is found to be a loss of our energy field in the affected bones. (See exercise 23.)

Fran experimented with magnets to find a way of realigning X-rayed bones. She found that by dropping or banging a magnet, the orderly arrangement of its energies could be permanently disrupted. She reasoned that by stressing our X-rayed bones, we could disrupt the foreign atomic arrangement in our bones. So she directed people to strongly stress the part concerned and then immediately align to their Vivaxis.

Later she developed a very simple technique. Stress the part by tapping it sharply and then apply carbon frequencies in the form of charcoal to all parts of the body. (Details of this technique are given in exercise 1.) Carbon appears to have an important role in maintaining correct energy flows through the bones, perhaps because of its polarity with calcium. Applications of carbon to the body are therefore valuable after exposure to ionizing radiation such as occurs in X-rays. The carbon used for this purpose needs to be charcoal made from untreated wood and is applied in turn to each part of the body after stressing with the closed fist.

After Fran found the energy layers, she discovered that carbon clearing was far more effective if undertaken

---

[79] Frances Nixon, *Mysteries of Memory Unfold* (British Columbia, Canada: Magnetic Publishers, 1978), p. 9.

when facing west and standing on the layer that contains the frequency of carbon—Force Flow 1. If you are unable to stand on this force flow, carbon can be located by facing north. (The compass direction for carbon is apparently changed as the energy flows through the Force Flow 1.)

In this book, when I refer to elements and their effect on the body, my reference is to the energy or frequencies of the substance and not to the actual physical molecules. Thus, when we apply carbon to the body, we produce changes in the frequency of our carbon atoms simply by holding the bag of charcoal on the body.

Neutralizing Foreign Energy Fields

Foreign fields result from linking our energy circuits with an outside circuit. Possible causes for this phenomenon are the use of diathermy, laser, electrolysis, electrocardiography, and the many types of electronic and diagnostic units used by some natural therapists. Fran found that we can be linked to the Vivaxis circuits of other people by holding bilateral meridian points on another person (which some therapists, such as acupressurists, are likely to do) or through hypnosis or from some forms of magnetic healing. Other types of disturbances to the Vivaxis may result from the ingestion of hallucinogenic drugs, pharmaceutical drugs, and chemicalized foods.

Sometimes a person is literally in a seething sea of energy with many foreign Vivaxes in their field. This means that each foreign Vivaxis is feeding energy into the person's acupuncture meridians and receptors but with wavelengths that are *in conflict* (that is, incompatible) with the wavelengths of the person receiving them.[80] Therefore, a foreign energy field establishes a semipermanent link with frequencies that are not compatible with our own.

---

[80] Nixon, *Vivaxis Manual, Part 3*, p. 39.

We remain connected to our own Vivaxis, but we may be also connected to foreign Vivaxes. This causes a chaotic condition of energies in our etheric body.

Fran found that foreign fields must be eradicated before a meridian can normalize its energy flow.[81] This finding has significance for acupuncturists, especially those therapists who use electric acupuncture, which may indeed generate a foreign field. However, needling without electrical pulsing will not correct a meridian connected to a foreign field. When we connect to a machine such as in electroacupuncture, a diathermy machine, or any therapy unit with a pulsed electromagnetic wave, our own frequencies are combined with those of the Vivaxis related to that machine. Earlier, I explained that a Vivaxis is created when a magnet is made, so any machine using electromagnetic energy will have an associated Vivaxis.

Sometimes a person is literally in a seething sea of energy with many foreign Vivaxes in their field. This means that each foreign Vivaxis is feeding energy into the person's acupuncture meridians and receptors but with wavelengths that are in conflict (that is, incompatible) with the wavelengths of the person receiving them.

Alternatively, we might be connected to the Vivaxis of our therapist. This may happen when the therapist holds bilateral points on our meridians (on both sides of the front or back of the body, such as on both arms or legs), as occurs in shiatsu or applied kinesiology. In this case, the normal routes to both Vivaxes are temporarily blocked, and the wavelengths or frequencies of the therapist and patient are combined so that the circuit is completed. This forms a new Vivaxis, which permanently remains at the site of the treatment. (See figure 32.) You can imagine that the treatment rooms of some therapists

---

[81] Nixon, *Vivaxis Manual, Part 4*, p. 11.

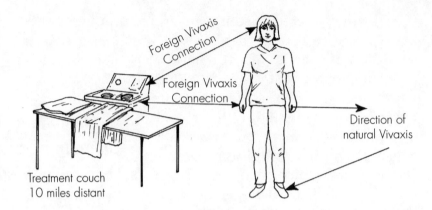

Figure 32. A foreign Vivaxis. The figure illustrates the foreign Vivaxis from the machine in the treatment room feeding semipermanently into the client. Her own Vivaxis is shown on her left-hand side. The patient will experience a conflict of energies, because two separate Vivaxes feed into her energy field. This conflict will remain until the foreign Vivaxis is eliminated. The actual points of contact are usually where the electrodes have been attached—in this case, the right hand and the right side of the head.

and doctors may therefore be a mass of Vivaxes that have been formed between the various diagnostic and treatment machines and many clients. Vivaxes may also be present on the treatment couch when they are formed between therapists' hands and client.

The following case history illustrates how this works. It concerns Jane, who unfortunately developed a foreign field through electrical treatment from a therapist, a very common problem.

Correction of a Foreign Field

Jane, one of my naturopathic clients who had studied Vivaxis with me, had treatment from a practitioner involving a machine that pulsed energies at different frequencies. Several people were hooked up to the machine, which had been set at a particular frequency. One day this practitioner would treat cancer patients, the next day asthmatic patients, and on another day arthritic persons. This situation allowed these different persons to become *permanently* linked together (electrically speaking) via the machine. Jane came back to me after experiencing sensations like electric shocks in her body and realized she had disturbed her Vivaxis energies.

On scanning Jane's field, I discovered that she had a foreign field connected to her wrist at the point where the electrode from the machine had been attached during the treatment. She had not informed me of this point of contact before the scanning took place. In her case, after attempting unsuccessfully to eradicate the problem, we had to make her a new Vivaxis. Jane was relieved of her symptoms from that point on.

Undoing Electric Shock Effects

A second case history involves Hannah, who had a long-standing foreign field from an old electric shock. Hannah, one of my Vivaxis students in a class of ten, was unable to record energies. Eventually, I scanned her energy field and found a foreign field attached to her left foot. There was a corresponding disturbance on the head. Hannah explained that she had suffered an electric shock many years before. From my perspective, this was the cause of the foreign field. She was advised to repeat the neutralizing exercise, after which the foreign field went away. She repeated the neutralizing exercise at home a number of times.

Although she did not learn to record energies with her arm, Hannah had a correct sense of the position of the energy layers on the ground and felt much better after the foreign field was eradicated. Two years after the Vivaxis course, she thought she had acquired another foreign field after being part of a research project by a psychologist. The project involved several persons being linked together with an electric circuit. She was sorry to have been foolish enough to become involved in that project, but she had not realized what he was going to do. Her symptoms included feeling vague and confused in the head.

A foreign field was affecting Hannah's head. She removed it by exercising on the energy layers, doing the neutralizing exercise, and drinking energized water. After she aligned to her Vivaxis (with my assistance), she felt better immediately. Her history of the electric shock had probably made her vulnerable to easily picking up another foreign field, although being part of an electric circuit involving a number of persons definitely invites trouble.

Here is a third case history involving the effect of magnets. I was in my clinic with a middle-aged patient named Paul, who was having naturopathic treatment for a severe problem of dizziness involving his inner ear (called Meniere's syndrome). He had collapsed in a faint with this problem during meetings at work and once when driving. Paul also had a severe hearing problem, and he had a large hearing aid in each ear. Hearing aids contain various electronic circuits and some contain small magnets.

After working out his supplements, I was balancing his chakras on each visit and I had placed both hands on his shoulders while doing my preliminary alignment for healing. On this occasion, as soon as I took my hands off his shoulders and started doing the healing, my left hand felt as if small electric shocks were continually passing through it. Resisting the temptation to think this was healing energy flowing through my hand, I realized that I had picked up a foreign field. This field was quite strong, and I had to go outside and sit on Force Flow 1 and undertake the neutralizing exercise twice before I was able to eradicate this field from my left hand.

I was completely mystified as to how I had received this foreign field and did not associate it with this patient in the first instance. Then I suddenly remembered his hearing aids. Putting both my hands on his shoulders near his ears had immersed them in an electrical circuit between his ears and thus attached me to this electro-magnetic field. It occurred to me that his dizziness and blackouts may have been caused in the first place by the electromagnetic field created *between* his hearing aids. Fortunately, his symptoms had already been completely alleviated by the treatment I had already given.

It was a lesson to me yet again as to how easy it is to get hooked into a foreign field and also the possible effects from magnets or an electronic circuit that acts a bit like a magnet. It also showed me how our vital Vivaxis connection can get compromised by "foreign" energies.

The client may have initial improvement in the problem area, because the flexible brain receptors are attached to the foreign field and do not send pain messages to the brain. However, the ultimate result is that the client's brain and receptors become connected to two Vivaxes. This causes congestion and chaos in that person's energy field, because there are now *two sets* of frequencies continually being received by the body.

Symptoms of a foreign field can include headaches, poor memory, confusion, muscle pains, and exhaustion—indeed many symptoms that are now grouped under the heading of chronic fatigue syndrome. This may be one reason these patients are so therapy-resistant and why common natural therapies do not always help. The disturbance in brain receptors may also be contributing to an increase of Alzheimer's disease.

I have one client (a woman in her sixties) who specifically came for help after feeling hypnotized by an ex-lover. I found disturbed brain receptors and a foreign field attached to her head. After treating her head by applying water impregnated by the force flows, plus having her undertake the neutralizing exercise, she was much improved in her concentration and memory.

Julie, a client with advanced cancer, had undergone surgery, chemotherapy, radiation, and eight CT scans, not to mention many electrical procedures. She had so many foreign fields I did not even bother to examine them in detail. Following extensive naturopathic treatment, all her main tumor symptoms had disappeared, but she continued to suffer a fuzzy feeling in her head and exhaustion for two years. I helped her make a new Vivaxis (see exercise 11) and within minutes her head felt clear and remained so many months later.

If we have a foreign field, these energies are *always* impinging on our own frequencies, even when we are physically or mentally resting. It is wise when learning Vivaxis techniques to presume that you may have some foreign fields and to use the neutralizing technique to remove them. In part 3, exercise 3, I give instructions on how to test for a foreign field. Basically, a foreign field is evident when we find a chaotic horizontal wave combined with a vertical wave attached to our body.

The neutralizing process saturates our energy field with *our own* energies so strongly that any foreign-induced energies are removed. To do this, a closed circuit is made between the fingertips and toes, because the end point of the meridians are situated on these digits. The fingertips and toes are pressed together while the subject breathes deeply. The neutralizing exercise is another instance where there is an enhancement of the procedure if we sit on Force Flow 1.[82] (See exercise 2.)

> *If we have a foreign field, these energies are always impinging on our own frequencies, even when we are physically or mentally resting. It is wise when learning Vivaxis techniques to presume that you may have some foreign fields and to use the neutralizing technique to remove them.*

Removing Static from Receptors

Fran's techniques changed and evolved over the years of her research. One of her earlier techniques involved using the hand to make particular spiral motions over the receptor. Next came the use of the individual's personal Vivaxis color frequencies (as described earlier), applied by holding small pieces of colored material over the disturbed receptors for up to thirty seconds or so. The Rose Aura material also was used until Fran discovered it had detrimental effects if the person inadvertently stood on a vertical energy flow while using it. The final technique Fran developed involved lining up to the Vivaxis, turning the disturbed part of the body out

---

[82] Nixon, *Search for Vivaxis, Part 1,* chap. 5.

of alignment to the Vivaxis, jarring it sharply, then realigning and immediately aligning to the Vivaxis. As with the carbon clearing, jarring the receptors stirs up the disordered energy before bringing in the energies from one's own Vivaxis. (See exercise 15.)

In my work with clients, I have found that even before they can find their Vivaxis, it is valuable to go through the three procedures I have just outlined: the use of the energy layers for clearing by exercising on each flow, carbon clearing, and neutralizing foreign fields. Having done these, you are then in a position to learn to record energies and to find your Vivaxis.

The Arealoha Forces and the Vivaxis

A large section of Fran's early writings was devoted to exploring what she called the "Arealoha forces." This term was coined by Fran in memory of the word used as a greeting in Hawaii: *Aloha*. She concluded the research on Arealoha forces and light in 1973. Before Fran discovered the force flows (as described in chapter 3), she discovered she could harness certain planetary energies with the use of sea salt and sodium bicarbonate. In Fran's work with light, she often talked about the directions and vectors of light. It seems to me that she meant the light also carried other subtle forces. The forces appear to vary according to the seasons. This research started during one of her lecture tours in the United States, when the atmosphere in California was so static that she almost canceled the seminar. She awoke on the morning before the seminar with the idea of correcting this atmospheric static by using the same elements (soda and sea salt) she used in the bath for treating static as in exercise 3.[83]

Fran had previously experimented with soda (sodium bicarbonate) and salt in a mixture that was passed over the

---

[83] Nixon, *Vivaxis Manual, Part 3*, chap.1.

head to remove static and as a means to align the body energies toward the Vivaxis. This was an alternative measure she used to clear the energy field before her research moved to Vivaxis aligning. However, the effect of the soda and salt only lasts ten minutes, instead of twenty as with aligning, so she assumed the aligning procedure to be more powerful.

Fran had also experimented with a quarter cup of pure sea salt and the same amount of soda placed two inches apart on a table. The result was that a vertical stream of energy going both up and down was found at the center point between the two boxes. When she held her testing finger over this point, she noted a counterclockwise spinning pattern and when she held the finger below the level of the compounds, the motion was clockwise. (The reverse directions appear in the Southern Hemisphere.) Fran found that a healthy atmosphere can be created, extending up to forty feet or more, by placing an open jar of sea salt and a jar of sodium bicarbonate in an east/west line about ten inches apart. (See figure 33.) A force emerges between the jars in a vertical stream, and it balances the ion flow in the atmosphere; it can also be used to clear and enhance our own energies. In particular, this force gives our adrenal glands some stimulation.

The Arealoha forces, health-giving forces associated with the energy field of our planet, are focused by the alignment of the soda and salt in relation to the angular relationship of Sun, Moon, and Earth. For this reason, Fran considered that these forces appear to be related to light waves and to the same

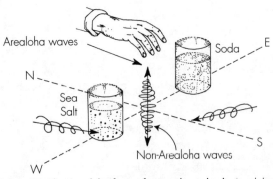

Figure 33. The Arealoha forces from soda and salt. Arealoha forces are formed when jars of soda and salt are placed in an east/west direction a few inches apart. One force field flows down in an angled line from the west, and another one from the south. These fluctuate and change under various influences, relative to time and place. At times, only one of these fields is detectable. Hand direction is reversed in the Southern Hemisphere. The palm is held over the center of force between the jars.

Reprinted from *Born to Be Magnetic*, vol. 2, by Frances Nixon, 1973.

gravitational forces that control the tides. She reasoned that the forces were related to light, because if the jars are placed in a darkened room, no force field is generated. She also discovered that when the light vectors or waves come from the north and east, they come up through the ground and enter the body through the feet and legs. In contrast, when the light comes from the south and west, it comes down to the ground from above. Most of the time the light vectors travel toward the jars in a narrow stream.

Fran discontinued the use of Arealoha forces to treat the body after she discovered the energy flows on the Earth. However, her discoveries of the forces transmitted by the soda and salt give us important information about how light flows on our planet and an alternative method for balancing and recharging our energies if we do not have access to the energy flows on the ground.

Because the Arealoha forces are concerned with light, all testing is done with the eyes *open*. In addition, when the light is flowing downward, as it does when coming from the south and west, the head must be kept level during testing. Presumably, this is because the light is received vertically into the body when the light comes from these directions. When the light is coming from the north and east (traveling upward from the ground), we can test with our head tilted downward. For the purpose of clearing and recharging the energies, Fran found it best to undertake the exercise when light is coming from the south and west. (See part 2, exercise 3.)

It appears that the forces carried by the light in our environment can be drawn in by the soda and salt when placed in the east/west orientation. It seemed logical to Fran that because the jars need to be placed east and west, the forces would be drawn in from north and south on a horizontal plane. She postulated that the reason the soda and sea salt carried these forces from north and south related to the mineral frequencies associated with these compass directions. The direction for sodium (common to both substances) is magnetic north. It appeared to Fran that light is the carrier wave for these north and south forces and that the soda and salt were, in conjunction, able to process the forces so that they were compatible to our energy fields. The point of processing occurs at the center point between the jars.

It was at this point that Fran began to understand the meaning of our interaction with our Vivaxis and its connection with the gravitational forces acting on the planet. Her work with the Arealoha forces seemed to demonstrate the effect of some type of relationship between the forces of the north and south pole and gravitational forces from the Sun and Moon. These forces appear to be reflected in the vertical and horizontal waves of our Vivaxis.

Fran was fascinated by the realization that the frequencies of soda and sea salt were so basic to our energy field and that the same frequencies carried by light waves were related to the movements of the tides as governed by the changing position of Sun, Moon, and Earth.

Checking at half hour intervals, she detected a slow movement of energies carried by the light, traveling either north or south, inward and outward toward the center point between the jars.

These findings indicate how the forces on our planet relate to the larger system—the solar system—with the movements of Sun, Moon, and Earth affecting the forces. They show how extensive and all-encompassing is our Vivaxis connection. The movement and change in the direction of the light vectors through the days and months coincides with the changes in the tides. Therefore, the jars of soda and salt have to be placed in different positions according to whether it is a solunar flow time (that is, high or low tide) or new or full moon.

At both major and minor periods and for the three-day period over the new or full moon, Fran found the vectors for light transmission to be very unstable. At these times, the sea salt usually needed to be placed east of the soda. During solunar flow times and when the light was coming from the south, the sea salt was placed west of the soda. During major and minor periods, Fran found that the light energies were vertically oriented. She also tested the directions for light reception at different times of the year. In the Northern Hemisphere, she noted that from July to October light came from south and west and flowed downward, and from November to February it came from the north and east and flowed away from the Earth. She stated that these findings needed further substantiation but apparently went on to other work.

As there are a number of factors that change the direction for light reception, this exercise is only suitable for those who can test accurately for the direction of light, because this angle changes continually. A person with cleared circuits can test the direction by facing in the four directions of the compass with hands by their sides and the backs of the hands held facing forward. The hands will move strongly back and forth toward the direction of light reception.

With correct positioning of the jars, the non-Arealoha forces in the environment are drawn into the ground below the area of the jars. The non-Arealoha forces could be described as static, in the sense of imbalanced ion flow leading to chaotic energies. This appears to be the reason that a disturbed atmosphere can be corrected. Fran found that it was very important to place the jars on the ground floor of the building concerned so that the floors above would be free from static. If the jars were placed on a higher floor, the static would be drawn into those rooms below the jars, defeating the purpose of the exercise.

The extent by which the healthy field emanates from the jars diminishes over time. The size of the field can be ascertained if you scan outward from the jars and visualize a direction in space. Your arm should follow the direction of thought. At the place where the protective field ends, your arm will move at right angles to the direction given by the brain and thereby indicate static. Once the soda is saturated with static energies, as measured by the diminishing healthy field, it must be discarded and renewed. The salt can be recharged by leaving it in the sunlight for several hours. When not in use, the materials should be stored at different levels in a dark cupboard, so that they do not interact and create a field when it is not wanted.

The absorption of Arealoha forces was an important method Fran used to clear the body energy circuits, including erasure of foreign influences. (See exercise 3.) In the Northern Hemisphere, you place each hand in turn with fingers pointing south for about half a minute over the center point of each jar. The soles of your feet should also be placed one at a time over the center point between the jars. (In the Southern Hemisphere, the fingers and toes need to be faced north because of the reversed spin of energies between the jars from one side of the equator to the other.) When your hand is faced in the correct direction, the skin feels smooth and silky. In addition to the energizing effect, your immune system is enhanced by strengthening the energy circuits.

The techniques involving the use of the energy layers and aligning to the Vivaxis largely replaced this work, because with these latter approaches, no equipment such as soda and salt is needed. However, the Arealoha technique is obviously useful at times when we do not have access to the energy layers. The technique is of great value in clearing a house or conference room when their atmospheric conditions are poor.

Using Soda and Salt to Create a Positive Field

After some experimentation with the Arealoha forces, Fran found that a semipermanent correction to the field around one's home or office could be created despite changes in light direction by placing the sealed jars of

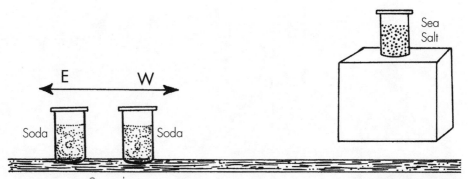

Figure 34. Creating a compatible field with salt and soda. Method: Place two glass jars on level ground, each containing one and a quarter cups of dry baking soda. Space the jars approximately six inches apart and aligned east and west. Place one and a quarter cups of dry sea salt in a glass jar, which is set off the ground and three to four feet higher in elevation than the baking soda jars. The sea salt must be five to nine feet horizontally distant from the soda.

Reprinted from *Vivaxis Manual* by Frances Nixon, 1974.

soda and salt in an east/west direction on a bed of charcoal on ground slightly lower than the floor of the house. The compatible field extended six hundred feet and appeared to be stable for some months. The field only operates in daylight. By the time we received our first instruction in 1980, Fran had discontinued this process because of increasing environmental disturbances, such as nuclear testing. (See figure 34.)

The Inactivating Process and Vitamin C

In place of the above procedure, Fran taught us how to neutralize detrimental energies in our environment by using vitamin C powder that had been exposed to all the energy layers. (See part 3, exercise 24.) The powder is dispersed in one pound of organic bran and enclosed in a clear plastic bag. The bag is then swung systematically through house, office, or over the car. It can also be used to inactivate detrimental frequencies such as insecticides in fruit and vegetables and can be tied on the pipes delivering water to the kitchen or bathroom sinks. (See figure 35.) The frequencies in the powder appear to be imprinted on the water as it passes through the pipe. These health-giving frequencies neutralize harmful frequencies in the water.

I have found that the vitamin C powder remains active for years. Since 1980, I have undertaken double-blind tests to see if students could detect fruit and

Figure 35. Inactivating the home using treated vitamin C powder. Start on the far side of the room and move backward toward the door. The inactivator bag is swung back and forth systematically over all areas.

vegetables that had been inactivated. We have found considerable consensus on the part of the participants in these tests. The same trials have been successfully conducted with beakers of inactivated water. In these tests, the inactivated samples were marked so that neither assistant or tester knew which samples were already inactivated. The samples were then juggled around and the tester endeavored to identify the inactivated specimens, and was usually successful.

Fran made an enormous contribution to our understanding of particular energies connected with our planet and the body. However, there are other well-recorded energy phenomena from other researchers that also deal with Earth energies. Phenomena such as ley lines, Curry and Hartmann grids, and the teachings of feng shui were not featured in any of Fran's research. These areas have not to my knowledge been researched in such depth or detail as the Vivaxis energies have. But they are important phenomena, and they therefore will be described in the next two chapters. Wherever possible, I will relate these phenomena to the Vivaxis connection to better illuminate both.

Suggested Reading

Coats, Callum. *Living Energies: Victor Schauberger's Brilliant Work with Natural Energy Explained.* Bath, U.K.: Gateway Books, 1996.

CHAPTER 10

Important Earth Phenomena Related to the Vivaxis Connection

Let us reflect on the relationship between the energies associated with the human body and those connected with our planet—in other words, the Vivaxis connection. In the human body there are major energy centers called chakras, minor centers with conduits called meridians connecting major and minor centers; and smaller energy lines that are the chains of triple groups discovered by Fran Nixon. Acupuncture points or receptors feature on these various lines of energy. These can be seen as tiny transmitters of electrical energy around the body. All these etheric or electromagnetic manifestations form the interface between the human nervous system and those more subtle expressions, which relate to our emotions, minds, and spiritual being.

On the planet, we also have major energy channels called ley lines that criss-cross the surface of the Earth. From my perspective, they are planetary meridians. They carry subtle energies from one place to another just as do the meridians in the human body. Located at certain places on these ley lines are major foci of energy called power spots, just as in the human body the major power transmitters are called chakras. On the horizontal plane of our planet, Fran Nixon discovered the fine planetary layers of energy to be like the skins of an onion that surround the planetary surface. The ley lines are like rivers that intersect the flat landscape of the Vivaxis layers.

Although the ley lines are not specifically related to our Vivaxis work, to ignore them would be like making a map of a terrain and ignoring the rivers and streams that run through it. If for no other purpose, we need to know where the ley lines exist so as to avoid them when we are doing Vivaxis work.

Although the ley lines are not specifically related to our Vivaxis work, to ignore them would be like making a map of a terrain and ignoring the rivers and streams that run through it. If for no other purpose, we need to know where the ley lines exist so as to *avoid* them when we are doing Vivaxis work. We need to be aware of ley lines so that they do not compromise our Vivaxis connection.

The energy in the ley lines is very strong and overrides other energies in the same area in the same way that a fast-flowing river sweeps away the sand and mud in its path. I found that the direction of energy flow in the ley lines reverses at the new and full moons. Because the energy in the ley line overrides our own, it is impossible to test our own energies, such as ion flow, while standing in a ley line. In fact, it was the absence of normal ion flow that led me to discover the ley line running through our house in Ringwood, Australia.

When holding my Vivaxis seminars in my first Ringwood house east of Melbourne, I had to keep the class off the ley lines or they could not sense any Vivaxis energies. Not that the ley lines are harmful; they are just a different, very strong level of energy. Fortunately, there may be at least a mile of distance between ley lines, so there is lots of space between them. Whenever I run a Vivaxis seminar, students always ask me what the difference is between the Vivaxis layers and ley lines, so it is important to clarify the matter of ley lines to some extent.

Apart from the previous suggestion that the ley lines are like rivers running through the Vivaxis layers, I suggest that our planet is composed of many different electromagnetic frequencies and grids through which these currents and frequencies are transmitted. Since science is only recently coming to grips with the relationships between the known forces of physics, it is not surprising that I cannot explain the relationship between the Vivaxis system, the ley lines, and yet another energy system called the Hartmann grid, to be discussed briefly in the next chapter. We need to know that these different systems exist and a little about their differences to understand how the Vivaxis connection differs from them.

We have established that the force flows Fran discovered are health giving and connect to us via the Vivaxis. The ley system is associated more with the planet itself and is not connected to the human system. It contains powerful energies that appear to have been used in ceremonies, and this, no doubt, is why sacred sites appear to be situated on ley lines. (See figure 36.)

The concept of long straight tracks connecting sacred and meaningful sites was revived in the early twentieth century by Alfred Watkins. He was born in Hereford, England, in 1855 and was a county councilor, magistrate, and a miller of flour by trade. He took a great interest in

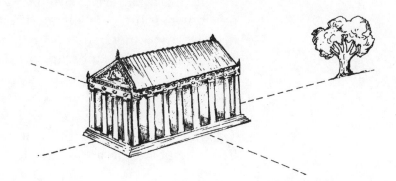

Figure 36. Ley lines crossing under center of Greek temple

Reprinted from *Healing through Earth Energies* by Judy Jacka, 1996.

the countryside and noted how various hilltops appeared to connect sites of interest. Initially, he thought these may be ancient trader's tracks. Later, using ordinance maps, he found a number of cases where four and five churches could be seen as connected in a straight line. When he made a similar number of random markings on a map, he was unable to duplicate this phenomenon.[84] Watkins formed the Straight Track Club in the United Kingdom in 1926.

Literature on ley lines is now profuse, although most of the work and writing appears to be from Europe and England. One of the central concepts about ley lines is that power spots exist where the lines cross. The "energies" noted in cathedrals, temples, and sacred sites in Europe, India, and Egypt have been investigated by French geobiologist Blanche Merz. She and her colleagues used Geiger counters, plus a more subjective measurement called a Bovis biometer, to measure the intensity of energy at many sites.[85] They found significant power spots in places like Chartres Cathedral in France and the Great Pyramid in Egypt. Often, in the middle of the sanctuary there would be a "silent" place, as if free from these strong energies.

In his book, *New View over Atlantis*, British ley line researcher John Michell pointed out the similarities between the American and British ley systems in terms of the features of the landscape. In both cases, these include rocks, caves, hilltops, mounds, sacred trees, and sacred buildings as features that appeared to be part of the leys.[86]

Paul Devereaux, a leading researcher on this subject, together with Andrew York, conducted a project to establish whether there are connections between sacred sites,

---

[84] Alfred Watkins, *The Old Straight Track* (London: Abacus, 1974).
[85] Blanche Merz, *Points of Cosmic Energy* (Essex, U.K.: C. W. Daniel, 1985).
[86] John Michell, *The New View over Atlantis* (London: Thames and Hudson, 1983).

geological faults, meteorological events, and even UFO sightings. Every known stone circle in England and Wales was found to be within one mile of a surface geological fault. Devereaux also investigated the phenomenon of "Earth lights" in these areas. These are mysterious lights reported in the area of sacred sites. The lights often dance around the site, appearing and disappearing in a random fashion. A further investigation, Devereaux's Dragon project, looked at the ultrasonic pulsings emitted from some stones in sacred sites; specifically, the Rollright Stones in the Cotswolds of England were chosen for this project. Pulsings from some of the stones were found to occur during winter before sunrise at the new and full moons.[87]

During my travels through Europe, I examined many sacred sites and found that ley lines usually run down the longitudinal axis of sacred buildings. (Refer again to figure 36.) In Greece, I checked several temples, including the Parthenon at the Acropolis in Athens, where I found an intersection of ley lines in the middle of the building.

In ancient times, it is possible that people understood how to work with Earth energies by holding rituals at sacred places situated on ley lines. We can think of these sites as acupuncture points on the surface of the Earth meridians; perhaps, through ceremonies and beacon fires, the energy was distributed from one meridian to another. The standing stones are like acupuncture needles placed in special points on ley lines to transmit energy. It is also possible that ancient cultures had some kind of telepathic communication through ritual from one site to another via the ley line system.

While these energies are suitable for spiritual purposes, it is not wise to live on top of them. I discovered this for myself when I lived directly on a ley line in a house east of Melbourne in the south of Australia. Despite

---

[87] Paul Devereaux, *Places of Power* (London: Blandford, 1990).

the very challenging experience, it enabled me to understand these energies intimately during the ten years of my
residence there. It was by chance that I discovered the ley
line.

Discovery of a Ley Line

We had been resident there for several years and
many people who visited us mentioned that they felt our
house was in a "special" place. The house was surrounded
by several acres of forest in a quiet street of the Melbourne
suburb called Ringwood. With its sloping grounds, the
property was eminently suitable for teaching Vivaxis.
Before our purchase, I had carefully checked that the site
was a sufficient distance from the nearby power lines to
prevent energy disturbance in our living area. However,
because of its large size, I had not checked every part of
the five-acre property for normal energy flow.

About six years later, during the mid-1980s, we were
disturbed during the night for some weeks by a strange
repetitive, penetrating sound, like an electronic beeping.
We checked the various electrical appliances in the house
and pondered the origin of this disturbing sound.
Meanwhile, I was becoming exhausted from lack of sleep.
One night at about 4 A.M., I went outside to trace the
sound. I moved toward the noise and began testing the
energy flow on the ground to see if there was anything
unusual. As I drew near to the sound, which seemed to be
coming from a large eucalyptus tree, the normal ion flow
cut out. Suddenly, there was a movement in the tree and
an enormous black bird flew out. I had never seen such a
bird before. It was pitch-black and larger than a raven. The
noise near the tree appeared to be coming from the bird.

I had solved the mystery of the noise, but I was now
fascinated to find that this tree was the center point of a
very strange energy phenomenon. It was almost as if the
bird had called me to the place. In daylight, I investigated

these strange energies and found that the tree was at the intersection of a line that went straight through the house and beyond for as far as I could test. Another line was at right angles and also continued into the distance. I found these lines by looking for areas where the normal energy or ion flow was absent, and then I switched my focus to sense the type of energy in the line. It was a strong energy that pulled my hands and body along in the direction of the line. It was about three yards wide and traveled through the house, just missing my bed.

I wondered why I had not noticed this energy line earlier. It is interesting how we can miss a phenomenon until we are actually confronted with something out of the ordinary. When we focus on a particular area, we tend to notice only general effects or whatever we are expecting, and this accounts for how we can develop a tremendous bias against the unusual, especially in our home surroundings. We need to check and recheck our findings whenever we come across a new manifestation of energy, and we should not ignore our findings because they do not fit into an existing model.

The Type of Energy in a Ley Line

The energy at the site of the tree was a spiral. If I stood at the intersection of lines near the tree and relaxed, my body started to gyrate in a slow circular fashion from the feet upward. In later months, I found that the direction of the spiral reversed at each new and full moon and that this coincided with a change in direction of the flow within the lines.

One line was running north to south and the other east to west. I found that at the full moon, the lines expanded considerably and became as wide as the whole house. This made sleep difficult, because my bed was now within the energy flow. It gave me a feeling of restlessness in my legs, although I found it was a positive force when meditating. When we are meditating, we can use the powerful type of energy in the ley lines, but when we are trying to relax and fall asleep, it just keeps us awake. I began to understand why places of worship and sacred buildings, but not residential dwellings, were located on these sites.

Another interesting phenomenon was observed by my coworker from Canberra when she came to assist me with my healing seminars. She had trouble going to sleep because of the extra energy rushing through the house; she also suffered from the restless limb problem. She described her experience as like trying to "sleep on a walking track with disembodied entities wandering through each night." This was an aspect I had not considered, but it seemed logical that a ley line could have a psychic dimension and carry a lot of "traffic." Later, I learned from Phillip Heselton that ley lines are traditionally paths of psychic activity and lines of a seasonal flow of spirit.[88]

We can imagine that if there is strong and subtle planetary energy flowing through a ley line, it may carry discarnate spirits along its track. This is probably why the Australian Aborigines named ley lines "dreaming tracks." I once asked an Aboriginal elder who sat on many government committees about ley lines, and he said he believed they were the dreaming paths of his people.

I decided to have the position of my ley lines confirmed by a well-known Australian dowser, Alanna Moore, who was experienced in working with subtle energies. She was living hundreds of miles away in New South Wales but was experienced in map dowsing. Alanna confirmed my evaluation by sending back a street map marked with the lines, and she made some suggestions about how to deflect the energy. Her suggestions involved placing mirrors to reflect the energies away and planting

---

[88] Phillip Heselton, *Earth Mysteries* (Dorset, U.K.: Element, 1991).

trees across the line, but I was not attracted to either of these propositions.

As I became more familiar with the characteristics of the terrain and the vegetation on the ley lines, I noticed that a tree with an unusual formation often grows at an intersection of lines. The tree near my house had two trunks, twisted strangely, which is not typical for the eucalyptus species. I reasoned that the energies of the two lines with their spiral formation had contributed to this double trunk.

Perhaps we are attracted to unusual home sites because of an interest in subtle energies, but I found it increasingly difficult to live in my house. Continual changes to the etheric field of the Earth during the early 1990s caused the ley line to become wider each year. So, as there were other reasons to sell the house, I decided to move into a small cottage elsewhere. After my recent experience, I carefully checked the new house, but it seemed free of unusual energies.

After a few weeks, I began to muse about the enormous eucalyptus near the front gate. This tree is over one hundred feet tall and has no less than five huge trunks. I wondered if it was on a ley line and soon found that it is on a powerful ley line which runs from Mt. Dandenong (where I was now living) to Melbourne. This line had been researched by the Fountain Group, which is an international group devoted to sending healing energies into the planetary grid system. This line did not go through the house; and even with its expansion at the Full Moon, it was at least sixty feet distant. This find allowed me to again monitor a ley line at close quarters and to confirm the reversal of the energy flow at new and full moon. On my walks in the nearby forest, I found another intersection of lines also marked by a eucalyptus with five trunks.

It is not necessarily the case that all such intersections will be marked by a multitrunked tree, but there is usually some indicator. Some years ago, a friend with a fifty-acre property asked me to find a ley line. I started out on foot and allowed my instincts to carry me to a particular area. In this area, I noted a very large white-trunked eucalyptus and began detailed checking. Sure enough, this tree was marking the intersection of two energy lines. One line led to a magnificent spring, which fed a sizeable lake providing water for the surrounding farms. It is not uncommon to find springs in the vicinity of ley lines.

In Australia, we do not have many ancient buildings or known sacred sites as in Europe and Asia, and our checking of ley lines is therefore mainly confined to open sites. There are sacred sites that are known to the Aboriginal community. Over time, some of the knowledge accumulated by these very sensitive and psychic people may have been lost, but there are indications in Dreamtime stories that ley lines were used by the Aboriginal people. Because sacred sites in Australia are not marked with architectural features, we must note more natural signs as manifested by rocks, trees, and contours of land to give us clues.

To summarize the significance of energy lines, the Earth is covered by a grid that probably has the purpose of distributing energy from one place to another and of nourishing the Earth with the energy received from the Sun. Because of the relationship of the Earth with other celestial bodies, energies in the grid fluctuate from day to day and week to week. Humans versed in the ancient wisdom have always known how to find this grid and to use it for both sacred and sometimes profane purposes. Master builders have raised edifices and structures to concentrate and distribute the energy, and this is why many cathedrals, churches, and temples are found on ley lines and on the intersection of ley lines.

The Vivaxis layers are a much finer grid and are possibly connected to the ley lines in much the same way as very fine energy lines exist on the human body that connect with the larger meridians. As yet, we do not know the mechanism for this connection, but we do know we have to keep the leys in mind when we are working our Vivaxis connection.

Suggested Reading

Miller, Hamish, and Pavel Broadhurst. *The Sun and the Serpent.* Cornwall, U.K.: Pendragon Press Cornwall, 1990.

CHAPTER 11

Harmful Earth Energies: Geopathic Stress

So far, we have looked at a number of beneficial energies flowing through the Earth as well as some of the harmful energies in our environment. There are many human-made problems, from X-ray radiation to atomic fallout, that have been shown to be potential causes of genetic alterations in living things. In addition, there is a growing body of scientific evidence that indicates people and animals can become ill and even die if exposed to energy phenomena called geopathic stress, which means "pathology from the Earth."

In this chapter, I will first cover the naturally occurring stresses that affect the surface of our planet. These are now the subject of the popular feng shui workshops and of practitioners whose art is based on this ancient Chinese art of reading the health of the Earth from features in the landscape. However, the fairly modern term, "geopathic stress," was developed in Germany. Our Vivaxis connection and associated electromagnetic field can be profoundly and adversely affected by both naturally occurring and human-made geopathic stress. This negative affect to our Vivaxis derives from the debilitating and interfering effect of energies that *override* our own subtle energies.

What Is Geopathic Stress?

The term "geopathic stress" has been used increasingly to cover a wide range of both naturally occurring and human-made problems that exist in our environment. Geopathic stress literally means "Earth pathology," and because we live on the surface of the Earth, we are sometimes affected by this Earth disease. The concept was first publicized in Germany in the late 1940s. The knowledge was applied in particular by the German electroacupuncturists, who found that patients were very therapy-resistant if they were living or sleeping over an area of geopathic stress. These therapists diagnosed such disturbances on their patients with electronic diagnostic instruments and were able to differentiate one type of disturbance from another. A person trained in geopathic stress would then visit the home of the client and, using their dowsing skills, would examine the ground under the beds or favorite chairs of those affected. They would then make suggestions as to how furniture should be moved to avoid certain areas in the home or office. Underground watercourses, rock fissures, energy knots from intersections of the planetary grid system, oil deposits, electromagnetic pollution from power stations, power lines, transformers, microwave ovens, microwave transmitters, and dishes—all cause energy disturbances.

Underground watercourses are the most common form of stress encountered in our natural environment. Considerable research has taken place in Russia, France, and Germany on this subject in relation to cancer and other serious health problems. In some German educational institutions, architectural students are taught "building biology" (Baubiologie) to help them design buildings away from harmful sites that could produce

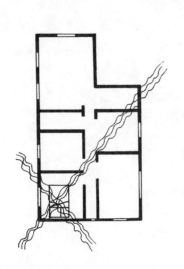

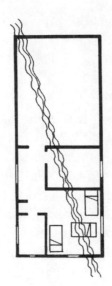

Figure 37. Underground watercourses. Streams of water passing under a house can sicken the occupants of the rooms directly above these watercourses.

Reprinted from *Healing through Earth Energies* by Judy Jacka, 1996.

disease in residents. (See figure 37.)

In southern Germany during the 1930s, Baron Gustav von Pohl conducted an evaluation of cancer sites, using dowsing techniques. With the help of local authorities in the town of Vilsbiburg, he accurately located the homes of fifty-four persons who had died of cancer. Initially, he mapped the detrimental sites in the whole town and then compared locations with the deceased victims of cancer. In many cases he even pinpointed the seat of the cancer from the exact section of the bed affected by upward-rising radiation, which originated from underneath the buildings. The Central Committee for Cancer Research in Berlin published his findings, and in 1930, von Pohl read the paper to a medical congress in Munich. His book describing this research is entitled *Earth Radiation, The Causative Factor in Disease and Cancer.*[89]

Before the Second World War, Pierre Cody, a French engineer, demonstrated over a seven-year period the link between ionizing radiation and cancer. With the support of an eminent physicist, Louis le Prince-Ringuet, an Elster and Geitel electrometer was used to register energy disturbances under the beds of seven thousand persons who had cancer. These readings, when compared with

---

[89] Gustof Von Pohl, *Earth Radiation, the Causative Factor in Disease and Cancer* (Feucht, W. Germany: Fortschritt fuer Alle, 1932).

readings a few yards away, were ten times higher directly *under the beds* of the cancer sufferers. The radiations appeared to rise directly upward, in some places through several floors, without any horizontal diffusion.[90]

In Switzerland, Dr. Hans Jenny carried out controlled experiments over twelve years with twenty-four thousand mice he tested in a radiation zone. The mice attempted to flee the affected area and, when forced to remain in that area, produced lower-than-normal birthrates and higher-than-normal infant mortality. When these mice were painted with carcinogenic coal tar and kept in the radiation zone, they formed tumors at a much higher rate than did those in the control group, which were housed in a radiation-free zone.[91]

In the 1960s, a research group from Heidelberg University and one from the Technical University in Munich, both in Germany, studied a house in the Nechar Valley, where three generations of people who slept in the same location in the house had all died of stomach cancer. Using scientific instruments, the researchers located the intersection of an underground watercourse and a geological fracture below the position of the bed. A geological fracture can be described as a fissure in rock. Mice in wooden cages were placed over this "cancer zone," and their behavior was compared with a control group of mice. The exposed mice were restless, more aggressive even to the extent of devouring their young, and produced one-third the number of offspring as compared to those in the control group.[92]

---

[90] A. Moore, "Are You under Geopathic Stress," *Australian Well-being* 15 (1986).

[91] J. A. Kopp, "Healthy Living by Elimination of Soil Influences Detrimental to Health," *Journal of Swiss Society for Housing (das Wohnen)* 11 (1970).

[92] J. B. McCreary, "Water Theory," *The American Dowser Quarterly* (November 1981): 22.

What is the explanation for this dangerous phenomenon? Some physicists and engineers have postulated that neutron radiation is generated from deep within the Earth, that it rises upward and is altered by coming in contact with the electromagnetic field created by the friction of water moving along underground. In this theory, the normal background radiation emerges as a mixture of neutron and infrared radiation that is partly converted into microwaves. Russian scientists at the Institute of Industrial Hygiene and Occupational Disease at the Medical Academy of the former USSR confirmed the presence and danger of microwave emissions, which travel upward in a direct line from underground watercourses. They found that these sites show ionization changes, acoustic anomalies, gamma radiation, and decreases in geomagnetic field intensity. A junction of water veins is considered to be a serious problem, especially if it travels through radioactive rocks. Supersensitive scintillometers can now be used above water veins to measure the increased radiation at these sites.[93]

Correcting Underground Water Disturbances

The following case history—my own—shows how geopathic stress can disturb our Vivaxis connection. I had an interesting personal experience with an underground water stream at the holiday property we owned for ten years north of Melbourne at Kinglake on the Great Dividing Range in Australia. We had been living in the place for about five years, during which time I had always found it very difficult to sleep. I would awake feeling unrefreshed and sometimes had the peculiar sensation of my body being pulled in a twisting direction from the bed.

---

[93] J. A. Kopp, "On the Physics of Geopathogenic Phenomenon," *Journal for Practical Medicine* (1 May 1971).

The house was an unusual T-shape I had designed myself, with cathedral-type ceilings that were high on one side. The house was built of natural materials with a pressed metal roof. I wondered if the shape of the house, combined with the metal roof, had produced some strange kind of energy.

At the initial Australian Vivaxis seminar held there in 1980, I complained to Fran that I was finding my Vivaxis at right angles to its proper direction. She suggested there may be a watercourse under the house and took me inside to investigate. She held her hand in the position to record a vertical flow, and it moved in a circular direction over my bed and in a line straight down the house. The width of the line was about six feet.

My concern at this discovery soon turned to amazement when Fran demonstrated how to treat the detrimental energy flow. She placed a heaped tablespoon of calcium ascorbate on all the energy layers and then sealed the powder in a glass jar. The jar was buried in the soil outside the window in line with the underground watercourse. We then found that the energies were completely normal throughout the whole house.

An interesting sequel took place a few years later. I had slept well in the house for some years and had almost forgotten the event, when the same sleeping disturbance returned. It occurred to me that the vitamin C powder previously placed in the jar and buried on the line of the water source may have become oxidized and spoilt after such a long interval. I dug up the bottle and found that the powder had become damp and yellowed. With renewed inactivator

> *Fran demonstrated how to treat the detrimental energy flow. She placed a heaped tablespoon of calcium ascorbate on all the energy layers and then sealed the powder in a glass jar. The jar was buried in the soil outside the window in line with the underground watercourse. We then found that the energies were completely normal throughout the whole house.*

powder, the negative effect was again removed and I slept well again until we sold the house. It is notable that the farmer next door had a large water bore that was in exact alignment with the watercourse as dowsed by Fran and myself, suggesting the existence of a substantial underground watercourse near our site.

A more scientific procedure to correct underground water disturbances is described in a building text entitled *Do You Want to Live Healthily?* by K. E. Lotz, a professor at a technical university in Germany. In an experiment, Lotz measured his students' skin resistance while they stood over underground water sources; he did this to indicate the disturbances induced in their bodies. Lotz used an interference or dipole transmitter in his research with disturbed sites. This instrument automatically overrides the type of microwaves emitted at any point in time. This treatment of the site is able to reestablish the normal background radiation field.[94] Lotz was able to establish that this device protected his students from adverse affects.

I once had a patient I deduced was sleeping over a watercourse in a hillside suburb. She had come to me with a benign throat tumor; even though it was scheduled for surgery, she was against having an operation. At my suggestion, she moved her bed into another room and her health improved considerably. She had naturopathic treatment to reduce the tumor and at the date of this writing she is well, although the tumor has not yet disappeared.

An interesting sign of the existence of a harmful underground stream is that ant nests are commonly found in the vicinity. Animals such as dogs, sheep, goats, and cows move away from harmful areas, but cats are well known for seeking out these places to sleep. In the

---

[94] K. E. Lotz, *Do You Want to Live Healthily?* (Remscheid, Germany: Paffrath-Druck KG, 1982).

Northern Hemisphere, forests of deciduous trees, oak and elm trees, are apparently more commonly found over watercourses than other trees such as beeches or birches.

The Hartmann and Curry Grids

Geopathic stress can manifest in yet another way. According to German research, our planet has a network of criss-crossing lines that have electromagnetic properties. The "Hartmann grid" was discovered by Dr. Ernst Hartmann of Germany after the Second World War. The grid consists of lines that run north/south and east/west. Hartmann postulated that these lines are somehow related to the magnetic properties of the north pole. He used a Geiger-Muller counter to find the pattern of the grid system in many countries and found that the grid lines had higher counts of radiation than that of the ground between. Hartmann found considerably increased counts of radioactivity in the grid system before earthquakes occurred. He also found a concentration of grid energies around pyramids and sections of famous cathedrals. In contrast, the center of these buildings presented a "silent" space, free from any radioactivity.

Hartmann interpreted this as a means of providing protection for those undergoing spiritual practices. The grid lines are much closer and more regular in their distribution than the ley lines. They are six to ten feet apart and each line is twelve inches wide. In a similar manner to the ley lines, the width of the lines increases considerably during the full moon, with sunspot activity, and with different weather patterns. We need to avoid the "knots," or intersections, on these grids when we do Vivaxis work, because they interfere with our Vivaxis connection.

The Curry grid was discovered by Drs. Whitman and Manfred Curry, following research by Curry at the Bio-Climatic Institute in Germany. This grid runs at a diagonal to the Hartmann grid and is also charged with electromagnetic energy. The lines are about eleven and a half feet apart. This grid does not alter with the Moon cycles.

As yet, no researchers have been able to show exactly how these grids relate to geology and physics. However, many therapists, including myself, have evaluated the effect of the grids on clients over many years. Problems only seem to occur in the places where the overlapping of the two grids cause a knot of energy, especially if an intersection from each grid overlaps. Problems may occur if someone is sleeping over an intersection of the two

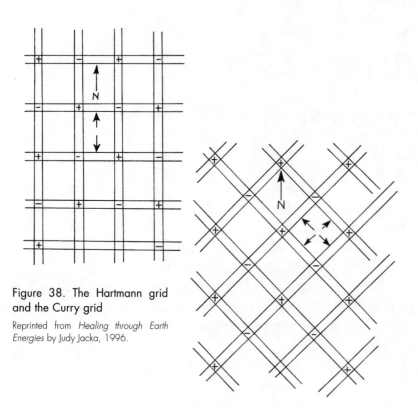

Figure 38. The Hartmann grid and the Curry grid

Reprinted from *Healing through Earth Energies* by Judy Jacka, 1996.

grids. The energy disturbance found at these points is increased if the charges on the grids have a similar polarity such as two negatives or two positives. (See figure 38.)

In my naturopathic practice, if I determine that someone is suffering from geopathic stress associated with these grids, I suggest they move their bed about three feet from where it is. This action frequently results in improved health, particularly in terms of vitality. When I dowse for these energy disturbances on the grids, I usually find my recording hand moves in a circular motion when I focus on the disturbance. The intuitive impression I receive is of a dense knot of energy in that particular spot. You will gather that, as these grid lines are fairly close together, they will be present under and in all buildings. Problems only occur if a bed or frequently used chair is over one of the energy disturbances. The situation is further compounded if the knot of energy is over a watercourse.

Other underground deposits such as oil and minerals can also cause energy disturbances. This subject has not been as thoroughly researched as underground water, but nonetheless, geopathic stress can result from these other deposits under our homes or workplaces. If we find a disturbance that appears to be a substance other than water, we can experiment by visualizing other elements. If we find the correct substance through such visualization procedures, there will be a positive response in our recording arm, pendulum, or dowsing rod.

I once conducted a Vivaxis seminar at a place called Tidbinbilla near Canberra and found disturbances in many of the rocks nearby. When sensing the vibration of the rocks, by simply looking at the rocks and keeping my mind still and focused, my hands moved in a circular motion, two turns one way and then two turns in the opposite way. This is an indication for radioactivity in the environment. In this case, we had to stay clear of such disturbance when testing or teaching the various procedures. Once we become habituated to testing the health of our environment by evaluating the ion flow in the area, we become very quick at picking up abnormalities.

Earthquakes, Volcanic Activity, and Radiation

At a seminar I was conducting with Fran Nixon on Victoria Island, Canada, in 1983, we found that our recordings of the environment were very disturbed and we all felt very heavy in the head. Later, we received news of a disturbance in the area of Mount St. Helens in Washington state—the same volcano which had erupted three years earlier. Strong disturbances can also be recorded from earthquakes sometimes many thousands of miles away.

As described in exercise 26, we can often monitor an imminent earthquake by the circular recording in our hands when we test the energy pattern in the ground. Toward the end of 1999, I experienced a very thick feeling in my head one morning. I decided to go outside and align to my Vivaxis to improve my clarity. However, on checking the direction of my Vivaxis, it appeared to be at right angles to its normal direction. When I looked at the ground, my hands recorded the energy in an egg-beater type movement instead of the normal back and forth motion. I felt sure there must be an earthquake somewhere. After half an hour of observations, I tuned on the midday news. An earthquake had occurred in New Zealand several hours earlier. The quake registered at over 6 points on the Richter scale, but was well away from an inhabited area. I noticed that the disturbance cleared in about half an hour, but of course it may have been present for many hours before I tested.

Electromagnetic Pollution

It is only a little over one hundred years since electricity revolutionized our lives, and there probably is a significant esoteric parallel to this lighting up of our planetary environment. The extent of this revolution confronts us when we fly into a large city at night and see the amazing electrification of the whole area with its millions of twinkling lights far below. However, a century is a very short time to gauge the effect of this technology on the human and animal kingdoms.

Remember while you are reading this section that your Vivaxis is, in part, an electromagnetic phenomenon and will therefore be potentially affected by all other electromagnetic phenomena. Before electricity was harnessed on our planet, there obviously was less electromagnetic interference to your Vivaxis. If we reflect on the criss-crossing of electric cables and wires throughout the planet, we can understand the astronomical number of human-made electromagnetic fields that now exist. We are also subject to the microwave frequencies from cellular phone towers and from satellites as they circle the Earth.

We can be adversely affected by these human-made fields because of the electromagnetic aspect to our Vivaxis and the associated bands of our aura. I have discussed how the layers of our Vivaxis aura are associated with both positive ions (zinc/iodine layers) and negative ions (iron/copper layer). There is a basic electrical phenomenon associated with our body here that is not yet acknowledged by modern medicine.

However, the electrical flow in our body (as demonstrated by Burr and Becker) is measured in millivolts, whereas human-made fields result from much higher voltage and can therefore override the sensitive human fields. Hence our Vivaxis connection and our electromagnetic field can be profoundly affected by electromagnetic sources. In fact, we can say that our planet now suffers from profound electromagnetic pollution.

The more I study the Vivaxis connection, the more I realize it is intimately related to the human electromagnetic field and therefore that all Vivaxis phenomena are probably related to the electromagnetic phenomena of Earth. There are many indications for this connection, such as the various polarities and reversing spins of the receptors on the body that seem like electrical phenomena.

It is hard to separate the electromagnetic forces in our human aura from the etheric ones, because the electromagnetic is like a mirror image of the etheric. For this reason, scientist William Tiller uses the term "magneto-electric" when referring to the etheric. With the skills described in part 2, you can easily learn how to test human-made electromagnetic fields and thus at least know how to avoid them. In addition, through the Vivaxis exercises we can enhance our own energy fields.

Since the 1980s, many studies have been conducted on the biological and health effects of electromagnetic radiation. Studies have included cell cultures exposed in the laboratory to artificially produced fields, humans exposed similarly to electromagnetic radiation, populations exposed to environmental radiation, and groups of workers who were exposed in the course of their work. Probably the most controversial study in recent decades was carried out in 1979 by Wertheimer and Leeper, who reported on 344 people aged eighteen or less who died from cancer in Denver between 1950 and 1973.[95] The factors taken into account were electromagnetic field strength from power lines or transformers within about one hundred feet of their homes. Those who died of cancer were found to have lived in homes with higher exposure to electromagnetic radiation than those in the control group, who were matched for ages. The study originally was rejected by government authorities, but it was reexamined and found to be valid by the electrical authorities themselves.[96] Wertheimer conducted another study in 1982 with 1,179 adults and controls who were not only matched for age and sex but also for social class. Again, cancer was more likely to have occurred in homes with higher ambient electromagnetic field exposure.[97]

As part of a project by the New York Power Lines Project, studies were undertaken by Savitz on cancer in children up to the age of fourteen years. Very detailed measurements were undertaken within the homes of the

[95] N. Wertheimer and E. Leeper, "Electrical Wiring Configuration and Childhood Cancer," *Journal of Epidemiology* 111 (1982): 273-84.
[96] New York State Power Lines Project, *Biological Effects of Power Line Fields* (New York: U.S. Department of Health, 1987).
[97] N. Wertheimer and E. Leeper, "Adult Cancer Related to Electrical Wires near the Home," *Journal of Epidemiology* 11, no. 4 (1980): 345-55.

subjects, and these measurements included all the electrical appliances. The final causal association indicated that 10 percent to 15 percent of all childhood cancers are attributed to magnetic fields.[98] Apart from the likely increase of cancer after such exposure, it has been found that the incidence of headache, depression, and suicide is increased in persons living within about one hundred and fifty feet of overhead power lines. Both electric and magnetic fields are emitted from power lines, and it is the magnetic field that is the most penetrating.

One of the problems in establishing a safe distance from such lines relates to the fluctuations in the strength of the field that occurs with changing power-load demands and weather conditions. There are also sudden peaks of voltage that can occur for very short times but that may have a significant effect on anyone in the vicinity at the time. For instance, a cable carrying 400,000 volts may sometimes carry a million volts for a millisecond. It has been suggested by electrical engineering researchers Smith and Best that this sudden surge of current can create a field that may adversely affect the human immune system. (See suggested reading at the end of this chapter.)

Testing for Electromagnetic Fields

Developing an understanding in this area is one of the most useful skills we can have for our home, work, and travel environments. If you know how to check the normal energy flow (ion flow), then you are equipped with this essential skill. Remember that testing ion flow in the environment is a measure of the balance in the

---

[98] D. A. Savitz, "Childhood Cancer and Electromagnetic Field Exposure," Report to the New York State Department of Health, Power Lines Project, New York, U.S. Department of Health, 1987.

electromagnetic field associated with our bodies, and this includes our Vivaxis energies. Outside electromagnetic interference overrides the subtle electromagnetic field of the body, so by testing for ion flow balance, we can gauge whether our own field is at risk in any environment. It is a practice that can be carried out quietly without anyone noticing.

When buying a new home, changing workplaces, or choosing a hotel room, you can easily check the ion flow for health-giving energies. In one house I lived in, high-voltage power lines were located about three thousand feet down the street. I carefully checked the block for any disturbance before we bought the house. The boundary of the electromagnetic field from the lines was just near our boundary on a clear day. Several homes were built between our property and the power lines—one house was situated directly underneath the lines.

It was a good opportunity to investigate the phenomena, and I regularly checked the ion flow of the houses closer to the lines. At no time did I ever note a normal ion flow on these properties. It is amazing that the residents could remain in such a lifeless environment, and I wonder if they felt perpetually tired. On one occasion, I engaged a professional engineer to measure the magnetic field around my home. I was interested to see whether his findings correlated with my own. He found the field strength well within the safety range in our home; then, for interest, he checked the house next door, which was nearer the power line. His instrument measured 0.9 milligauss, which he said was acceptable according to government standards, yet this was a house without any normal ion flow from my perspective. In other words, when I tested for ion flow around the house, my testing arm was "dead," so there was no normal flow at all.

In this instance, the human body is a more sensitive and reliable "instrument." At any time and despite the many variables, we can assess the total effect on our body from the surrounding environment. I have found the extent of disturbance around the type of transformers placed in suburban streets somewhat variable, but there usually is a disturbance for at least thirty feet. In many cases, this disturbance penetrates the living rooms of the home nearby. Again, our electromagnetic field and our Vivaxis connection will be disturbed if we live in such an environment.

Radiation from Television and Computer Screens

This is a controversial area. Some of the studies conducted on women to check for incidence of fetal malformation have been rejected by the authorities. But in 1988, a study of 1,583 women that was conducted in Oakland, California, by the Kaiser Permanente Health Group found serious problems. Female workers using computers for more than twenty hours a week had a 40 percent increase of miscarriage compared to those in a control group; other problems included insomnia, headache, and skin rashes.[99]

According to Robert Becker, all video display terminals (television sets, video games, and computer monitors) emit varying amounts of radiation over a broad spectrum. Microwaves, X-rays, and ultraviolet rays are all emitted by the screen. If the electronic assembly of a set is poorly adjusted, some of the terminals can emit enormous amounts of radiation. Regular maintenance and the use of lead impregnated glass or an acrylic screen can virtually eliminate ionizing radiation, but the problem of microwaves has not been solved.[100] Modern computers emit much less radiation than those of the 1980s and early 1990s.

---

[99] D. I. Dowsen, "A Review of Epidemiological Studies into the Health Effects of Electromagnetic Fields," *Complementary Medical Research 3*, no. 2. (1989).
[100] Becker, *Cross Currents*, p. 276.

We need to consider the new generation of children that is being introduced to computers in schools. These children are being subjected to regular doses of electromagnetic radiation from an early age. At home, the exposure continues with the constant use of computer games and the watching of television. It is important to consider the *cumulative* effects of the combined electromagnetic factors in the environment. There is still much we don't know. For instance, does the computer operator or student constantly use a cellular phone, live in a room next to the street power lines, watch a lot of television in their spare time, or have a poor diet?

In Australia over 50 percent of adults already have a cellular phone. The main problem with cellular phones is that when they are being used, the operator receives microwaves via the aerial held close to the brain. Exposure will obviously depend on the amount of time spent on the phone. Many parents are now buying these phones for their teenagers so that their children can keep in touch in case of emergency.

The advantages of technology in this age of communication cannot be ignored. There is no need to discard the endless possibilities for creative living provided by television, computers, the Internet, satellites, jet travel, and cellular phones. But we need to understand the health implications of such technology and to take appropriate measures to preserve health. Governments are gradually becoming alert to the health implications. We can hope that further appropriate legislation and controls will be instituted whereby power lines are kept away from residential dwellings and schools.

However, we do need to remember that the price of freedom is eternal vigilance, and in this case, it is freedom from health problems. We need to appreciate that our human-made electrical environment is yet another obstacle to the healthy operation of our Vivaxis connection. The privatization of facilities such as water and electricity poses extra problems for the general public, because private organizations will not have the same accountability as governments have. It behooves us to be alert to our exposure to detrimental energies as we move further into the twenty-first century. As people become more sensitive to energies, they are becoming more aware of positive and negative energies in the environment.

Suggested Reading

Becker, Robert, and Gary Seldon. *The Body Electric: Electromagnetism and the Foundation of Life.* New York: Quill, 1985.

Smith, Cyril, and Simon Best. *Electromagnetic Man: Health and Hazard in the Electrical Environment.* New York: St. Martins Press, 1989.

Thurnell-Read, Jane. *Geopathic Stress: How Earth Energies Affect Our Lives.* Dorset, U.K.: Element, 1995.

PART TWO

Practical Exercises for Working with Your Vivaxis Connection

Introduction

This second part of the book describes the various exercises you can do to remove disturbances from your energy field and to reinstate healthy energies. The exercises are in a necessary sequence, and it is preferable that you master each stage before passing on to the next. In some cases, this is essential, as for instance, you need to gain the ability to record energies (as in ion flow) before you chart the energy frequencies in the planetary layers. However, there are some optional exercises that relate to Fran's earlier work such as those connected with the Arealoha forces, and these can be conducted out of order.

You may feel a bit frustrated you cannot go straight to the exercise for finding your Vivaxis, which is exercise 11. There are some optional exercises you can do before this, such as removing static, to successfully and accurately find the Vivaxis direction. But otherwise, undertake the sequence as described below for best results.

The first exercises deal with carbon clearing for old X-rays and neutralizing of foreign fields. The next set is about learning to use your built-in magnetic sense to find the planetary directions for true north and south. This is one of the easiest exercises and is very rewarding in terms of its implications. Then you will develop your ability to test for ion flow; this brings in the dowsing sense that underlies so many of the later skills, and it enables you to become sensitive enough to sense your energy field and the energies in your environment. You can learn to sense energies as soon as you have cleared your circuits of emotional, chemical, and electronic disturbances. After acquiring the ion flow skills, you will learn to find the times of the major and minor periods and the solunar low times wherein you can undertake your testing and do the Vivaxis work. Having strengthened your own energies in this way, you can now develop the skills for finding the receptors for different elements on your fingers.

The capacity to visualize the elements prepares you to find the energy layers and to use them to make the inactivating powder for home and office, to purify food and water, and to find the specific directions for elements. Other skills involve checking yourself and others for energy disturbances of vitamins and minerals on the energy layers and then aligning to specific elements, if needed. The chakras can also be checked on the energy layers. Further, you can learn to find the vertical flows, which can be useful in a situation where there is no access to sloping land for marking the horizontal flows.

Then at last we come to the exercises that help you to find your Vivaxis (exercise 11) and give directions for aligning your Vivaxis energies (exercise 12). These exercises are the center point of your work with the Vivaxis connection.

The capacity to visualize and test for elements gives you the ability to learn the skills for improving memory and for testing the size of your aura from day to day. You can have fun exploring receptors on different parts of the body, such as those concerned with appetites for food and sex. Moving from sex to the sublime—identifying and correcting disturbed pineal receptors—is a skill that will correct the daily rhythms of your endocrine system and will enhance meditation skills.

Then you will master specific skills, such as how to cut short colds and the effects of viruses, reduce the effect of insect stings, test your eyes to monitor longsightedness and shortsightedness, and observe the effect of your thoughts on another person. After exploring the receptors, you will be in the position to work with many of the body receptors and to test when they are disturbed. You will gain the techniques needed to restore the correct energies. Fran's later work with the energy layers has minimized the need for detailed work in this area, but it is of great interest to keen students, especially those working as therapists.

Clearing Techniques with Carbon

The purpose of this exercise is to remove the negative effects of X-rays regardless of how long ago you received them. This exercise realigns the carbon atoms of the affected bones in the correct orientation to true north and south via your Vivaxis. You may need to repeat this more than once, but one application generally is sufficient unless you have missed an X-rayed part. The basic process is to jar the affected part so as to displace the disturbed energies and then to immediately apply the frequencies of carbon in the form of charcoal. In practice, it is best to treat the whole body, as X-rays have a scattering effect and it is hard to remember every X-ray we have experienced.

Students report a definite sense of well-being after this treatment regardless of whether they remember ever having been X-rayed. This is because we are subject to other forms of ionizing radiation throughout our life such as that from television and computer screens, and therefore our bones may be affected by many sources. Ionizing radiation involves streams of high-energy photons that knock out the outer electrons in the atoms composing

Students report a definite sense of well-being after this treatment regardless of whether they remember ever having been X-rayed. This is because we are subject to other forms of ionizing radiation throughout our life such as that from television and computer screens, and therefore our bones may be affected by many sources.

our body tissues. In sufficient quantities, these loose electrons can cause tissue damage.

1. Collect some charcoal (carbon) from a fire made with untreated wood and place it in a strong plastic bag. Do not use commercially produced barbecue briquettes unless they are pure charcoal. The amount of charcoal should be enough so that the bag will cover about seven to nine square inches of your body.

2. It is best to treat the body in sections. Jar each area first by tapping sharply with the heel of your hand to stir up the disturbed energies before applying the charcoal. Wrists, elbows, shoulders, coccyx, knees, and jaw may need special attention. Until you learn to find the energy layers, face approximately true north (the compass direction for carbon) and place the plastic bag containing charcoal on your head while focusing your thoughts on carbon for about thirty seconds. Then continue by applying the charcoal to your neck, shoulders, arms, chest (front and back), lower body, and legs after initially stressing each part by tapping with the heal of your hand.

3. After applying the charcoal to your head and arms, balance this carbon frequency by moving the bag of charcoal away. Face south and visualize calcium—think of chalk. Calcium is the mate to carbon, and their compass directions are directly opposite each other. Continue to treat the rest of the body in this manner by facing north, jarring the part, applying the carbon,

and balancing carbon by facing south and thinking of calcium after treating several body parts.

4. Pay special attention to any previously X-rayed areas. To remove the effect of dental X-rays, wrap a small piece of charcoal in plastic (preferably non-PVC type), then press and bite it between your teeth and press the charcoal onto the roof of your mouth.

5. Carbon should be applied to both top and bottom surfaces of your feet. Stamp each foot before and after activation by the carbon.

Remember that the affected area is always larger than the original X-rayed area because of the scattering and spreading effects of X-rays. Hips, pelvic bone, and knee joints can be stimulated by a hula-hoop motion while holding the carbon on the bones concerned. If you have difficulty reaching your back, a stocking filled with dried beans makes a convenient tool for stimulating your spine before applying the charcoal.

Once you have learned to find the Earth's energy layers, or bands, in exercise 7, this clearing procedure is enhanced if you stand on Force Flow 1. This is because the frequency of carbon is found on Force Flow 1. Note that when standing on Force Flow 1, the direction for carbon is west rather than north. Until you have learned how to find the energy layers, you should face north as previously directed.

Finding the Directions for Carbon and Calcium: True North and South

After the clearing exercise with carbon, you should be able to find the directions of true north and south through the natural magnetic response in your body to the compass directions for carbon and calcium. The ability to find true north will indicate that the carbon clearing exercise has been successful. This is your first experience of the compass directions for an element. Later, you will easily find the directions for each elemental frequency, provided your energy circuits are free of disturbances.

The basic technique for finding the direction of an element is to clearly visualize the chosen element and, at the same time, allow your arm or body to move in that direction. As long as the calcium and carbon atoms in your bones are in a state of confusion, the direction for these elements cannot be demonstrated. Finding the correct direction after the exercise proves that the effects of X-rays have been eradicated.

1. Stand on level ground and place your hands firmly on your thighs, with your feet, knees, and thighs together. (Positioning the body in this way produces a much stronger response than trying to test with one arm, although that is a valid procedure after you have learned to test ion flow.)

2. Visualize the element carbon by thinking of charcoal. In doing this, your energy body will become attuned to the frequency of carbon, which "travels" over the planet in the direction of true north. You should feel a strong pull in your body toward true north.

3. Visualize calcium (white blackboard chalk) and you will get a pull backward and toward true south. (See figure 39A.)

The only additional information you need for finding these directions relates to the major and minor periods. At these times, the frequencies of calcium and carbon are interrupted several times each twenty-four hours as a result of the changing relationship between Sun, Moon, and Earth, which causes the daily tides. Until you know how to find the tides, you will not know when the horizontal directions for calcium and carbon disappear.

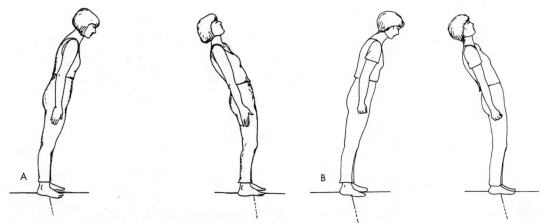

Figure 39. Testing the directions for north and south
39A. Carbon and calcium pulls during solunar flow time By facing north and visualizing carbon, you experience a forward pull through the North Pole Force Flow on your carbon atoms. Hands must be flat on thighs. By facing north and visualizing calcium, you experience a backward pull through the influence of the South Pole Force Flow on your calcium atoms.
39B. Carbon and calcium pulls during major and minor period. The hands are held as closed fists on the thighs, because the fingertips are then pointing upward, and this allows you to record the vertical waves of carbon during the major and minor periods when the horizontal waves are missing.

Reprinted from *Healing through Earth Energies* by Judy Jacka, 1996.

However, during those periods when the horizontal waves have disappeared, you can find the carbon and calcium pulls, using their vertical waves. So, if you don't get a response to north with your hands flat on your thighs, try the following: Place your hands against your thighs as before, but close your hands so that your fingers are pointing upward, allowing your body to respond to the vertical waves of carbon and calcium. In this position, your hands will be held like closed fists against the thighs. (See figure 39B.)

You could wait to do this exercise until after the exercise to find solunar flow (see exercise 5) so that you would then know how to avoid the major and minor period, but until the X-rays are cleared, it may be difficult to find the solunar flow.

While true north and south are related to carbon and calcium, magnetic north and south are related to the frequencies of sea salt and iron respectively. To find magnetic north, visualize sea salt, and for magnetic south, visualize iron. Again, your body should be pulled toward the source of the element that is visualized. Magnetic north is a variable degree east of true north. Indeed, the magnetic poles have moved many times during our planet's history. This movement has been charted by scientists who investigate the right- and left-hand spin of molecules that have been preserved for millions of years in the crust of the Earth.

Finding north and south can be handy if you are wilderness hiking on an overcast day when it is hard to tell the Sun's position. If you are unable to do this exercise correctly, repeat it after doing the neutralizing exercise (exercise 2) that follows. For if you have a foreign field, finding the directions for north and south may be difficult.

An interesting observation about the elements carbon and oxygen was offered by British atmospheric scientist James Lovelock in connection with his theory about the Gaia Hypothesis. He said that several scientists had attributed the amount of oxygen in the atmosphere to carbon burial and its release by the weathering of siliceous rocks as well as to the processes of methane production. This contrasts with the more widely accepted hypothesis of oxygen production and release from living plants and trees. It could be argued of course that if there were no forests, there would eventually be no carbon so that vegetation is still the indirect cause of oxygen production.

In the context of the Lovelock hypothesis, I think it relevant that Fran Nixon discovered that the frequencies of carbon and oxygen are connected and that for health we need a good alignment to these frequencies, which both relate to a northerly direction. She also discovered that carbon, calcium, and oxygen are related to the main health-giving key flows of energy on Force Flow 1.

This relationship between carbon and its pair, calcium, and between oxygen and its pair, cobalt, derives from the fact that they are directly opposite each other in terms of their compass directions. These directions in space are the first of many patterns that emerged from Fran's research. You will learn to check these patterns with your body in exercise 8. Further research into these frequencies will perhaps eventually give more understanding as to why the elements relate to different directions of the compass. (See figure 40.)

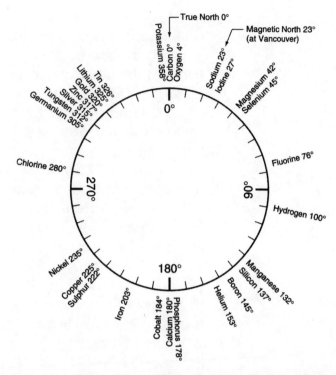

Figure 40. Compass direction for key elements. The compass directions for the elements depicted in this diagram were derived as follows: The researchers grounded their hands firmly on their thighs, while keeping legs firmly together at ankles and knees, and visualized the particular element in question. They then noted the direction in which the body was pulled. They next moved so that they were facing the direction of the pull, repeated the exercise, and noted the number of degrees clockwise from True North (direction of carbon) that they were facing.

Reprinted from *Healing through Earth Energies* by Judy Jacka, 1996.

Using Chalk and Carbon to Establish a Protective Force Field

This optional exercise is best done later, when you have learned to test energy flows. Some years after Fran died, Canadian researchers of Vivaxis discovered that a field of energy can be created between a plastic bag of carbon and some white blackboard chalk (calcium) placed ten inches away. This field is able to cancel out any detrimental field created by magnets.

The research project involved placing four bar magnets, each of 1,200-gauss strength, in the four directions of the compass. (Gauss is the unit of measurement for magnetic fields.) A strong vertical vector of energy was found at the center point between the magnets. The carbon was placed at northeast between two of the magnets and the calcium between the other two magnets at southwest. The vertical field from the magnets was now found to be canceled.

This finding proves the benefit of using the frequencies of calcium and carbon to counteract detrimental fields. Magnets placed on the human body or used near the human body can introduce a foreign field of energies into our own circuits. Many people have disturbed their energy circuits through regular applications of magnets for pain even while receiving temporary relief. As the use of magnets can cause the injection of a foreign field, it is not conducive to healthy energies to use them for pain relief. They block pain by blocking the reception of pain by the brain, but the confusion caused by foreign energies from another Vivaxis causes further problems. This brings us to the next exercise, which is the elimination of foreign fields.

Removing Foreign Fields

Having a foreign field means that we are connected to another Vivaxis as well as to our own. This connection causes a confusion of energies resulting from conflicting wave circuits. Our acupuncture meridians are connected to energy fields that are out of resonance with our own. The body can be charged up, but if we have a foreign field, it will be a mass of seething, conflicting energies. We may suffer from exhaustion, poor memory, headache, muscle pains, lack of concentration, and a total inability to relax.

I explored the causes of foreign fields in part 1, but as a reminder here, they can include any type of electrical circuit such as diathermy, electrocardiograph, electrolysis treatment for unwanted hair, or from connection to one of the electronic diagnostic units used by natural therapists whereby electrodes or probes touch the hands. The phenomenon can also take place through hypnotism and magnetic healing or through the use of magnets.

The rationale for the neutralizing exercise is to bring in and saturate our energy field with *our own* energies, and to do this so strongly that all foreign energies are removed. We accentuate our own energies by making a circuit with our fingertips and toes in the following manner:

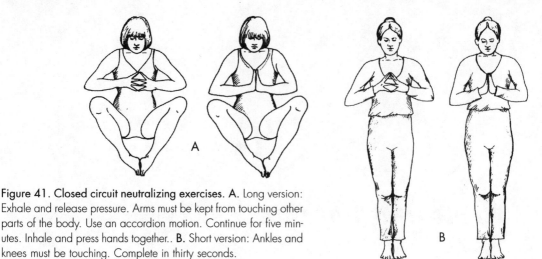

Figure 41. Closed circuit neutralizing exercises. A. Long version: Exhale and release pressure. Arms must be kept from touching other parts of the body. Use an accordion motion. Continue for five minutes. Inhale and press hands together.. **B.** Short version: Ankles and knees must be touching. Complete in thirty seconds.

Neutralizing Exercise: Long Version

Use the long version to eliminate existing foreign fields.

1. Find a quiet place where you will not be disturbed and assume a sitting position. (See figure 41.) Place the center whorls of your fingers together and likewise your toes. Your heels should also be touching.

2. Firmly press the fingertips and palms of your hands together, while inhaling.

3. During exhalation, release the pressure on your fingertips but keep them touching. Your hands should move as if you are playing an accordion. Provided your fingertips and toes stay connected, you can take short rests during this exercise.

4. Keep the exercise going for five minutes.

5. Keep your toes and heels in close contact throughout the exercise. At intervals, briefly press and release pressure on your toes and heels without breaking the circuit.

6. It is very important to hold your arms away from your body so that the energies are not short-circuited by your arms touching the clothing around your chest.

You need to exert considerable pressure on the hands for this exercise to be effective. However, pressure should be applied in such a manner that it will stimulate energy flow and not restrict circulation.

Neutralizing Exercise: Short Version

The short version is suitable to prevent foreign fields after working with clients (such as doing body work) or to prevent draining other people's energies after aligning to our Vivaxis. Normally, we would choose to stay away from other people for twenty minutes after aligning, but this is not always possible.

1. Stand with knees and ankles pressed together.

2. Make a circuit between your fingertips and use the same press and release technique while inhaling and exhaling for one minute.

It is useful for therapists to undertake a short version of this exercise between each patient consultation, because it prevents the energies of the therapist being drained by the client and, more important, because it prevents the formation of a foreign Vivaxis between client and therapist. Use this short version to cut short the effect of aligning to your Vivaxis, if necessary.

Like the carbon-clearing exercise (exercise 1), the neutralizing exercise is enhanced when it is performed on Force Flow 1. So, after you have learned to find the energy layers that include Force Flow 1, you can then do the neutralizing exercise sitting on that layer. This exercise preferably should be done during solunar flow time, that is, between major and minor periods. Until you know how to find the solunar period, undertake the exercise at different times on several consecutive days.

Later, when you have learned to find the energy layers (see exercise 7) and when you have charted the mineral frequencies on the fingertips, you can more quickly remove a foreign field by placing the chromium horizontal finger pad on the corresponding force flow—Force Flow 1—and the chromium vertical finger on the chromium vertical layer at the same time for a few seconds. Do the exercise with both hands. This is obviously useful if you are working with an instructor who has already marked out the force flows. However, the neutralizing exercise is also beneficial for bringing in *your* energies and should *always* be included in your preparatory exercises.

Optional Exercises for Removing Static

Static within our energy circuits can cause blurred vision, irritability, poor concentration, lack of coordination, exhaustion from leaking adrenal pathways, chronic aches and pains, and weakened immunity. This does not leave much else to go wrong. Exercising on the energy layers removes static. However, the following methods relate to earlier procedures discovered by Fran for removing static from the energy field. After she discovered the energy layers, she discontinued teaching these methods; even so, they can be useful before you are in a position to find the energy layers or when you do not have access to the layers, such as when traveling when the "hot shower method" can be used.

The Wire Hoop Method

This simple method requires that you stand in a galvanized wire hoop that has one end pointing into the circle (of the hoop) and the other end pointing outward. (See figure 42.) The ends of the wire must not touch the ground. The circle needs to be three to four feet in diameter. Stand in the center of the hoop with your hands grounded on your

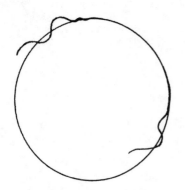

Figure 42. Wire hoop used for removing static. The galvanized wire hoop is approximately three and a half feet in diameter. The ends of the wire must not touch the ground.

thighs and your feet placed apart but not touching the wire. Undertake this exercise for about thirty seconds. The rationale here is obvious: the end of the wire within the circle picks up excess energy from you and carries it away. It is preferable to undertake this clearing outdoors because of the many electrical circuits in your house.

Fran found that a person standing outside the hoop could test the insulated area within the wire. When the tester thinks of any direction away from the hoop, their testing arm or angle wire will move in the direction of their thought. However, if thinking in the direction of the hoop, the arm or wire will not point in that direction. In other words, the area inside the hoop is free from interference. Perhaps the procedure in magic of drawing a circle around a person for psychic protection is based on this same principle.

This wire hoop method is suitable for simple static or excess energy problems, but it is not appropriate for some of the energy problems one encounters today. It is an old technique that has been used in many ways. For instance, a wire or strap was often attached to a car so that it dragged along the road and presumably discharged the static accumulated during travel; this was said to prevent car sickness.

The Soda and Salt Bath Method

This technique to remove static is based on Fran's discovery of the magnetic forces of the north and south magnetic poles, associated with the soda and salt. Bringing in these health-giving frequencies eliminates a buildup of static; however, it is not the most convenient method and is costly because of the price of pure sea salt. Normal salt would not be suitable, because it usually is refined and contains aluminum to keep it free running.

Again, this method is mainly suitable for general static and probably works best with fairly pure water, which is not available in most cities today. The many chemicals in our water supply may interfere with the exchange of energy between the soda, salt, and body. Do not employ the soda and salt bath for three days over the full moon period, because the energies transmitted by these compounds are unstable at such times.

Here's how to do it: Add a pound of sodium bicarbonate and the same amount of unrefined sea salt to a bathtub of warm water. Soak in the bath for about ten minutes and immerse your head a few times.

Charging Your Body with the Arealoha Forces

The following exercise involves a further exploration of the forces involved in the previous exercise. When Fran discovered the Arealoha forces, their absorption was found to be the most lasting and effective method of clearing one's energy circuit, including erasing foreign influences. In addition, the immune system was enhanced through strengthening the energy circuits. (The theory for the Arealoha forces was discussed in part 1.) This exercise depends on your ability to find the light vectors at any particular time of day, month, or year. It appears that the directions for light flow are the same for both Northern and Southern Hemispheres.

During the years I worked with Fran, she no longer taught this exercise, because her work with the energy layers had taken over her time and was found to be generally more useful and convenient. The technique of aligning on the force flows has largely replaced the need for this exercise, but it can still be useful at times when you are not able to use the force flows because of your location or because of extreme weather conditions.

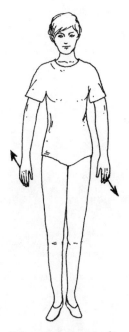

Figure 43. Testing for direction of light vectors. Tester faces different directions with backs of hands faced forward to test light vectors. When the direction of the light vector is found, hands during solunar flow period will move back and forth while held in this position.

1. Test that the light is coming from west and south by facing both these directions in turn with the backs of your hands facing forward so that your thumbs are next to your legs. (See figure 43.) Your hands should move forward and

backwards. If they remain stationary, it may be a major or minor period or at a time of the year when light comes from a different direction. In this case, turn to face east and north with hands in the same position. If the light is coming from these directions, your hands will again move forward and backward. It is best to only undertake this Arealoha exercise when the light is coming from west and south; this is usual in solunar flow times.

2. Place containers of soda and salt in an east and west direction with the soda east of the salt. (If the light is coming from the east and north, place the jars with the soda west of the salt but bear in mind that the light is more unstable when coming from these directions and may change direction suddenly.)

3. Bring blood to all your head receptors by hanging your head down for about eight seconds. Stand clear of the jars during this time.

4. Lift your head and immediately hold the palm of your right hand, pointing south in the Northern Hemisphere and pointing north in the Southern Hemisphere over the center point between jars for about six seconds to absorb Arealoha forces. Breathe deeply. Repeat with your left hand. (See figure 33.)

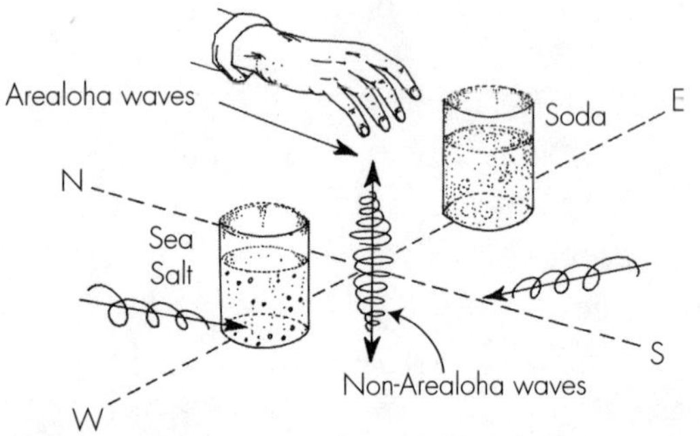

Figure 33. The Arealoha forces from soda and salt. Arealoha forces are formed when jars of soda and salt are placed in an east/west direction a few inches apart. One force field flows down in an angled line from the west, and another one from the south. These fluctuate and change under various influences, relative to time and place. At times, only one of these fields is detectable. Hand direction is reversed in the Southern Hemisphere. The palm is held over the center of force between the jars.

5. Now expose each finger and thumb in turn to the Arealoha forces between the jars for about six seconds.

6. Jog around the room for one minute to spread Arealoha energies to your foot receptors.

7. Do the short form of the neutralizing exercise (exercise 2) for about six cycles to further spread the energies throughout your body.

You can try an interesting side experiment by placing a lump of white sugar in the jar of sea salt. You'll find that no energies can be recorded between the jars and that they no longer have any positive effect on a static room. This illustrates the effect of refined foods and especially refined sugars on our energies.

Hot Shower Spray Method

This is a means whereby your receptors all over your body are stimulated by hot sprayed water. For this exercise, you need access to a moveable shower head.

1. Undertake the short neutralizing exercise (see exercise 2) as a preparation for this method.

2. The temperature of the water should be as hot as comfortably possible. Stand in the shower with your feet well apart and your head bare. Direct a strong spray of water over every part of your head and face, including around each eye. Spray inside your mouth, including soft and hard palates, tongue, and teeth.

3. Treat your neck, back, arms, hands, centers of fingertips and palms of each hand.

4. Start at your knees and work around your legs and feet giving attention to the instep and toes.

5. After finishing, do not touch your head or face for at least ten minutes and preferably allow your hair to drip dry. This is obviously not a technique for the middle of winter or if preparing for a cocktail party!

Finding Ion Flow

Finding ion flow is the basic skill for testing your Vivaxis energies. You might remember that this technique measures the healthy pulsation between the two main Vivaxis layers of your aura. As part of that process, the balance between negative and positive ions in your energy field is established. The procedure also enables you to monitor the balance of ion flow in your environment, demonstrating whether your environment is healthy at any point in time. Pollution and Earth disturbances like earthquakes, sunspot activity, and electromagnetic fields will unbalance the ion flow in the environment.

The mastery of this skill is important for all the procedures that follow. Note the difference between the element iron, and ion, as in ion flow. The element iron is one of the many elements we need for a healthy body, for example, blood iron. An ion, however, is an electrical term and in Vivaxis work we use it for denoting energy flows on the body and in the environment. Therefore, an ion means an electrically charged particle.

The clearing exercise with carbon and the neutralizing exercise must be undertaken first because effective testing of energies *depends* on your having cleared circuits. Again, as with the previous exercises, they can only be conducted during solunar flow periods, so until the skill for finding this period is developed, you need to practice this exercise at different times of the day. If you are lucky enough to be with a Vivaxis instructor, he or she will have already assessed suitable timing for you.

This technique is based on the dowsing response. The great majority of persons with cleared circuits can learn to use their arm and hands as recording or dowsing instruments for energy flow in any part of the body. It is wise to do this new exercise in calm weather conditions and in a state of calm emotions. Doing this just after meditation would be an ideal time, because the emotions have a profound effect on body energies and they are usually quiet after a meditation.

Ion flow is a measure of energy in our body and the environment. In balanced environmental conditions, there will be equal numbers of negative and positive ions in the atmosphere. If there is an excess of positive ions, such as occurs on very hot days, we feel exhausted. Air conditioners and many forms of industrial equipment create an excess of positive ions, which is why we feel exhausted in a stuffy room. Computers, photocopiers, and heaters also create positive ions; modern city and office life constantly expose us to an excess of positive ions. Our electromagnetic fields need negative ions if we are to feel energized.

Ion imbalances can disturb the lymphatic system. The antibodies of our immune system appear to depend on the regular exchange of energies between our Vivaxis and the receptor points for these energies on the body. It has been noted that epidemics and infections are more common when a prolonged period of positive ions in the atmosphere has occurred.

You can measure this basic energy through either sight or touch, although the following exercise deals mainly with touch. Use the middle finger of either hand to check each part of the body, while your other hand will then have a stimulated motion if there is a normal energy flow in that part of the body. However, you can also simply look at the body part being tested, or if the part is inaccessible to the eye, you can concentrate on it.

If there is no energy flow in the recording hand, your energy field is not penetrating the bone underlying the tissue being tested. If there is a disturbed or chaotic energy in the part being tested, your recording hand will move in a circular pattern.

Checking for Energy or Ion Flow

1. Remove any watch, mobile phone, jewelry, glasses, or coins you may have in your pockets. Any metal object or battery will change energy flows. Your clothing should be of natural fibers and of a light color, but definitely not black, because that color negates the effect of light flow. Just as we put up a black curtain to keep out daylight, there is a parallel phenomenon at subtle physical levels. Wearing black clothes tends to denude our bodies of subtle energy. Tight belts and ties should be removed.

2. Stand with your legs apart and make sure your shoulders are down and relaxed with your arms held loosely at your side. Practice while facing different directions in case you are facing your Vivaxis, because this might give a false positive. In addition, when starting the practice, energies may more easily be noted when standing in certain directions as we receive energies the body needs. This is a bit like suddenly noticing a welcome breeze when we turn our heads in a particular direction in a stuffy room.

3. Test first one side of your body and then the other in the following manner. Place the tip of your middle finger very lightly on the part of the body you choose to test. Allow your mind to be as relaxed as possible. Allow your other recording hand to hang loosely at your side,

but make sure your sleeve is not touching your body, because this short circuits the testing. It takes a bit of practice to hold the recording arm relaxed but in a slight curve so that it is not touching the body. (See figure 44.)

The recording movement is denoted by a back and forth movement of the hand in the direction away from the body and back toward it, in response to whatever part of the body is touched by the middle finger on the other hand. Initially, before you become familiar with using your arm in this way, you may respond to the energy flow by feeling a tingling in one or both hands. Hold the recording hand for horizontal flow. (See figure 45B.)

4. Use the middle finger of your right hand for touching and testing the right side of the body and the left middle finger for the left side. Do not cross the midline when testing for ion flow. Keep the middle finger of each hand on the same side of the body while you are using it to test.

5. To restore a balanced ion flow, exercise briefly and vigorously facing

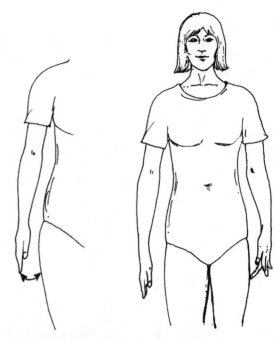

Figure 44. Recording technique for ion flow. Record ion or horizontal flows with a back and forth movement—keep fingers straight. Testing for ion flow: keep your shoulders down and relaxed; recording arm must not touch the body; only the middle finger of the testing hand can touch your body; arm should move gently back and forth.

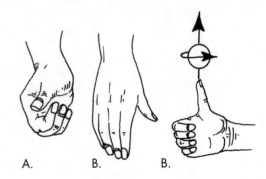

A.   B.   B.

Figure 45. Three different hand positions for testing
A. Hand position for testing vertical waves.
B. Hand position for testing a horizontal wave.
C. Hand position for testing direction of spin.

first approximately north and then south (in stable weather conditions). Later, after having found the energy layers, you can restore and enhance ion flow by exercising on specific energy flows. The magnesium and Force Flow 3 enhance negative ions, while the phosphorus and Force Flow 4 stimulate positive ions.

When you first practice finding ion flow and your arm moves back and forth, you may wonder if it is your imagination working too hard. In other words, you may think your mind is making your arm move; however, after further practice, it will become obvious that your arm is moving independently of directed thought. You may need to practice for about fifteen minutes on a number of days before you note any movement. Some people take time in learning to sufficiently relax the arm and shoulder so that the arm can respond to energy flows.

Testing Ion Flow in the Environment

After you have become proficient at this testing, you will notice that in unsettled weather you will record a weaker ion flow when you are facing a particular direction. In this situation, "a weak flow" means hardly any movement of the arm. Overall, it is preferable to have a slight predominance of negative ions in your body. We feel energetic when there is a slight predominance of negative ions and lethargic when there is an excess of positive ions.

As a general guide to environmental conditions, stand in a north/south line facing north. If conditions are balanced, ion flow should be approximately the same on both sides of the body. This means that the right side of the body is facing east, and the left is facing west. Negative ions tend to come in from the west and positive ions from the east.

As you gradually turn in a full circle, test the ion flow from each direction by noting the movement in your recording hand. You may find that the recording hand becomes weak when your body is placed in a particular direction. If the recording is weaker when the side being tested is facing west, this means negative ions coming from that direction are deficient. If the weakness is on the east, positive ions are deficient. In our polluted cities and countryside, it is more usual to have a deficiency of negative ions.

Usually, we feel very tired if positive ions accumulate as they do in many buildings with air-conditioning or heating. Test this fact by standing north/south in an over-heated room and test for ion flow. If the ions on the west side of your body are weak, this will prove to you that negative ions come from a westerly direction. Go outside in the fresh air and exercise vigorously, first facing north and then south. Then still outside, retest ion flow on both sides of the body while facing north/south. Balance should be restored, provided the atmosphere is also balanced on that day. In other words, at times our own ion flow is imbalanced because it is reflecting an atmospheric disturbance.

Recording ion flow is a very accurate way to find energy blocks in the body without the need of any electronic gadgets. After you have been using the method of touch for a while, try just scanning objects in the environment with your eye, but still using the recording hand. All your senses can be used to note energy flows. We started here with touch, because using a finger easily defines a particular area and is therefore very specific.

It is quicker to use the eye when scanning a number of objects, especially if they are far off. Check all the furniture and fittings in your home. Many soft furnishings will show a lack of normal energy flow if they contain

Recording ion flow is a very accurate way to find energy blocks in the body without the need of any electronic gadgets. After you have been using the method of touch for a while, try just scanning objects in the environment with your eye, but still using the recording hand. All your senses can be used to note energy flows.

foam plastic and if the upholstery is made of synthetic materials such as vinyl, nylon, or acrylic. Note the striking difference in recording energies between a tree or flower and a painted or plastic surface.

Inability to Record Energy Flows

You may not be able to record energy flow for a number of reasons. If the clearing exercise has not been adequately performed, effects from X-rays may still cause blocks in your arms and shoulders. Sometimes there are energy blocks in the head, which are partly caused by stress and negative emotions. These spots often correspond with old injuries on the opposite side of the body. On occasion, a very persistent foreign field needs clearing over several weeks with the neutralizing exercise (exercise 2). If there are persistent difficulties, it may be necessary to seek the help of a Vivaxis practitioner to help locate the difficulty.

Diagnosing a Foreign Field

Whenever the recording hand registers a circulating motion when you are testing some part on the body, you will know that there is a disturbed wave in a horizontal direction. In the presence of a foreign field, a vertical wave will link part of the body with the foreign Vivaxis. To test for this or any vertical wave, hold your recording hand with the fingers pointed upward. (See figure 45A.) If you get a back and forward response in the recording hand in addition to the previous horizontal disturbance, you have a foreign field around your body.

Testing for Compatible Foods and Medicines

This simple technique to test energies allows you to monitor energy flow in your body, environment, home, car, and food and is an invaluable aid in attaining health both at home and when traveling. You can use this technique to select appropriate foods and remedies and their correct dosages for yourself, family members, and friends.

This technique is an invaluable guide for homeopathic practitioners in determining the correct potency to prescribe. The one golden rule to remember is that your mind and emotions must be neutral at the time of testing and have only a visualization of the person concerned under way. The benefit of daily meditation for the purpose of diminishing emotional and mental conditioning in our testing procedures is worth repeating here.

To test food for your own use, hold a sample of the item in one hand and record the energies with the other. Hold the hand with the sample for testing at the same level as the recording hand. A normal strong ion flow in the sample will tell you that the food is compatible with your energy field. After some practice on food items, try testing your vitamins and minerals in the same way and also assess the best dosage for yourself.

You can also test foods and remedies for other people by thinking of them while holding the sample of the food or remedy. This is a valuable procedure for therapists and can be carried out at any distance from the subject.

When shopping or eating in restaurants, it is more appropriate to test by simply looking and observing the food and noting the reaction in your recording hand, which you are holding quietly by your side. With cases of food poisoning in restaurants forever on the increase, this is a valuable skill. There have been occasions when I have used my recording hand quietly under the table when eating out. Of course, it is difficult to know what you can actually say to the waiter if the food tests negative.

You will probably realize that ion flow testing using your arm is a version of dowsing, but without needing to use a pendulum. It is also in the same category as kinesiological muscle testing for suitable foods and remedies. However, with muscle testing there is always the problem of whether the tester is using the same pressure each time they push down on the subject's arm, rendering this approach less than reliable.

Finding the Solunar Flow Times

We need to conduct all the energizing exercises during the solunar (Sun and Moon) period so as to have access to the full range of frequencies. This period lasts approximately six hours between the major and minor period. During the major and minor periods that correspond to the peak of high tide and to the minimum of low tide, the force flows corresponding to the Sun and Moon cancel each other out. We cannot then receive frequencies of important elements like oxygen, calcium, chromium, zinc, and iodine from Force Flows 1 and 2. (See figure 46.)

The following exercise resulted from the finding that the light vectors from the Sun and Moon are reflected in our spinal cord at different angles as they change their daily positions relevant to the Earth. At the major period, the light is received vertically down our spine and at the minor period at right angles. This seems to correspond to the position of the Moon in relation to the rotation of the Earth. Our recording finger can pick up these shifting positions on the front of the body in relation to the spine and also on the mastoid bone behind the ear.

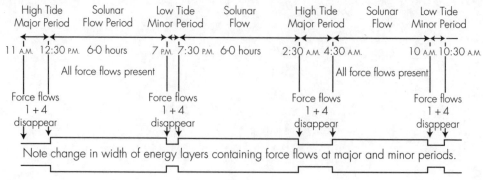

| High Tide Major Period | Solunar Flow Period | Low Tide Minor Period | Solunar Flow | High Tide Major Period | Solunar Flow | Low Tide Minor Period |

11 A.M. 12:30 P.M. 6-0 hours   7 P.M. 7:30 P.M. 6-0 hours   2:30 A.M. 4:30 A.M.   10 A.M. 10:30 A.M.

All force flows present   All force flows present

Force flows 1 + 4 disappear   Force flows 1 + 4 disappear   Force flows 1 + 4 disappear   Force flows 1 + 4 disappear

Note change in width of energy layers containing force flows at major and minor periods.

Figure 46. Solunar flow period over a twenty-four-hour period and change in width of force flows. Note that tide times will be one hour later each day. Note change in width of energy layers containing force flows at major and minor periods. Remember that this pattern will vary by one hour every day.

In her book, *Mysteries of Memory Unfold*, Fran first reported that the lines of force from the Sun and Moon are recorded at right angles to each other. At the minor period, she found the Sun's line of force recorded toward the west and the Moon's toward the south. She found that during the solunar flow period the line of force from the Sun gradually moved through an arc of twenty-two degrees toward the north. After peaking at the major period, this line gradually returned toward the west. Throughout this period, the recording direction of the Moon's flow remained at right angles to the Sun.

You can test these directions for the Sun and Moon yourself, as follows: If you face west and think of the Sun, a positive response will take place in the recording hand, but when you concentrate on the Moon, the recording arm will not move. Conversely, when you face south and think of the Moon, the recording hand will respond but will cut out as soon as you concentrate on the Sun.

Before starting this technique, establish the correct recording finger. In this exercise, we do not use the middle, or ion flow finger. Once you establish your receiving finger, it will be used for all testing above the waist apart from ion flow. Use either the first (index) or fourth (ring) finger on the left hand, depending on whether you are above or below your Vivaxis. If above the Vivaxis, the index finger will be the recording finger, and if below, it will be the ring finger. However, remember that to test ion flow, you use the middle finger and this finger is *always* used for ion testing regardless of our location.

Until the method for finding whether you are above or below your Vivaxis is described (see exercise 26), the simplest approach is to try first the index and then the ring finger of the left hand until a response is obtained in your recording hand. The left hand is used, because the flow of our Vivaxis energies is received via the left leg and arm.

As you will find in the exercise for finding mineral frequencies (exercise 26), the testing finger on the left hand is the one containing the frequency for iron (the magnetic group). From henceforth, we will always call this finger the testing finger, and it will always be the index or ring finger of the left hand. It is the magnetic layer of our Vivaxis sphere around the body that gives us the ability to receive information about energy flows on the body via the corresponding finger that contains the magnetic frequencies for iron.

Finding Solunar Flow: Method 1

The gravitational influences of the Sun and Moon travel up and down a one-half-inch band. Fran Nixon called this band the "solunar flow tract." It is located in a straight line from the navel to the notch on the front of the body just below the meeting point of the clavicles, (shoulder girdle). This slight hollow is over the thymus gland. The top of the tract registers energy at the major period which corresponds with high tide and the section at the navel corresponds to the minor period, or low tide. (See figure 47.)

1. Check ion flow to establish that it is reasonably balanced as you face into the four quadrants, and if necessary, balance your ion flow before locating the solunar flow. (See exercise 4.) Then face in a westerly direction and think of the Sun.

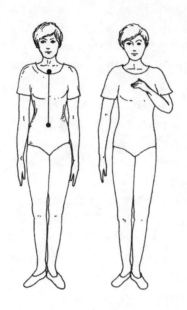

2. Place the tip of your testing finger (either the index or ring finger of the left hand) lightly on top of the solunar flow tract. Hold the other hand ready for recording lightly away from the body and with fingers relaxed but extended.

3. Move your testing finger in small distances of about one quarter of an inch gradually down the tract. Do not drag your finger, because this causes static on the surface of the body. It is also important not to press too hard; in fact, you can perform this test with your finger not quite touching your body, because you are measuring subtle energies. At some point along the tract, the recording hand will start to move back and forth. Stop moving your finger at this point and wait about thirty seconds. After some seconds, your recording hand will cease its motion. This is because the spine has already recorded a slight change in the position of the light vectors from the Sun and Moon.

4. Find out whether there is a movement toward a major or minor period. Move the testing finger further slightly to determine the new position. As the flow may be going up or down the tract at the time of testing, you may have to move the finger either up or down to relocate the new position. You can thus ascertain whether you are moving toward high or low tide. You can then know what intervals to expect later in the day and when, therefore, to do any Vivaxes exercises. The point

on the solunar tract where we record the flow at a particular point of time shows us the approximate time between the major and minor periods, that is, how far we are into the solunar flow period.

Some people may find it easier to concentrate on the Moon instead of the Sun, but in this case, you will need to face south while doing the exercise. If you try facing directions other than south or west while testing, you will record a slightly different position on your body for the tide flows and this will be less accurate. This relates to the fact that the angular relationship of the Sun and Moon to the Earth (and therefore their light vectors) relates to west and south specifically.

If you record a major period, it may be important to find how long you are into a major or minor period. Keep the testing finger on the notch in front of the thymus and tilt your head slowly backward. At a particular angle of the head tilt, your recording arm will stop moving. Roughly divide this angle or space into the full head-tilting angle, which corresponds to eighty degrees. As an example, if your head is tilted halfway back from level to full extension of the neck when your recording arm stops moving, you will know that the major period is halfway over, and thus forty minutes of time remains.

For the minor period, keep your testing finger on your navel while tilting your head downward until the recording arm cuts out. Repeat the same type of calculation but remember that the minor period only lasts twenty minutes. For example, if your head is tilted halfway from level down to the chest when the recording arm stops, you will know that half of the low-tide period has gone (half of twenty minutes, or ten minutes).

Finding Solunar Flow: Method 2

The gravitational energies of the Sun travel behind the right ear in an arc on the mastoid bone, while those of the Moon travel behind the left ear. In testing the tides by using your ears, the position of the high and low tides is reversed from the position in front of the spine, with the major period or high tide being found at the bottom of the ear, and the minor period or low tide at the top of the ear.

As with method 1, check your ion flow. If using your right ear, face in a westerly direction and concentrate on the Sun. Place the tip of your testing finger on the right mastoid bone and move in small jumps in an arc from the bottom to the top of the ear. Record the exact position of the tide just as you did in method 1.

If using your left ear, face south and concentrate on the Moon while using your testing finger to move over the mastoid bone just as described for the right ear. Use the same method for finding the distance into a major or minor period as described in method 1.

In working with students, I find method 2 can be problematic because so many people have a history of ear problems, and this seems to affect the recording of energies on this part of the body. Also, the ear is a very small area, whereas the solunar flow tract between thymus and navel is bigger and allows for greater differentiation. There can be difficulties using method 1 if there is a history of spinal problems, so it is appropriate that you have a choice of two methods.

Once you have acquired the skill of finding the force flows or energy layers, you can stand on the Sun band (Force Flow 1) when thinking of the Sun and on the Moon band (Force Flow 4) when thinking of the Moon. This strengthens the reception of the Sun and Moon energies, but is not essential.

The tides occur approximately an hour later each day, so it is not possible to use the same time for your Vivaxis exercises every day. You also need to remember that we are basically evaluating the position of the Earth, Moon, and Sun and not the position of the oceans at any point of time. It is the angular relationship of Sun and Moon to the Earth that determines the force flows on the energy layers. The oceans are simply responding to the Moon and Sun, as do our body fluids. In addition, the body of water that composes the ocean takes a while to respond to the gravitational forces of the Moon and Sun, so it is not wise to go by the tide positions in local papers or to your casual observation of the sea in any particular place. The tides will also vary according to the little bays and inlets found on any coastline. Our body is the most accurate receiver of the Sun and Moon positions in relation to the Earth.

When you have learned the skills for finding the solunar flow period, you are in a position to evaluate all the mineral frequencies on your body. During major and minor periods, you can observe how some of these mineral frequencies disappear. This confirms the importance of this solunar flow exercise. You need to do all the Vivaxis exercises when all the mineral frequencies are available. Otherwise, you will imbalance your energies. The next step is to examine these mineral frequencies in detail.

Finding Your Mineral Frequencies

With cleared circuits and knowing how to record ion and solunar flows, you are ready for the next adventure in the Vivaxis connection. All the elemental frequencies are present in a balanced state during the six-hour solunar periods. Therefore, this is the right time to test and correct your energy flows. Minerals are the basic building blocks of the cells. Of course, we can become mineral deficient as a result of poor diet and inherited predispositions, but Fran's research indicates that disturbances in our body receptors for minerals may also be a major contributing factor to health disorders.

All the elemental frequencies are present in a balanced state during the six-hour solunar periods. Therefore this is the right time to test and correct your energy flows.

You must learn to visualize each element clearly before you can check the receptor points for them on your body. It is useful to build up a collection of samples for this purpose. To start with one of the most important elements, purchase a small amount of chromium oxide, which is available from any ceramics or potter's supplier. Chromium oxide powder is grass green in color. It is essential for you to register this frequency in your brain, because you will need to visualize chromium when you are looking for the energy layers. Once you can visualize a substance in its material form, you can usually recall its *vibration* just by thinking of the original sample. It is not always necessary to have the sample visible when testing.

Readers will be familiar with the frequencies of many elements in the course of daily living. For instance, we have all seen copper pipes or kettles, iron nails, chalk (calcium), and salt (sodium). Other substances such as iodine or zinc can be purchased from a pharmacy, and the rarer elements, such as selenium, can be obtained from chemical suppliers; some elements can be obtained from vitamin and health-food stores. It is necessary to buy the elements in a form in which they are not combined with other vitamins and minerals so as to avoid confusion when identifying a particular wavelength. Magnesium for example, should be obtained in the form of magnesium oxide or orotate.

When you visualize the elements, it helps if you imagine that the element is actually on your finger. This prevents you from keeping the awareness of the vibration or frequency only in your brain. Some people are more gifted with visualizing than others, but I have rarely found anyone who was not able to test the elements on the fingertips. Occasionally, a person will have difficulty finding a mineral if their body is deficient in that mineral. In one of my seminars, a woman was unable to find iron because she had a tendency to anemia. She was more successful in this task when she was helped to "channel" iron from the appropriate layer of the energy flows. Other people are deficient in zinc and selenium and yet others may need supplementation with chromium and iodine. Increasingly, these mineral deficiencies are becoming tabulated through hair analysis and blood serum tests.

The exact position of the receptor is in the center of the whorl on the fingertip. When you look closely at your hand, you can see it is covered in fine lines that are called dermatoglyphics. On the fingertips, these lines usually form a loop, or a tent or, more uncommonly, a small whorl pattern. It is not necessary to be looking at this exact spot when testing; just look approximately at the center of your fingertip.

The visualization of the main element on the fingertip is important, because there are other minerals arranged around the central mineral that are individual for each person. The visualization process involving a particular element allows you to concentrate on that element, and this concentration automatically blocks out other frequencies from your awareness.

Once you learn to discern mineral frequencies on your body, you are on the way to a new life adventure in which you can visualize and diagnose the frequencies of *anything* on the planet and test whether these elements are compatible with your well-being. I have found over the years of teaching frequencies that starting with those frequencies present in our body comes easily for most people.

Technique for Finding Mineral Frequencies

1. Turn one hand palm up a comfortable distance from your eyes and look at the center of the fingertip on your middle finger. Visualize chromium oxide on this point and hold your other hand in the position for recording a horizontal flow. The fingers of your recording hand should be straight (as shown in figure 45B) when recording the horizontal flow of an element. If horizontal chromium is present on the fingertip, your recording hand will move back and forth. If there is no response, this means that the chromium horizontal wave is on the middle fingertip of your other hand and you should repeat the procedure for the other hand.

2. Test for the iron frequency receptors on both hands; these will be found on either index or ring finger with the position reversed from hand to hand. Visualize iron nails or pots on the fingertip to establish the right frequency. If you have iron on the index finger pad of your right hand, you will also find it on the ring finger pad of your other hand. Usually the horizontal flows are on the pads of these fingers and the vertical flows on the back, except for chromium, where one finger pad will have the chromium horizontal and the other, the vertical flow. Remember to change the position of the fingers on the recording hand to find the vertical flows by curling the fingers upward (as shown in figure 45A).

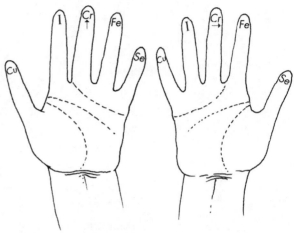

Figure 48. Examples of mineral frequencies on fingertips. Note how the iron hand and iodine positions are reversed from hand to hand, as are the selenium and copper. Some people will have zinc instead of iodine as the key element in their gravitational group. Remember we are testing frequencies and not tangible physical substances.

Having discovered which finger on each hand has the frequency for iron, you can consider the remaining index and ring fingers. It is helpful to make a chart of these associations as you go through these tests. (See figure 48.)

3. The index and ring fingers will be either zinc or iodine, depending on the individual. It is still a mystery why some are "iodine people" and some zinc, but it may have something to do with the associated endocrine glands. Zinc is associated with the gonads (ovaries and testes) and iodine is associated with the thyroid. Over the many years of teaching these techniques, I can often tell beforehand which mineral a person has by their personality and body type.

The "zinc" type is more common. People with zinc receptors on the fingers appear to have a stronger type of constitution. The "iodine" person is more mentally active. Test first for zinc by visualizing zinc cream on your fingers, and if there is no response, visualize iodine. Most of us have seen the yellow color of iodine as it looks when painted on the skin.

4. This leaves the thumb and little finger. They are associated with the elements copper and selenium. If the right thumb pad has selenium, the left thumb pad will have copper. The positions on the other hand will be reversed. Repeat the procedure as for the other elements, visualizing first copper and then selenium on the center of the thumb pad. You will probably have to purchase a small amount of selenium from a chemical company to help you with that visualization, because most selenium vitamin tablets are mixed with other ingredients. Having established whether copper is present on the pad of your thumb or little finger, even without testing you can assume selenium will be on the other digit.

In summary, everyone has horizontal and vertical pairs of elements on both right and left hands. The direction of flow reverses from back to front, and the position of the minerals reverses from hand to hand on each person. To repeat, if iron is on the index finger pad on your right hand, it will be on the ring finger pad of your left hand. In addition, if you have iron with a vertical flow on one side of the fingertip there will be a horizontal flow of iron on the other side of the fingertip and so on for the other elements mentioned. At this stage, we do not fully understand the significance of these patterns.

All these energy switches keep us alert as to our recording. There are occasions when the vertical and horizontal chromium groups appear to be together on the same side of the finger; these occur if we are facing our Vivaxis or standing in the energy layers. In these positions, our gravitational (electric) and magnetic waves are moving in a parallel direction. In other positions, they are at right angles to each other just as they are around an electric wire.

We are now in a position to evaluate these same two flows—magnetic and gravitational—as they form the two main layers of the electromagnetic aura that surrounds our body. The aura will change in size according to our health and provides a protection from frequencies that would otherwise interfere with our well-being. As mentioned earlier in connection with recording ion flow, it is the space *between* the two layers that provides the means for us to record energies with our recording hand. One layer is magnetic and one is gravitational or electric, and depending on whether we move above or below our Vivaxis, these layers will switch.

Evaluating Your Energy Layers

The inner and outer layers of your energy field correspond to two of the force flows in the energy layers on the Earth with which we will be working. If we are above our Vivaxis, the outer layer will be the magnetic layer and the inner layer will be the gravitational layer. If below the Vivaxis, the positions will be reversed. The magnetic layer has iron as the central element, and the gravitational layer has either iodine or zinc as its main element.

You are now in a position to visualize these elements in the layers of your energy field. Again, we will have two groups of people in terms of the element associated with the gravitational layer—either zinc or iodine, corresponding to whichever of these elements is on the fingers.

By discovering whether you are above or below your Vivaxis in terms of altitude above sea level, you will also know whether your testing finger is the index or ring finger of the left hand. If you are above your Vivaxis, it will be the index finger for testing everything above the waist, if you are below your Vivaxis, the ring finger will be used for testing energies above the waist. For testing below the waist, reverse your testing fingers so that if your index finger is used for testing above the waist, your ring finger is used for testing below the waist.

This means that the magnetic energies from your Vivaxis come in via the left foot and index finger of your left hand if you are above your Vivaxis, and into the ring finger of your left hand if you are below your Vivaxis. Finding the testing finger is easier than may be imagined and does not entail finding the Vivaxis itself. It is also a useful exercise for other reasons, because it enables us to test the size of our energy field at any point of time. See figure 49 for the general structure of the aura and its two main energy layers—the magnetic and gravitational.

When the outer layer of your aura contains the magnetic frequencies, such as iron, the left index finger will respond to the iron frequency. This will therefore be the recording finger for testing all your body receptors and also for finding the solunar flow. In other words, it is apparent that we test with the finger that corresponds to the magnetic layer, or Force Flow 3. This is the most permanent flow on the body, because it does not disappear during major and minor periods.

If you are below your Vivaxis, the positions are reversed. The gravitational band containing the frequency of iodine or zinc will now be the outer band on the energy field, and you will find a reversal of positions on the fingers. Your left fourth fingertip will then respond to the iron or magnetic frequency and will therefore be your testing finger for above the waist.

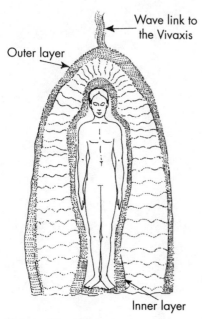

Wave link to the Vivaxis

Outer layer

Inner layer

Figure 49. The two energy layers in our aura. The outer layer is "magnetic" when we are above our Vivaxis and "gravitational" when we are below our Vivaxis. These two layers correspond to the magnetic and gravitational groups of elements on our body and are connected by the two-way wave links to our Vivaxis.

Use the following sequence to find your energy layers:

1. To find which is the outer layer, think of one of the magnetic elements, such as iron or copper. While visualizing this element, gradually move the fingertips of your left hand out horizontally from the body. If the magnetic band is on the outside, there will be a response in the recording hand when the fingertip with iron touches this band. You will then know you are above your Vivaxis and that the first finger with iron on its pad will be the testing finger for areas above the waist. You will also know that the inner band of your aura in your present position is the gravitational one. To prevent the possibility that you are standing in one of your Vivaxis directions, move a few degrees clockwise and repeat the test.

2. If you receive no response in the recording hand when visualizing iron, repeat the procedure, concentrating on iodine or zinc, depending on which of these elements you found on your hands during the previous exercises. If you get a response to iodine or zinc, you will know you are below your Vivaxis, and the testing finger for areas above the waist will be the fourth finger.

It is interesting to test the size of your energy field when tired and then again, when filled with energy after aligning to your Vivaxis or after meditating. In other words, how far outward from the body do you stretch your arm before the tips of your fingers touch the outer layer of your auric field?

It is the area between these two layers in which we hold our hands for all the testing procedures. Occasionally, if a person is in a very depleted state, she may not be able to test anything, because her energy layers will be too close to the body. We will not worry about the opposite and unlikely possibility that a person has such an enormous energy field they cannot reach the outer band with their recording hand! Such an occurrence can happen after aligning to our Vivaxis, but otherwise your fingertips will touch the outer rim before your arm is quite straight.

In summary, when you are above your Vivaxis, use the left-hand index finger when testing areas of the body above the navel and the left-hand ring finger when testing areas below the waist. When below your Vivaxis, the sequence is reversed: use the left hand ring finger for testing above the navel and left-hand index finger for testing below the navel. The middle finger is used for testing ion flow no matter what your position.

You may remember from part 1 that a group of four minerals also form around the central one on each fingertip. These minerals give more individuality to each person. An optional exercise for you is to research these other elements at some stage and make a chart. Repeat the same process you followed when finding the central mineral frequency. Visualize different minerals, one at a time, in each position around the central one (as shown in figure 18, page 109). Ascertain whether these minerals are the same as in figure 18. You will receive a movement in the recording hand when correctly visualizing each mineral on your fingertip.

You can now start to explore the elements on other points of your body. Start with the triple groups or lines of mineral groups down the front of your body, which respond to the elements associated with your Vivaxis. The following exercise will enable you to test some of their properties.

Testing the Minerals in the Triple Groups

1. Start by testing groups on the front and back of your head. Touch the center line of your forehead with your testing finger just below the hairline, while holding

your recording hand for a
horizontal flow and visualize chromium oxide. (See
figure 50A.) If there is no
response, hold the recording hand in the position for
a vertical flow.

2. Move your finger slightly
down your forehead and
repeat, noting that if the
previous group has a vertical flow, the next group
will have a horizontal flow.
Move down and repeat the
procedure a few more
times.

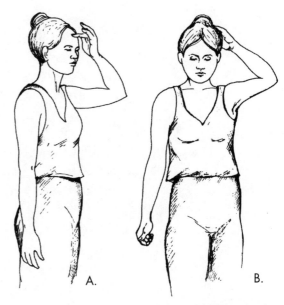

A.   B.

3. Move your testing finger slightly to one side of the
midline and find an iron group by visualizing iron
and testing for horizontal or vertical flow. Having
established whether the iron flow is vertical or horizontal, remember that all the other energy flows on
the front of the body will be the same except for the
chromium groups, which contain both horizontal
and vertical flows.

4. Move your testing finger down a bit further and visualize the other mineral previously found on your fingers, either iodine or zinc. Continue moving down
the same line and experience that the iron alternates
with iodine or zinc.

5. Now move your testing finger to the back of your head
on either side of the midline and move the finger down
until you find an iron group. Note that the energy flow
will be different to the flow on the forehead; that is, if

you find a vertical flow on your forehead, the flow will be horizontal on the back of your head. You can continue moving down the back of your head and find the other mineral groups containing zinc or iodine and chromium. (See figure 50B.)

6. Now come back to the front and test for the reverse spin of the groups as you move down the line of minerals. Curl the fingers of your recording hand and hold the hand horizontal with the thumb pointing upward (as in figure 45C). Move your testing finger slowly down a line of groups, noting how each successive group has an opposite spin from the one before. In other words, the recording hand will move in a circle first one way (such as clockwise) and then the other way, with the next group down the line.

Finding the
Energy Layers

You have now undertaken sufficient visualizing of minerals to find the energy layers with their various force flows for all the elements, both those that occur naturally and those that are human-made. Apart from finding the direction for your Vivaxis, this is the most important skill to learn, because these energy layers can be used for so many purposes, as you will remember from part 1.

We have a connection between our etheric layers and those of the Earth via our Vivaxis. The reason we find the energy layers before finding the direction of our Vivaxis is to enhance the strength and accuracy of that procedure. Finding our Vivaxis while standing on the energy layers also protects other people in the area from any energy disturbance as we align to our Vivaxis.

As a preliminary measure, make sure your clothes are not synthetic and check that your shoes are made of

> *We have a connection between our etheric layers and those of the Earth via our Vivaxis. The reason we find the energy layers before finding the direction of our Vivaxis is to enhance the strength and accuracy of that procedure.*

leather or rubber. Working in bare feet is ideal. Do not wear hats or glasses while attempting to locate the layers, because they create distortions in the recording process. As with all testing, remove watches, coins, necklaces, and bracelets; earrings are usually not a problem unless they are very large, but I would recommend removing all but very small earrings. You will need to find gently sloping land so as to mark the layers far enough apart to have room for you to stand on each force flow. The ground selected needs to be (preferably) free of plant growth except for short grass. It must also be free of underground electric cables and water pipes.

Method for Finding Energy Layers and Force Flows

1. Choose a time during the solunar flow, that is, between the major and minor period. Also check for normal ion flow in the environment.

2. Face a gentle slope where the layers will be wide enough to exercise on. The steeper the slope, the narrower the layer, and it is difficult to stand straight during the clearing and aligning exercises if the ground is too steep.

3. Check for neutral ground by placing your left hand face down toward the ground at the level of your heart. If there is no movement in the other recording hand, you are on neutral ground. Neutral ground means that there are no particular force flows from the energy layers, underground water, electrical conduits, or other sources. Standing on any of these would interfere with the accurate finding of other flows, because you are then conditioned by that energy under your feet.

4. Locate Force Flow 1 by humming a tune aloud or silently with your eyes shut while gradually tilting your head

from front to back and facing the slope. Singing stimulates the horizontal chromium receptors on your head; these are connected to the layer of chromium horizontal next up from where you stand. While singing, you will find one hand swings back and forth, and when the center point of the brain is in alignment with Force Flow 1, both your hands will swing. Keep your head still at this point and open your eyes without moving your head so as to note the position on the ground of Force Flow 1. (See figure 51.).

5. To find the exact position of chromium, keep your eyes open and visualize chromium at the position previously noted while humming. Mark this spot with a golf tee or stick. You can further cross-check this flow by visualizing one of the other elements on this layer, such as carbon or calcium, and noting a positive response in the recording hand. It is wise to vary the frequencies you visualize in this way so as not to oversaturate your system with any one frequency by concentrating on it for too long.

6. Turn ten degrees to right or left and repeat the procedure. This is to ensure you are not facing in the direction of your Vivaxis or its four quadrants while marking the position of chromium, because you will always register a positive response to chromium, calcium, and carbon when facing your Vivaxis. Also move a few inches

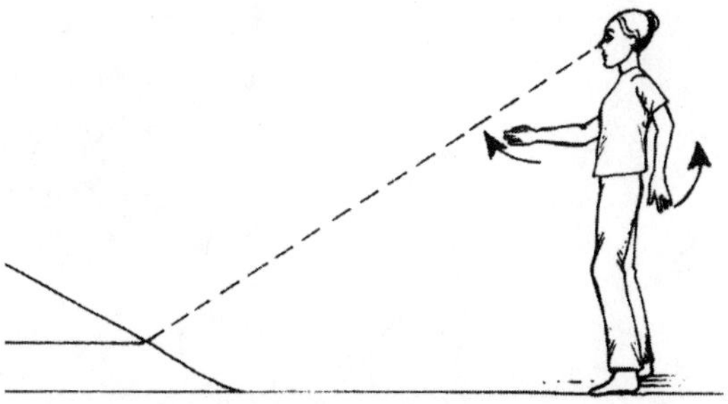

Figure 51. Finding the energy layers: method 1. Face a gentle slope after testing for neutral ground. Gradually tilt your head either up or down while humming a tune. One hand will record energy flow when you stimulate your chromium receptors by humming. When your pineal gland is in line with Force Flow 1 (chromium horizontal), both hands will record a back and forth motion. Stop moving your head and open your eyes while keeping your head still. Note the position on the ground where your eyes naturally fall. Mark this spot with a stick or golf tee and cross-check this position by visualizing chromium oxide powder at this spot. If your position is accurately marked, you will get a back and forth movement in the hand while thinking of chromium. Use the same procedure when marking the layers on a tree or wall. After marking the chromium layer, proceed to mark the other layers by visualizing an element from each force flow as depicted in figure 52.

Reprinted from *Healing through Earth Energies* by Judy Jacka, 1996.

to the right or left so as to be sure you are not standing on a vertical chromium flow. If you have correctly located the chromium flow, you will continue to get a positive response in these new positions.

7. Having marked the top of Force Flow 1, scan down the slope, visualizing chromium, and mark the spot where your arm stops recording, because this will be the end of this force flow, or layer. Note that on a gentle slope this band will be much wider than when marking it on a vertical surface, where it is only 0.25 of an inch wide. You can extend this width up to twelve inches by marking it on a gentle slope for the purpose of exercising. In other words, you cannot exercise on a vertical surface, but if you mark this layer on gently sloping land, it will be about six inches wide and there is room enough for your feet.

8. The end of Force Flow 1 marks the boundary or beginning of Force Flow 2, which contains a vertical flow of chromium; even so, it is distinct from the main vertical flows to be discussed below. The recording hand must now be held in the vertical position, with your fingers curled up pointing toward the sky. Keep visualizing chromium and mark the ground at the position the recording hand stops moving. During this procedure, continue visualizing chromium. The boundary of Force Flow 2 has then been reached. This is the only vertical flow charted in connection with the horizontal layers; the width here is also 0.25 inches.

9. The next flow to mark is Force Flow 3. Mark this by visualizing iron or copper while moving your eyes down the slope. This flow will be wider than the previous one (1.0 inches on a vertical surface). Again, when the recording hand cuts out and while you are still thinking of copper or iron, the boundary for this flow

has been reached. Using the same method, proceed to mark in all the layers below and above Force Flow 1, using figure 52 as the guide to the elements and to their placement and width. Visualize zinc cream or iodine lotion for Force Flow 4, the next one down. This layer will be the same width as Force Flow 3.

Next down is the phosphorus layer. For this, you can visualize match heads or bread, which is very rich in phosphorous. This band will be more than twice as wide as the previous force flow (2.75 inches on a vertical surface) and makes a pair with the magnesium band found above Force Flow 1. To mark in the magnesium force flow or layer that is above the chromium layer, visualize a tablet of magnesium oxide or magnesium orotate. These can be purchased at health food stores. Although you may think all white tablets are the same, the eye will also absorb the actual frequency and pass it on to the brain. Fran called the phosphorus and magnesium bands "carrier bands," because they contained the frequencies for many elements.

Below the phosphorus band is the foot band, with a section for each toe. Above the magnesium band is the hand band, with a division for each finger. These bands are wider again than the phosphorus carrier bands—3.75 inches on a vertical site. When marking the foot and hand bands, visualize your own feet or hands on the appropriate levels to find the boundaries. It is not necessary to visualize each toe and finger separately.

You will realize that although the layers marked on a gentle slope are much wider than on a vertical surface, the proportion of one to another on an even slope will be much the same as shown in figure 52. Therefore, you have a guide as to whether you are marking the layers accurately. For instance, if you mark in the magnetic band or Force Flow 3 and find it is twice as wide as the magnesium band, you will realize that something is wrong.

Alternative Method for Finding the Position of Force Flow 1

For people who have difficulty using their eyes and who are perhaps more tactile or kinesthetic, I devised an alternative system for finding the energy layers. You still need to visualize chromium, but while visualizing, you can sense chromium through your feet rather than constantly scanning with your eyes. The scanning approach can be tiring, especially if you are preparing ten sets of practice bands, such as for a seminar as I have conducted on many occasions. I often find the continuous visualizing very tiring. This alternative method can also be used to cross-check the results of the first method.

It is especially important in this procedure that any shoes you wear have leather or rubber

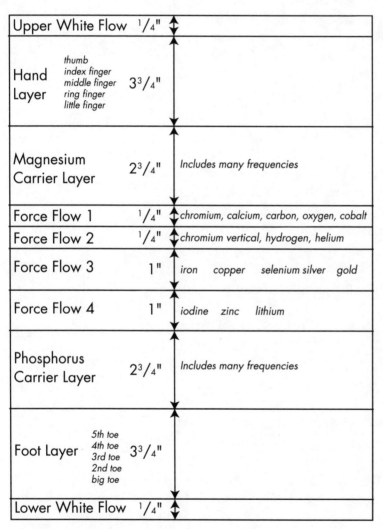

Layer		Width	Contents
Upper White Flow		1/4"	
Hand Layer	thumb index finger middle finger ring finger little finger	3 3/4"	
Magnesium Carrier Layer		2 3/4"	*Includes many frequencies*
Force Flow 1		1/4"	*chromium, calcium, carbon, oxygen, cobalt*
Force Flow 2		1/4"	*chromium vertical, hydrogen, helium*
Force Flow 3		1"	*iron copper selenium silver gold*
Force Flow 4		1"	*iodine zinc lithium*
Phosphorus Carrier Layer		2 3/4"	*Includes many frequencies*
Foot Layer	5th toe 4th toe 3rd toe 2nd toe big toe	3 3/4"	
Lower White Flow		1/4"	

Figure 52. **Simplified checklist for energy layers.** Not to scale. Width of layers as found on a vertical position (for example, the trunk of a tree). Complete width is sixteen inches. Remember that when these layers are marked on gently sloping land, they will take up more space, according to the slope of the land.

soles so that the energy flows can be correctly and accurately sensed. You also need to be able to balance easily on one leg when marking the borders of each layer.

1. Follow steps one to three as described in the first method (see above), then hold your recording hand in the position for recording vertical flows and visualize chromium. At the same time, find a chromium group with your testing finger on the center of your forehead. This will help you connect with the Force Flow 2 layer further up the slope from where you are standing. It could be a distance of several yards up this slope. The vertical distance will be indicated by the number of circular swings of your hand while visualizing chromium. (See figure 53.) Although you will be finding Force Flow 2 rather than Force Flow 1 (as in the previous exercise), these two chromium flows are very close together and give a good indication of the position on the slope for Force Flow 1.

2. Your hand will swing in a circle a number of times one way, and then the direction will reverse and repeat the same number of swings. Each swing represents about eleven inches in a vertical line above your present position on the ground. For instance, if the next band is about forty-four inches above your head, the recording hand will swing four times one way and four times the other. This motion of the hand continues with a reduced number of swings as you move further up the slope toward the chromium layer. (See figure 54.)

3. Walk up the slope until your hand stops circulating and moves back and forth or remains almost still.

4. Mark this chromium level with a stick or golf tee and, having found this approximate position, move back to where you originally stood and cross-check the top of

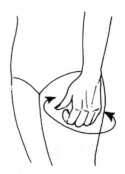

Figure 53. Counting hand spins to the nearest chromium force flow. Your hand will proscribe a number of circles, first one way and then the other. The number of circles diminishes as you approach the nearest chromium force flow.

Reprinted from *Healing through Earth Energies* by Judy Jacka, 1996.

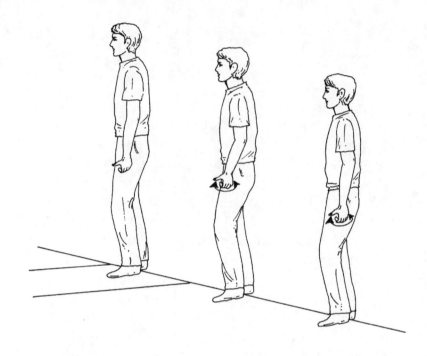

Figure 54. Finding the energy layers: method 2. The hand is held in position for vertical flows, and swings of hand reduce as you walk up the slope toward the chromium layer. When you are standing on chromium vertical, the hand stops swinging and just moves back and forth. You must concentrate on chromium while testing. Obviously, this recording of Force Flow 1 through the feet is not as accurate as when standing back and looking with the eye, so after you have marked this approximate position, stand back and cross-check as depicted in figure 51.

Force Flows 1 and 2 by undertaking steps four and five of the first method. Then move back to stand on the force flows and continue to mark the layers by sensing them through your feet. Whether visualizing via the eyes or feet, you will still use the recording hand to respond to the frequency.

5. When you have marked the top of Force Flow 1, stand facing across the slope with the edge of your left foot against the top of the horizontal chromium band. Visualize chromium, calcium, or carbon and record these flows with your recording hand. To cross-check, visualize another element further down the band, such as zinc, and the recording arm should stop. In other words, you are recording whatever is visualized as under your feet. Lift up your foot and test whether chromium horizontal is still coming through the lower piece of ground under your right foot. Move this foot further down the slope and test whether it is now on

the Force Flow 2 area by holding your hand in the vertical position with fingers curled upward. This position of the hand will record a vertical flow of chromium that corresponds to Force Flow 2.

6. Move down the slope, visualizing elements in each layer, and mark the ground with a golf tee as you go at each level. You can move your foot inch by inch to find the exact edge of the band. Once you become proficient at this method, you can do it quickly by standing first on one foot and then the other as you proceed downward, with your feet always placed sideways to the slope.

   The reason you need to lift one foot while testing is so you do not cover too much ground at once. For instance, you may have one foot over Force Flow 2 and the other foot over Force Flow 3 and it would not be possible to know exactly where to mark each band unless you lift one foot so as to only be recording one force flow.

7. Mark the foot band and then the magnesium band above the chromium band, using the same method. However, note that Fran advised against actually standing on the hand band. (See figure 44.) To mark the hand band, stand off the force flows on neutral ground and mark it as you would for the first method. Visualize your hand on the area above the magnesium flow, and when the response in your recording hand ends, mark the point on the ground where your eyes are focused.

   It will also be good practice to mark the layers on a vertical surface such as a tree. You can use chalk or a knife for marking these positions. The advantages of using a vertical surface is that the width of the layers will be exactly the size as marked in figure 52. You may wish to experiment with these main areas of the energy layers before marking in the White Flows. You can practice skills such as exercising on each force flow, purifying food, and finding your Vivaxis before marking in the white bands. However, for the sake of completing the instructions for finding all the force flows, the techniques for marking in the white bands will be described here.

Techniques for Finding Upper and Lower White Flows

You may remember from part 1 that upper and lower White Flows are present *only* between the hours of 10 A.M. and 2 P.M. local time. During summer time, or "daylight savings time," you will have to translate the time back to Sun time rather than clock time; this usually involves subtracting one hour from your clock time. You may also recall that these force flows correspond with the pineal gland and with purification, and therefore, are especially useful when you energize water, because they seem to preserve all the mineral frequencies from all the layers for many weeks. In fact, the White Flows seem to contain *all* the frequencies of all the force flows.

Finding the Upper White Flow

To locate the upper White Flow, you need the stimulation of light through your opened eyes. Perhaps this is because the pineal gland needs the stimulation from light falling on the retina in connection with finding this force flow. All the other force flows, including the lower White Flow, can be found with the eyes shut. In keeping with a correspondence to light, the pineal flows can only be found during peak daylight hours, that is, when the Sun is near to its meridian, between 10 A.M. and 2 P.M. This force flow has a frequency that can be found by visualizing either the color white, or garlic.

After marking all the energy layers, you are ready to mark in the white layer. Stand with your arms and hands straight down, with your palms facing your sides, and concentrate on white or garlic as you slowly tilt your head backward from a position in which your eyes were level with Force Flow 1. When the pineal receptor on the bridge of your nose is in line with the White Flow on the ground, both your arms should pull toward the top of this force flow, which is directly above the hand layer. Of course, once the hand band has been marked, you will automatically know the position of the white layer.

Finding the Lower White Flow

With your eyes shut, arms down, and hands with palms facing forward, gradually tilt your head downward below the phosphorous band, while thinking of white or chlorophyll. When the pineal receptor on the bridge of your nose is in line with the lower White Flow, your arms will pull forward toward the bottom of this force flow.

Now you have marked the complete set of life-giving energy layers from upper to lower white. During major high and low tides, when Force Flows 1 and 4 disappear, the layers contract inward, and the force flows, including the White Flows, will have temporarily moved their positions and will not return to their original positions until the solunar flow resumes.

This is an important point to remember, because some detrimental force flows are found not far from the White Flows, and these may also contract inward during the major and minor periods. This apparent contraction is a result, in part, of the disappearance of Force Flows 1 and 4 during major and minor periods. This is another reason to be precise with the timing of the exercises and to use the solunar flow times for most exercises.

If you have been working with another person, ask them to check the positions you have marked for each layer by repeating the steps in this exercise. We should always work by ourselves initially to prevent confusion of energies, but it is wise to cross-check with someone else.

Exercising on the Energy Bands

The first exercise to do after finding the various layers is to exercise on each layer. You can now use the energy layers for removing static from your body and to help you prepare for finding your Vivaxis.

Starting at the magnesium band, exercise on each band for about two minutes. Keep your feet firmly on the ground but well apart, while twisting and turning in various directions. Firmly tap all reachable parts of the body with the heel of the hand. The jarring is to knock out old areas of static so that the force flows may move through these blocked areas. Pay special attention to any areas that have been injured or X-rayed. Finish your exercise on the foot band. (See figure 52.) You can saturate your body with an excess of energies during this procedure, so it is wise to complete the exercise by moving off the band and grounding your hands on neutral ground for ten seconds. Simply squat down and firmly place your open hands on the ground for a few seconds.

Correcting Energy Disturbances in Your Belongings

Recall that healthy energy is recorded as an ion flow whether we are testing animate or inanimate objects in our environment. Select articles you have found not to have a normal ion flow. You can use the energy layers of the Earth to restore a normal ion flow to articles with a disturbed energy in the following manner:

Find a plastic or nylon article among your belongings and test it for ion flow. A plastic toy would be a good article to test, but any object made of these substances will do. Test this article for ion flow while standing well away from the bands on neutral ground. The recording hand will usually turn in a circular motion, indicating a confusion of energies in the plastic object. We can use all the force flows to reenergize objects, but I usually choose

Force Flow 1 because of its connection with oxygen. Ideally, if time permits, place the articles to be treated on all the force flows for about one minute so that they are subjected to the full range of health-giving frequencies.

Now place the specific article on Force Flow 1 and stand back. Retest for ion flow after about twenty seconds. Your recording arm should now record a back and forth movement, indicating a normal and healthy energy flow. You can now inactivate all nylon underwear and other synthetic articles of their disturbing energies. After twenty years of these experiments, I am still amazed at the permanent energy changes that appear in synthetic materials using the energy layers. Many people are disturbed by wearing synthetic clothing, because the static from these articles affects their body. By "inactivating" such articles, you are no longer restricted to wearing only cotton, wool, and silk.

The one synthetic plastic that cannot be improved by using the energy bands is acrylic. There must be something in its molecular structure that strongly resists energy flow. This is probably why it can be used to resist ionizing radiation emissions from television and computer screens. However, acrylic also screens out the beneficial energies from the Earth when used in clothes. Many clothes and shoes are now made of acrylic, and this presents a problem in terms of disrupting normal energy flow between the Earth and our bodies when we wear this material. You can select an acrylic sweater and test this finding for yourself.

Devise your own research program. Collect a number of plastic and nylon articles. Treat half of the them on the force flows and leave the others untreated. Mark those that you have treated in an inconspicuous way. Ask a group of fellow students to test which objects have been treated by checking them for ion flow. I have carried out this experiment at many seminars and have found a high degree of correlation in the findings of those participants who could accurately test for ion flow.

Finding the Detrimental Force Flows

As you will remember from part 1, the detrimental frequencies include elements like cadmium, lead, and mercury. These elements, when present in your body, tend to displace the health-giving elements, such as magnesium and calcium. They are also detrimental to your immune system and, in general, can be said to cause toxemia (accumulation of toxins). Cadmium is one of the most carcinogenic elements on the planet, while the effects of lead on the brain and nervous system are well documented. Children living on busy roads are adversely affected by the lead in gasoline fumes.

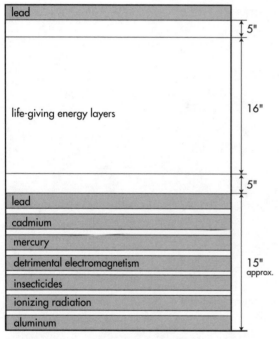

Figure 10.

Therefore, after you have experimented with the life-giving flows, it is important to know how to evaluate and mark in the detrimental force flows. You can then monitor yourself to see whether your body contains these frequencies, and you can also evaluate whether your food or personal items (such as hair dyes and cosmetics) contain these elements. These flows are found a few inches above and below the White Flows. However, unlike the main health-giving structure of the layers, their position is not always consistent from place to place. (See figure 10 for a fairly typical model of this.)

The method you use to find detrimental flows is exactly the same as you have already used for finding the life-giving energy layers. First visualize the element concerned and scan the area above and below the main band where the detrimental flows are located by tilting your head and keeping your eyes open. Your recording arm will move while visualizing a detrimental element, if that element is present in your body. The vibrations from these elements are taken into your system while you scan, so limit the time you take to perform this exercise.

To help neutralize the toxic substances associated with the detrimental force flows, drink water that has been energized by all the main force flows, including the White Flows, and exercise on all the force flows, from magnesium to phosphorus. Align to your Vivaxis on a regular basis. This regimen will neutralize any negative effects from these elements and will also create resistance in your body to the over-absorption of negative frequencies.

Finding the Directions for Elements

So far, we have worked with the compass directions for the elements of carbon and calcium. However, all of the elements have their compass directions. Perhaps we can envisage the energy layers on the Earth as being the grounding plates for the elemental frequencies as they travel through space. As this type of research is in its infancy, we have not established whether the directions are similar for all places on Earth.

All of the elements have their compass directions. Perhaps we can envisage the energy layers on the Earth as being the grounding plates for the elemental frequencies as they travel through space.

In *Mysteries of Memories Unfold*, Fran pointed out that, unless we are concentrating on one element, the various frequencies are recorded as radiating out from our energy field in all directions. When we focus on one mineral and face its compass direction, such as true north for carbon, our wave field becomes temporarily restricted to one direction, or more strictly speaking, one plane; in this case, the wave is toward true north. This focused orientation obviously helps us to absorb the frequencies of the element in question.

Gradually over the years, individuals working with these force flows have compiled a table of the directions of all the elements. Members of the Vivaxis Energies Research International Society, based in Vancouver, British Columbia, in Canada, played a big part in this evaluation of directions; figure 40 (see page 219) is largely based on their findings. The compass directions on this chart should be compared with other locations, but generally, I have found the elements in the Southern Hemisphere to be at the same compass directions as in figure 40, which is for north of the equator.

1. For the purpose of charting directions, use the same techniques of visualizing carbon as given in the earlier exercise (exercise 1). Stand on neutral ground and visualize the element concerned during a solunar flow period. One arm should move toward the direction of the element concerned.

2. Face this direction and ground your hands firmly on your thighs, while continuing to visualize the element. Your body should then be pulled in the direction of the element. (See figure 55.) Keep a compass nearby to record the result, but place it well away from the area of testing. Like magnets, a compass will distort your evaluations, yet it is needed as a tool to give the degrees as measured from magnetic north for each element.

3. For research purposes, it is a good idea to have several people check the directions of the elements without reference to one another and then to cross-check later. It is also useful to do these experiments at different times and on different days so that the most consistent or basic direction for each element is found.

Direction for copper

Figure 55. Finding compass direction for an element. The individual concentrates on copper with her hands on thighs and receives a pull forward when facing in the correct direction. She can then align in the four directions, after marking the ground. The process of aligning is identical to aligning to the Vivaxis.

After you have learned how to align to your Vivaxis, you can also sometimes align to individual elements, if these are found to be deficient in your energy field. The Canadian research group developed a technique for restoring the frequencies of an element in the following way. If, for instance, when attempting to visualize silica in the parathyroids, no response was received in the recording hand, the subject would face in the direction of silica, while holding a sample of silica on the parathyroids (same location as the thyroid gland, in the front of the neck). The person then discarded the sample and was retested to see that the frequency of silica had been restored to the glands.

Finding the Vertical Energy Flows

You are now in the correct energy state to find your Vivaxis, but to complete your understanding of the energy flows, we need to briefly discuss vertical flows. Fran discovered these in 1981 after she had researched the horizontal bands for some time. (See figure 11.) It is not essential that you learn this exercise, but it could be useful when gently sloping ground is not available.

To understand the model of the energy flows in a three dimensional way, visualize the following:

The energy layers throughout the Earth

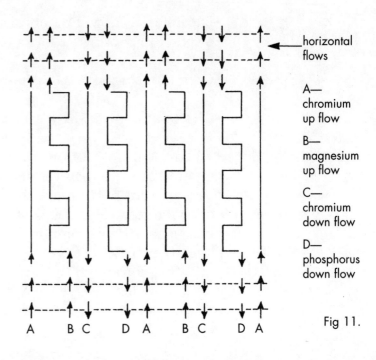

horizontal flows

A— chromium up flow

B— magnesium up flow

C— chromium down flow

D— phosphorus down flow

Fig 11.

A   B C   D A   B C   D A

275

and its atmosphere are like layers of an onion, and connecting each layer are vertical flows that could be visualized as threads of cotton connecting the layers of the onion. The horizontal layers are about sixteen inches deep, and the vertical connecting cords are a few inches only in width. Also in our model is knowledge of the compass directions for many elements that probably come into our planet from outer space and therefore connect us with the cosmos.

Method of Locating the Vertical Flows

Stand on very level ground and move your feet slowly sideways in an arc. At the same time, hold your hand in the recording position for vertical flows with your fingertips pointing upward and visualize in turn magnesium, phosphorous, and chromium. When your foot contacts one of the elements, you will note the following responses:

- Phosphorous downflow: a backward pull on the heels.
- Magnesium upflow: a forward or upward pull on the toes.
- Chromium upflow: a forward or upward pull on the toes.
- Chromium downflow: a backward pull on the heels.

You will notice from the step shape of the vertical flows in figure 11 that a beginner could mistake the vertical bands for horizontal ones when first looking for the horizontal flow. This could explain why beginners sometimes mark the chromium horizontal flow in strange places. (This is why it is suggested that when looking for horizontal chromium, we move the feet a few inches to the right or left in case we are standing on a chromium vertical band.) The elements carried in these vertical flows are listed in figure 11. It can be seen that the elements in the upflow of chromium differ somewhat from those of the downflow.

One point may need clarification. You may have noted when I described Force Flow 2 that vertical chromium is included together with helium and hydrogen. As this force flow is basically horizontal, I can only assume that this may be the expression of some type of locking mechanism between the horizontal and the vertical flows of chromium. It is interesting that the chromium vertical flow is never interrupted by the movements of Sun, Moon, and Earth.

It is not essential to complete the next exercise (exercise 10) before learning to find your Vivaxis. You may prefer to come back to checking your health on the energy layers after having learned to find and align to your Vivaxis. It is placed here only because it relates to the energy layers.

Checking Your Health on the Energy Layers

Keeping a regular check on your health is a major benefit of working with the life-giving energy layers. It is a good idea to have the horizontal layers permanently marked on your property so you can inactivate foods and synthetic clothing and use them for the regular exercise of aligning to your Vivaxis. If possible, the bands should be located conveniently close to your house to facilitate their everyday use, especially during inclement weather. However, the energy flows are not disturbed in wintry conditions. The location you mark with the energy flows will, of course, depend on the slope and position of your property.

For the purposes of scanning yourself or other people, mark a band with force flows on a vertical surface such as a tree or wall. This should include both the life-giving and detrimental force flows. Be sure to use an unpainted wall and mark a position that is free of pipes and electrical conduits; otherwise the energy layers may be distorted. The advantage of marking the energy flows on a vertical surface is that it will only be sixteen inches deep and you can then scan it very easily. It is also useful if you live in an apartment with no gently sloping ground nearby.

Eyesight problems may reduce this option for some people who could experience difficulty focusing on narrow bands that are only one-quarter inch wide. In this case, the larger spread on a gentle slope is preferable. It is certainly desirable to become proficient at marking bands on both sloping ground and vertical surfaces. Sometimes, since you may be unable to find a patch of sloping ground near your house, it is useful to mark a band on a wall.

Frequently, people ask about the effects of sleeping on a particular layer, either a life-giving or detrimental layer. For instance, what happens if we sit or lie exactly on a lead band? There is no doubt that overabsorption of any particular frequency, even essential frequencies, can create an imbalance of energies in our body. But when we think about it, we do move around a lot, and we would have to be a long time on an exactly level surface to remain only on one energy layer. For instance, a mattress does not stay exactly level when we lie on it. My assumption is that the discomfort we experience in certain chairs or positions is a natural warning to place ourselves elsewhere. The discomfort can be viewed as a kind of biofeedback to give us information on safe places to lie or sit.

As we become more sensitive to energies, we find ourselves automatically choosing the right surroundings. A sensitive body apprehends disturbances easily and is immediately aware of discomfort or imbalance when contacting detrimental energies. However, there are times when we need to cope temporarily with a disturbance or pollution such as chemical, smog, or noise, and we can then plan to move our house or our workplace and take the necessary steps to restore our energy balance. All the life-giving elements on the energy band should be present in your body, and you should be able to assess your response to these elements by means of the energy flows present in your body.

The following instructions can apply to scanning yourself or another person. In the case of scanning yourself, picture yourself on the energy flows as you scan each one. In the case of another person, imagine/visualize/picture them on the energy flows.

1. Make the usual check for solunar flow and check that your ion flow is balanced. Do not stand in the direction of your Vivaxis, opposite it, or at right angles to it. In other words, in the four directions of the Vivaxis. Remember that the elements from Force Flow 1 and 4 will be missing at major and minor periods and also at new and full moon.

2. Stand back from the energy layers and, starting at the hand layer, scan visually downward while thinking of yourself as if you are mirrored on the different layers. Imagine this as if you are using the force flows as a mirror for yourself. If the time is between 10 a.m. and 2 p.m., the white bands can be included in this scanning process. You can also scan yourself on the detrimental layers.

3. Your recording hand should move back and forth or move in a wide sweeping motion at each level of the energy flows where your eyes focus. When you start scanning the detrimental flows, your hand should not record anything, because these elements, such as mercury and cadmium, should not be present in the body. Often, you will get a positive response to mercury from the fillings in your teeth. But ideally, you should not get a positive response.

4. If you are investigating a particular mineral frequency in your body, go to the layer that contains that element and visualize the element concerned while thinking of yourself. For example, to check your iron frequencies, look at Force Flow 3; visualize iron and then picture yourself on that level in Force Flow 3. Check for iodine on Force Flow 4 and so on.

5. If an element is deficient, your recording hand may not respond at all or, if there is a disturbance in the receptors involved with a particular element, your hand may move in a circular motion. For instance, when checking another person, such as a smoker, your recording hand will move in a circular motion when visualizing that person on Force Flow 1 because of a disturbance of the oxygen receptors in their heads. If you wish to further differentiate between different elements in this force flow, visualize the person in connection with the main elements one at a time—carbon, calcium, cobalt, and oxygen.

The most important criterion in assessing the energy status of ourselves or others is the response in the recording hand. A zero response means that a person is not receiving the frequencies emitted by a particular force flow at that point in time. A circular motion indicates a disturbance on a force flow that can be itemized by visualizing each element on that flow to find the problem. A healthy response is a strong back-and-forth motion as you got with a normal ion flow; also good is a wide sweeping motion. Do not be concerned with an inability to perfect all the skills related to working with the energy layers. Gaining some familiarity with the elements in the force flows connected with the energy layers prepares the way for the all-important central skill of finding your Vivaxis, the subject of the next exercise.

Finding Your Vivaxis

When Fran first began to teach people to find their Vivaxis, she used two galvanized angle wires bent in a right angle, with the vertical arm held in a copper sleeve. The person looking for their Vivaxis turned around slowly in a circle, and when they were in their Vivaxis channel, the wires crossed neatly at the tips. Alternatively, they used one wire that swung toward the tip of the index finger of the other hand when facing the Vivaxis. The body position was important; the spine was held straight, the head was held erect, and the wires were held out in front of the body, with the copper sleeve in a vertical position and the thumb in a vertical position pointing above the fingers on the copper sleeve.

For research purposes, I still sometimes play with a pair of angle wires, usually made of copper and without a sleeve covering one arm of the wire. On this basis, I can make a few interesting observations. For testing the body energies or dowsing of any kind, the wires must be held with the horizontal portion of the wire parallel to the ground. The wire must be able to turn freely above the first finger and the thumb, which is holding the vertical arm of the wire. If you are free from energy disturbances and concentrate strongly on a particular direction, one wire will turn in the direction dictated by the brain, while the other remains pointing toward your Vivaxis.

As the years went by, Fran discovered more about the elements and their frequencies. She noticed that impurities such as lead frequencies in the wire were absorbed into the body and affected the recording ability of the students. It was at this stage that she started to train people to use their arm as the recording instrument instead of using a rod or pendulum. I agree with these findings, having initially experimented with the wires. I also find it more natural to use my arm and hand.

There are several techniques you can use to find your Vivaxis. Clearing your circuits is essential before attempting to locate your Vivaxis. Do the carbon clearing for X-rays, the neutralizing exercise, and exercising on the energy flows *before* undertaking the next step. Also be aware that if you have blocked sinuses, you may not be able to find your Vivaxis until this trouble is resolved. This is probably because your magnetic sense is located near the ethmoid sinus, close to the root of the nose, and may be disturbed by the sinusitis.

As a prelude to this exercise, scan each side of your hands for the Vivaxis flows. From the previous exercises with the triple groups, you are used to finding iron and zinc or iodine in these groups. Remember that there are two main groups of elements—the magnetic and gravitational—that correspond to the two layers of your aura, or energy field. There will be a flow of the magnetic group, including iron down one side of the hand, and the flow down the other side will include iodine or zinc as the main element—the gravitational group. (See figure 56.)

Once again, we find a correspondence between the basic mineral groups of our Vivaxis and the energy layers of the Earth. Visualize the element iron while scanning one edge of your hand, and if there is no response in your recording hand, think of your element in the gravitational

Figure 56. Vivaxis flows along the sides of the hands. The magnetic flow will be on one side of your hand and the gravitational flow on the other. This forms part of the two-way flow back and forth to your Vivaxis.

Reprinted from *Healing through Earth Energies* by Judy Jacka, 1996.

group you have already established as zinc or iodine in exercise 6. You will find that the other side of the hand features the other mineral group; these two groups correspond to the two layers of your aura, as previously described.

Once you have become skilled at linking up with the Vivaxis, you will find that as soon as you pick up any of the Vivaxis flows in your body, your recording arm will move in the direction of your Vivaxis while you concentrate on that element. However, in the meantime, the following methods will help you find the exact direction for the flows connected with your Vivaxis. Remember, although you may know the general direction of the antenatal location, you need the precise direction within one or two degrees of the compass.

Finding Your Vivaxis: Method 1

1. Test for neutral ground and find an area at least seven feet away from buildings and trees and at least fifty feet away from street power lines, and be clear of the electric line leading to your house by some six feet.

2. Test for ion flow on yourself and include your environment in this test by turning clockwise. Never do any exercises if your hand records a circular motion, because this indicates chaotic energies in your body or the environment around you.

3. Test for solunar flow, because during the major or minor period, your Vivaxis link will not be fully present.

4. Find the energy layers and stand on Force Flow 1 or 3. Rest the three middle fingers of the left hand lightly on the side of your thigh at the place where they naturally touch; a triple group is located here. (The left side is

recorded because energies from the Vivaxis come in up the left leg on that side.) The recording hand (right hand) should now move as for ion flow. The three fingers will be matching their same groups on the thigh— iron, chromium, and

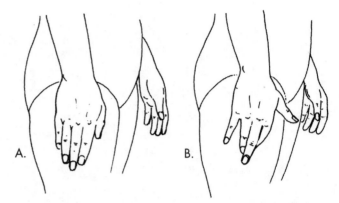

zinc or iodine—and when you lift the middle finger, your other fingers will remain connected to the Vivaxis flows of the magnetic and gravitational groups. (See figure 57.)

5. After you have lifted the middle finger, your recording hand and arm should now turn and start swinging toward the Vivaxis following the energies related to the Vivaxis fingers. Try turning in different directions, because in some positions the body may restrict your arm from swinging toward your Vivaxis. Facing different directions will also confirm the direction of the Vivaxis.

6. Mark the position with a stick, and turn your feet so that you are directly facing toward your Vivaxis. Ground your hands firmly on your thighs, place your legs tightly together, and hum a tune you learned early in life, such as a nursery rhyme. The reason for singing a nursery rhyme is because this melody was firmly in place in your memory receptors at an age before the occurrence of any disturbances to your Vivaxis. Reviving an early childhood musical memory causes a strong stimulation of Vivaxis energies, and your whole body should be pulled forward toward your Vivaxis.

Figure 57. Finding the triple groups on the thighs. When your three fingers are correctly placed on the side of the thigh (A), your recording arm will move back and forth (same as ion flow). Lift the middle finger, which leaves the two Vivaxis fingers on the Vivaxis groups (B), and your recording arm should now move in the direction of your Vivaxis. After turning to face your Vivaxis, both arms should swing back and forth toward your Vivaxis.

Reprinted from *Healing through Earth Energies* by Judy Jacka, 1996.

Note also when facing your Vivaxis that you will be pulled forward when you visualize any of the elements in the Vivaxis flows, such as iron, copper, or selenium. For this reason, when testing compass directions for the elements as described previously, it is important not to be facing any of your Vivaxis quadrants. When facing your Vivaxis, and even its opposite direction or at right angles, you may also obtain a pull when visualizing the associated elements, such as iron, iodine, or zinc.

If you are ever pushed backward when facing your Vivaxis, it is possible there is a thunderstorm or some other disturbing influence in your Vivaxis area, and testing and aligning should be postponed until that influence disappears. However, in the early stages of learning this exercise, it is wise to check that you are not standing with your back to the Vivaxis. Check by reversing directions and humming a nursery rhyme again.

I usually suggest that a person cross-check this first method with another, because finding your Vivaxis direction is very important and students often seek further clarification. The second method is as follows:

Finding Your Vivaxis: Method 2

1. Stand on Force Flow 3 and repeat steps 1 through 3 of method 1. Then place the middle finger of your left hand lightly on your navel.

2. Turn slowly clockwise if you are in the Northern Hemisphere and counterclockwise if you are in the Southern Hemisphere. When you face your Vivaxis, your recording arm will swing toward your Vivaxis. This is the only direction you will get a recording on the midline of the body while using the finger normally used for testing ion flow. It is almost as if we have an invisible umbilical cord of energy attaching us to our Vivaxis.

In fact, when facing your Vivaxis while testing for ion flow on any part of the body, your testing hand will move toward the Vivaxis. This is why when you practice ion flow testing, you should face a variety of directions so as to be out of your Vivaxis channel. This phenomenon also illustrates the point previously made that when we face our Vivaxis, the electric and magnetic fields of the body are in phase rather than at right angles to each other. For, as demonstrated in method one, placing the Vivaxis fingers of the left hand on the thigh causes the recording hand (right) to move toward the Vivaxis. But when we place the Vivaxis fingers (first and fourth) of the right hand on the thigh, our recording hand (left) will move at right angles toward our Vivaxis, unless we are facing toward our Vivaxis.

Once you have cleared your energy circuits of X-rays and other disturbances, you should be able to stand facing any direction in a relaxed state with a quiet mind; one arm should swing in the direction of your Vivaxis. Standing with legs tight together will enhance the effect. To make sure that your X-rays have been removed, press your middle finger firmly on the parts that have been X-rayed or move these parts vigorously; the recording arm should still swing toward your Vivaxis. If it moves in another direction, this means you are still receiving energy from two Vivaxes, your own and one connected with an X-ray machine or some other electromagnetic source. You must then repeat the carbon technique for X-rays, repeat the neutralizing exercises (exercises 1 and 2), jar the area concerned again, and exercise on all the force flows again, concluding by bringing in the Vivaxis energies by aligning them as described below.

Helping a Person to Find Their Vivaxis

Fran discouraged instructors of Vivaxis from trying to find a person's Vivaxis for them. The reason for this caution is to prevent the instructor becoming linked to the student's Vivaxis. Therefore, it is wise not even to watch another person undertaking any Vivaxis work.

However, exceptions can be made as in extreme cases such as paralysis. Fran reported looking at the earlobe of the subject and noting the direction in which her own arm moved. The subject could then be aligned to their Vivaxis and undertake the channeling procedure. The energy waves from receptors above our waist travel toward the Vivaxis, while below the waist they travel toward us from the Vivaxis. Hence a focus on the earlobe or other spot above the waist will lead us toward the Vivaxis of the person.

The other method Fran sometimes used was to muscle test the person when they faced different directions. As the direction for alignment must be accurate within a degree or so of a circle of three 360 degrees, this option would be fairly tedious. The arm will test much more strongly when we are facing our Vivaxis. I have successfully used these methods to help a person find their Vivaxis.

Testing the Strength and Radius of Your Vivaxis Energies

The Vivaxis can also be found when you stand on neutral ground. However, when you face your Vivaxis on ordinary ground, the energies of anything in your environment within a radius of two hundred feet are drained. This indicates the amazing energies of the Vivaxis, and it can be demonstrated as follows:

Arrange to have several people who are proficient at finding ion flow situated at various distances up to about two hundred feet from person A, who is standing on neutral ground. Have these testers find the ion flow and then retest when person A is facing her Vivaxis. The testers' recording arms will go lifeless when a person aligns exactly to their Vivaxis, thereby illustrating the strength of the energies with which we are dealing. This test should not be conducted for more than a minute, because it drains energy from everyone in the vicinity.

The phenomenon results from frequencies of the Vivaxis forces being drawn into the aura of the person aligning with their Vivaxis. This experiment indicates the amazing protective effect of the energy layers, and for this reason, all Vivaxis work should be conducted on these force flows to protect and strengthen our energy field and to protect other people.

People often ask me about a person unknowingly aligning with their Vivaxis when talking with someone. However, the alignment is only significant if the subject is standing completely erect, with hands by their sides and their head facing directly ahead. Fran postulated that this might be one reason soldiers fainted when on duty after becoming oversaturated with their Vivaxis energies. However, fainting in a person who has stood still for a long time can also be caused by low blood pressure.

Creating a New Vivaxis

Sometimes it is necessary to create a new Vivaxis if a person is unable to eradicate a number of foreign fields causing chaos in their body and aura. These unfortunate people are usually unable to find the direction of their real Vivaxis no matter how hard they try. With a new Vivaxis, they will have a fresh and permanent link to the energy field of the Earth, one that will automatically cancel out all foreign Vivaxes.

This is not something to be done lightly, for there must be a reason why your Vivaxis is situated in a particular area. The soul coming into incarnation may well choose to have the Vivaxis at a particular place for reasons we cannot understand. However, there are times when the creation of a new Vivaxis appears to be the best therapy.

1. Select a place preferably at least one hundred yards away from any electrical installations. Take into consideration the possibility of future technology in this area. Be some distance away from large trees, because they may attract a lightning strike during a storm. Test the area carefully for ion flow and look for underground disturbances, such as watercourses and electrical cables. Near the far end of a peaceful private garden is often the safest place.

2. Check that you are in a solunar flow period.

3. Mark the energy layers on the ground.

4. Exercise on all the bands from magnesium to phosphorus to strengthen your energies before you create a new Vivaxis and to minimize the old chaotic energies.

5. Stand on Force Flow 1 and turn slowly clockwise if in the Northern Hemisphere and counterclockwise if in the Southern Hemisphere while you concentrate on chromium oxide. It is a combination of the concentration on the chromium frequency plus turning on the force flow for chromium that realigns your body frequencies to this new geographical point. Establishing your Vivaxis on Force Flow 1 makes a strong and direct link to the energy layers, although all Vivaxes associated with living beings are linked by waves to the nearest chromium layer.

6. Move away to ground lower than the Vivaxis so that another person can test the success of the procedure. The tester stands next to the Vivaxis and places their left hand face down over the Vivaxis. Their recording hand is held in the position for recording vertical waves (fingers curled with tips pointing upward). A vertical wave should be flowing from where you stand

below your Vivaxis to your new Vivaxis site. A horizontal wave should also be recorded at the Vivaxis site. If you move above your Vivaxis, the vertical wave cannot be recorded by a person standing at the Vivaxis site.

Aligning to Your Vivaxis

Over the years, I have learned many practical ways to use Earth energies to restore health to myself, my clients, and the environment around me. The great advantage of this work with Earth energies is that it costs nothing and can be accomplished by each individual for himself. It is especially useful after traveling, during stress, during illness, or at any time when you are thrown completely back on your own resources and do not have therapeutic assistance.

Aligning or facing directly toward your Vivaxis energies is the most significant exercise you can do in relation to your Vivaxis. It is a means of consolidating your life-giving Vivaxis energies and restoring them to disturbed parts of your body. By receiving these energies, you bring the energies of your body into balance with the health-giving parallel flows to and from the Vivaxis. The alignment of all the elements in your body is strengthened, and this, in turn, corrects any nervous and muscular abnormalities you may have. There is also a dramatic effect on your lymphatic system and immune function, such that foreign disease-generating viruses and bacteria can be overcome. In addition, all the endocrine glands are aligned and balanced when you align to your Vivaxis energies.

The following factors need to be observed and avoided when you align to your Vivaxis, as they can interfere with your Vivaxis energies: jets passing overhead; nearby electric motors such as chainsaws, power-drills, or garden mowers; thundery weather conditions; tree branches overhead; nearby power lines; standing on acrylic carpet; or standing directly under lights or near television or microwave receivers and transmitters. Select an open space outside during calm weather away from these interferences.

You need not align to your Vivaxis every day; the need will vary and perhaps twice a week may be a rough guide for maintaining or restoring your health. To guide myself in this respect, I walk slowly across the energy layers and observe whether I get a response in my recording arm on any force flow. If so, I use that as an indication to align on that force flow. It is usually on Force Flows 1, 3, or 4. Occasionally, for a specific purpose such as the need for more negative or positive ions, it is appropriate to align on the magnesium or phosphorous band.

Aligning or facing directly toward your Vivaxis energies is the most significant exercise you can accomplish in relation to your Vivaxis. It is a means of consolidating your life-giving Vivaxis energies and restoring them to disturbed parts of your body. By receiving these energies, you bring the energies of your body into balance with the health-giving parallel flows to and from the Vivaxis.

Before aligning, check that the following key areas on your body have a healthy ion flow: top of the skull, coccyx, center points on the hands and feet, back of the hard palate in your mouth. Use the tip of your thumb to test the palate. If you find any disturbance in these parts, jar the part before aligning the energies.

Aligning to the Vivaxis

1. Remove watches, mobile phones, jewelry, hats, and shoes (unless they have rubber or leather soles) from your person.

2. Check ion and solunar flows. Never align during a major or minor period or at new or full moon for a period of at least five hours before and after these events. The exact time of full and new moons is given on many calendars. Be careful to adjust for summer daylight savings times, because calendars do not include these times. If it is summer, you will need to subtract one hour from the clock time to revert to real time.

3. Find the most appropriate force flow by slowly walking over the layers from the foot band to the magnesium band until your recording arm gives a strong response. If in doubt, use Force Flow 1 or 3.

4. Stand on the chosen flow and find the direction of your Vivaxis. Then mark the four quadrants exactly on the ground; each direction will be exactly ninety degrees from the next. Now align in the four directions in the following manner, starting and finishing by facing your Vivaxis: Stand with feet apart, spine erect, eyes

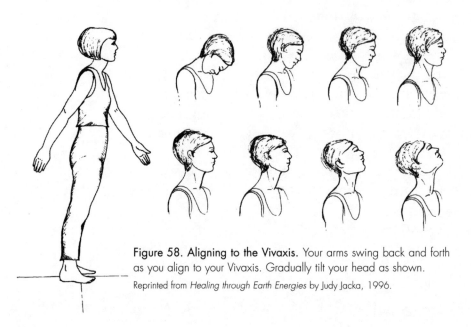

Figure 58. Aligning to the Vivaxis. Your arms swing back and forth as you align to your Vivaxis. Gradually tilt your head as shown.
Reprinted from *Healing through Earth Energies* by Judy Jacka, 1996.

shut and tilt your head as far forward as possible. Gradually raise your head and move it as far backward as possible. (See figure 58.) Note the response in your arms. If your arms respond very strongly at any point, keep your head at that tilt and wait until your arms have stopped moving, which indicates that sufficient energy has been absorbed.

5. Turn clockwise for the Northern Hemisphere and counterclockwise for the Southern Hemisphere and repeat in the four directions; finish by aligning a fifth time when you are facing your Vivaxis again.

6. Exercise briefly on the other force flows, except on the hand band.

7. Move off the band and ground your hands on neutral ground to remove excess energy.

8. Test if the process has been effective by observing whether one arm will only move toward the Vivaxis even when concentrating on another direction. This indicates that your body is still strongly aligned to the Vivaxis.

9. Walk around for twenty minutes to ground your energies and stay away from other people while your body fluids are strongly aligned to your Vivaxis. The fluids in your body remain aligned with your Vivaxis for about twenty minutes after aligning. This fact can be verified by touching any of your lymph nodes (for example, in the groin or under the arm) with the testing finger of your left hand. Other readily accessible nodes are the side of your neck. The recording arm will be stimulated to move for twenty minutes. This means that your immune system is stimulated and energized for this period of time. The alignment can be cut short at any time by briefly doing the neutralizing exercise, using

the accordion method. (See exercise 2.) After this, you will find that the arm will move toward any direction that is visualized.

Aligning for Specific Elements

There are occasions when it is important to align for specific elements. For instance, aligning to iron in cases of anemia; to selenium to improve immunity, or to iodine in cases of thyroid deficiency. At other times, we need extra oxygen such as for bad headaches and various infections.

1. Stand out of your Vivaxis directions on the force flow that contains the element you wish to absorb. For example, Force Flow 3 for iron or selenium, Force Flow 4 for iodine, the magnesium band for magnesium, and so on.

2. Stand erect and visualize the element and note the direction in which the recording arm moves. Face that direction and ground your hands on your thighs while visualizing that element. If you are facing the correct direction, your body should be pulled forward while you are visualizing the element concerned. Mark the ground in four directions at points ninety degrees apart from the first and main direction for that element.

3. Align in the same way as you do to your Vivaxis, facing the four directions associated with the element; meanwhile, visualize the element concerned.

4. Exercise briefly on the other force flows (except the hand band) to balance with the other elements.

Remember that, except for the elements on Force Flow 3, aligning must be done during the solunar flow, because otherwise the energy flows from elements like chromium, calcium, iodine, and zinc will have disappeared temporarily. Absorbing selenium is particularly strong during the minor period, and you should always try to align to selenium at that time, if it is needed. As selenium is very important for immunity, this can be a valuable exercise. Fran made the point that the selenium exercise was more potent if we took in both the horizontal and vertical flows of selenium. Thus stand on Force Flow 3 for horizontal selenium and then stand on Force Flow 2 for vertical selenium. Both these flows are present at all times, but they more strongly present at the minor period.

Stimulating and Improving Your Memory

Memory is probably at the top of the list of the many health concerns clients discuss. It is a serious concern to us all when we start to experience memory lapses. We worry that the brain is no longer a reliable instrument. The fear of some form of senility lurks in the thoughts of many, especially as we approach middle age and observe severe memory lapses in our elderly parents and associates.

There are many nutritional supplements containing substances such as the vitamin B complex, vitamin E, magnesium, and potassium phosphate, and herbs like Ginkgo biloba and Gotu Kola, and these can be of great assistance. However, if the basic receptors on the head for minerals are disturbed, you need to get to the cause so that you can absorb the minerals effectively. The professions of conventional medicine and naturopathy have not yet clearly established why some people on identical diets vary in their absorption and tissue levels of certain nutrients like iron, zinc, copper, and iodine. It is likely this variation depends on the correct functioning of the receptors/acupuncture points associated with each mineral.

This part of Fran's research is unique and, in terms of memory problems, may solve some of the mysteries as to why some of us become senile in old age and some do not. Remember that in finding your Vivaxis, you used an old memory, like a nursery rhyme, to verify the direction of your Vivaxis. This was done because the memories of such rhymes were formed before any damage to your receptors from chemicals, deficiencies, or electromagnetic sources had occurred. In this exercise, you stimulate the key memory receptors, which are in a band around your head at the level of the bridge on your nose. (See figure 59.)

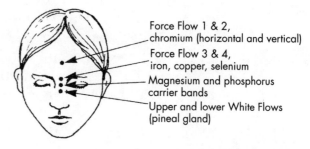

Force Flow 1 & 2, chromium (horizontal and vertical)

Force Flow 3 & 4, iron, copper, selenium

Magnesium and phosphorus carrier bands

Upper and lower White Flows (pineal gland)

Figure 59. Receptors for the various force flows on center line of face

1. Check your ion and solunar flow.

2. Drink energized water that has been rolled between the magnesium and phosphorus bands.

3. Stand on Force Flow 3, because the elements associated with these memory receptors are in this flow.

4. Find the direction of your Vivaxis.

5. While facing your Vivaxis, find the memory receptor on the bridge of your nose with the tip of your testing finger by visualizing the elements associated with magnetic group: iron, copper, selenium, and gold. Your recording arm should swing in response to each visualization. Repeat the process to find the corresponding receptors at the back of your head and those at the side of your head above your ears. These receptors will be in a direct line with those on your nose.

6. Use your index fingers to alternately press the memory receptors on your nose and then the corresponding receptors on the back of your head. Do this five or six

times while facing your Vivaxis. Stand erect during this procedure and press very firmly on the receptors. Drop your hands and allow the Force Flow 3 energies to flow in. This energy flow may take up to twenty seconds. Many people feel these energies as a vibration or energy flow through the head.

7. Turn ninety degrees to the right in the Northern Hemisphere or ninety degrees left in the Southern hemisphere. Your ears are now in line with the Vivaxis. Repeat the stimulation of receptors, but this time press the receptors above the ears. Then drop your hands and allow the energies to flow in.

8. Exercise briefly on all force flows to balance your energies. Ground off excess energy by pressing your hands for a few seconds on neutral ground.

After this exercise, your memory receptors will remain stimulated for about twenty minutes. To check, place your testing finger on a memory receptor; your recording arm should move without any visualization or humming process. Remember to use your testing finger, because it will differentiate the force flow energy from ion flow, which is recorded by the middle finger. In other words, you cannot test receptors using your middle finger, because this would just give the usual response to ion flow both before and after the stimulation.

Another, less specific, way for stimulating memory receptors is to align to the Vivaxis on Force Flow 3, while you hum a nursery rhyme from in childhood. This stimulation relates to the strong connection between the receptors on your head associated with memory and rhymes that were learned at a time when these receptors were in a healthy state during early childhood. Singing these rhymes restores the original healthy pattern in the receptors.

EXERCISE 14

Testing the
Pineal Receptors

In part 1 we explored how the pineal gland is the leader of the endocrine "orchestra" and how it is intimately related to all our daily rhythms as well as to our spiritual experiences and expression. It is therefore important to keep this gland healthy and energized.

An important group of pineal receptors is located about one quarter of an inch below the bridge of your nose. (See figure 59.) Other corresponding receptors are spaced in a band around the head at that level, including a pair on the back of the head, and also just above the auditory canal in each ear. In addition, there are further pairs of pineal receptors on different parts of the body. In each case, one of the pair will receive energy from the upper White Flow and one from the lower White Flow.

These pineal pairs behave in the same way as the other receptors and swap their functions as you change your orientation toward your Vivaxis. As you respond to the upper White Flow with your eyes open and to the lower White Flow with eyes shut, by changing your position you can check how these receptors change their function. Use your testing finger while thinking of "white" to find whether one of the pair is responding when your eyes are open or shut. If, when thinking of white, there is a response with your eyes open, move ninety degrees to the right; there will now only be a response when you think of white with your eyes shut. In other words, the pair of receptors have swapped their function.

Testing for Calcification in the Pineal Receptors

Start with the receptor pair on the bridge of the nose and confirm its position by thinking of white while holding the point. There will be a response in your recording hand if you are touching a pineal receptor when thinking of white. To establish whether this pineal receptor is calcified, visualize chalk, which is a form of calcium. If your receptor is calcified, a positive response in your recording hand will take place when you concentrate on chalk or calcium. The response in your recording hand may be a circular motion, which indicates disturbance.

I have reflected on the meaning of finding calcium in pineal receptors. Calcium is one of the most important elements in the body, but it causes problems if it is found in the wrong places. Examples of calcification include kidney stones, hardened arteries, gallstones, arthritic joints, and cataracts. We seem to have a polarity between the pineal gland (the master gland of the endocrine glands), which is linked to light in both a physical and spiritual sense, and calcium, which signifies hardness, materiality, and crystallization. The various factors to consider in this interesting polarity are these: The pineal needs a balance of light and darkness to function normally. It appears to be sensitive to physical light, and as mentioned, nonovulating women (of an age when they should ovulate) have been helped to ovulate by sleeping in a lighted room around the time of ovulation. The pineal is also traditionally associated with our ability to receive spiritual light, and if it becomes calcified, we could expect that all its capacities will be reduced.

There may also be a polarity within the pineal gland itself, because it produces both serotonin and melatonin. Seasonal Affective Disorder (SAD) occurs in some people during winter when there is less sunlight. Such people are helped both by exposure to bright light for a period each day and by taking melatonin supplements. Perhaps we need to understand further the role that serotonin plays here, because it is a hormone that appears to give relaxation and happy mood.

We then come to the part played by sunlight in relation to calcium absorption. The body needs vitamin D to absorb calcium, and vitamin D is manufactured by the skin through the influence of sunlight. So it appears that the reception of light may actually enhance calcification. However, perhaps the mystery clears when we remember that melatonin is manufactured by the body in the middle of the night for the purpose of keeping the pineal gland healthy. If this gland is healthy, then the calcification process, despite being stimulated by sunlight, may perhaps be kept in balance.

Regardless of these mysteries, it seems apparent that the pineal gland should not be calcified if you want good health and spiritual development. By using the energy from the White Flows, the effect of calcification in the pineal receptors seems to disappear. There is no easy way to establish whether the actual physical calcium deposits disappear, but I expect they would. Perhaps magnetic resonance imaging scans (MRIs) could establish this fact, but who would wish to expose themselves to radiation for this purpose?

Removing the Effects of Calcification in the Pineal Receptors: Method 1

Check the pineal receptors on your head by using your testing finger on the key receptors just below the bridge of your nose above the auditory canals and on the corresponding level at the back of your head. Their position is established by visualizing white and by obtaining a response in your recording hand. If your recording hand responds when visualizing calcium (chalk) in the pineal receptor, undertake the following steps between the hours of 10 A.M. and 2 P.M.:

1. Check for normal ion flow in the environment and check for solunar flow.

2. Fill a hot water bottle with very hot water, as hot as can be borne by the skin.

3. Roll or drag the hot water bottle across all the energy bands on the ground from the lower White Flow upward, being careful to include the upper White Flow, but to not go beyond it because of the detrimental flows five inches above. Drag the bottle down and then up again each time, including the white bands. Do not rest the bottle on the ground before treating your disturbed receptors, because this may partly dissipate the energies in the water.

4. Hold the bottle against all disturbed receptors for a minute.

5. To balance the other energies, exercise on all the energy bands except the whites and stimulate your memory receptors by singing a nursery rhyme or by remembering a pleasant incident in early childhood.

6. Check that your pineal receptors are now free of calcium by visualizing calcium while touching the receptor with the testing finger. If there is no response in the recording hand, then the effect of calcification has been removed. Obviously, the gradual dissipation of the calcium may take days, weeks, or months and

therefore the receptors should be rechecked weekly over a period of several months.

Removing the Effects of Calcification in the Pineal Receptors: Method 2

1. Check for normal ion flow in the environment and for solunar flow time.

2. Stand on the lower white band. (Fran advised not to stand on the upper white band for any exercise.)

3. Use your middle fingers to stress alternately the front and back pineal head receptors, while facing your Vivaxis. Drop your hands and allow energy to flow in.

4. Stand sideways in your Vivaxis channel and repeat the procedure, using pineal receptors located above the auditory canals.

5. Move to Force Flow 3 and stimulate your memory receptors by singing a nursery rhyme.

6. Exercise on all force flows from magnesium to phosphorus and then ground your hands on neutral ground after moving off the energy bands.

The method you use to help your pineal gland is optional. Because this research is unique, it is useful to cross-check and explore as many options as possible; either method should be successful.

Testing the Brain Receptors

The next set of exercises involves the receptors, and in particular, the brain receptors, such as I have already described in the context of testing the triple groups. The electrical pattern of your body may gradually be emerging in your mind. We are indeed electrical beings, and our electromagnetic energy field is associated with thousands of energy receptors. Each receptor is like a tiny transformer, able to receive the subtle currents that flow if the right mineral frequencies are present in the receptor and if it is correctly tuned to our Vivaxis.

Basically, the receptors are responsible for the final energy transmission involved with memory, creative thought, mathematical thought, movement, and all the automatic functions of the body such as heartbeat, breathing, digestion, and endocrine function. The many types of receptors were

We are indeed electrical beings, and our electromagnetic energy field is associated with thousands of energy receptors. Each receptor is like a tiny transformer, able to receive the subtle currents that flow if the right mineral frequencies are present in the receptor and if it is correctly tuned to our Vivaxis.

explored in part 1 and now I present the skills to find and test the brain points.

Once Fran began to teach students to use the energy layers, she did not feel the need to teach about the individual receptors. She gave the impression that any disturbed body part could be corrected by jarring the disturbed receptors and aligning to the Vivaxis while standing on an energy layer. While the study of the role of the receptors is a fascinating science and is particularly useful for anyone involved in healing work, it is not essential that you master this section of the exercises for the purposes of healing with Earth energies. However, if you have poor memory or concentration, then I strongly recommend you become familiar with this section.

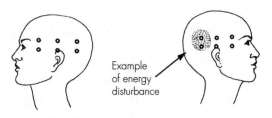

Example of energy disturbance

Testing the Lower-Brain Receptors

The twenty-four lower-brain receptors are shown in figure 20. Each of these brain groups contain the three types of receptors—the central one for mathematical thought, and the one for involuntary and voluntary movement on either side. Because these receptors are very close to each other, we need to use our testing finger carefully to differentiate each type. To do this, use the tip of your fingernail to test each type within the group of three.

Figure 20.

The central brain receptors of both the lower- and higher-brain groups are the only ones on the body that are stimulated by mathematical exercises. Locate a brain receptor by moving your testing finger down the central line of your forehead while thinking of a simple

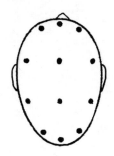

Figure 20B.

multiplication calculation (such as 2 x 2 = 4). Halfway down the forehead you will come to a brain receptor and your recording arm should move back and forth. If the receptor is disturbed, your hand will move in a circular movement. (In contrast, the recording hand will stop moving altogether if your energy field is partly displaced from the bone as can result from X-rays.)

To test the receptors on either side of the central one, move your testing finger slightly to the left or right. Your recording arm will move toward your Vivaxis if you are touching the involuntary receptor. Now move your finger to the other side of the central receptor and concentrate on an object in the room. Your recording arm will move in the direction of the object only when you are touching a voluntary receptor. Remember, this type of receptor makes a temporary horizontal link with the object of your thought. Now take up the opposite direction in relation to your Vivaxis and note that the two receptors just tested will reverse their roles.

These receptors on either side of the central brain receptor have alternating spins, one with a clockwise motion and the other counterclockwise. This can be checked by first finding a central brain receptor on your forehead, then moving your testing finger slightly to the right while holding your recording hand like a fist with the thumb pointing upward. Your hand will circle in one direction, which will reverse if you turn so that you face the opposite direction in relation to your Vivaxis. The receptor on the left-hand side can then be checked and will be found to have the opposite spin.

Testing the Higher-Brain Receptors

Each of these twelve receptor groups (Figure above the hairline—see figure 20B) measures half an inch in width. To find a higher-brain receptor, conduct a simple mental exercise as you did to find the lower-brain

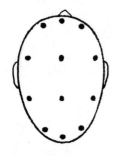

Figure 20B.

receptors, that is, think of a simple multiplication calculation, such as 2 x 2 = 4. These receptors are also stimulated by recalling an incident from your past, or by thinking of your Vivaxis. Fran made the point that it is significant that the center point of the higher-brain receptors is linked exclusively both horizontally and vertically to our brain and Vivaxis. In other words, unlike the lower-brain receptors, these higher receptors are not accompanied by a receptor that can be disturbed by linking with another person or object in the environment. They are thus protected from interference.

If you are above your Vivaxis, you can test a clockwise spin in the higher-brain receptors. This means there is a vertical wave traveling down toward your Vivaxis. To test for this wave, hold your testing finger on the receptor and hold your other hand as a closed fist with your thumb pointing upward. Note that your hand turns clockwise; if you are below your Vivaxis, the hand will turn counterclockwise. In the case of the higher-brain receptors, those on either side of the central one appear to have the same direction of spin as the central one. Note also the different phenomenon of spin from the lower-brain receptors, where those on either side of the central one have reverse spins from each other, switching according to your position in relation to your Vivaxis. This bit of information may seem very technical, but it becomes simpler when you slowly develop the requisite skills to test the spins.

On one side of the central higher-brain receptor is a receptor for Sun energies and on the other side is one for Moon energies. To find the Sun receptor, think of the Sun and move the tip of your recording fingernail to the left or right of the central receptor until there is a response in your recording arm. The opposite side will then give a response to the Moon. These side receptors will switch their wavelengths for Sun and Moon if you change your position in relation to your Vivaxis and also as the Earth rotates and changes its position in relation to the Sun and Moon. These intricate patterns illustrate some of the many polarities in our universe. These polarities are related to such phenomena in nature as vines growing clockwise in the Northern Hemisphere and counterclockwise in the Southern Hemisphere.

All the brain receptors must be in good working order before we can effectively use the brain and receive Earth energies. Dysfunction can be caused by earthquakes; electric storms; magnetic disturbances; electrical equipment, including diagnostic equipment in hospitals and clinics; televisions; computer terminals; fluorescent lights; and any other sources that emit electromagnetic frequencies.

Five particular brain receptors (apart from the higher and lower receptors already discussed) give distress signals in response to these causes. They are positioned in the center points of the ears, two more are in the same line at the center of the nose and back of the head, and one is on top of the head. (See figure 26.) If you hold your testing finger on these points, your recording hand may move in a circular direction or in a direction at right angles to your Vivaxis.

A simple exercise will show you how these five brain receptors can become temporarily affected so that your Vivaxis appears to be at right angles to its true direction. Use your testing finger to find one of these receptors while standing on neutral ground during the solunar flow period and note how your arm immediately swings in the direction of your Vivaxis. Then stand under any type of light that is switched on. Within a few seconds, you will find that your arm swings at right angles to the true direction of your Vivaxis.

If you have been subjected to electromagnetic interference for some hours or days, this disturbance can remain *until* you correct the disturbed receptors by jarring and then aligning to your Vivaxis. Working many hours at a computer can have the same effect as standing

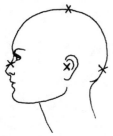

Figure 26.

under a light, but the effect may be more significant, because we usually only stand or sit under a light for a short time. Once you learn to find the direction of your Vivaxis, it becomes a simple skill to know when these five brain receptors are affected as described above.

Testing the Brain Groups

This is a method Fran Nixon devised for testing the brain receptors to check that they are in good working order and not disturbed by static, foreign fields, drugs, chemicals, or psychological stress. Before you test brain receptors, you must establish that the center point of each thumb pad has normal energy waves to your Vivaxis in order to relay wave patterns to your brain. Look at your thumb pads and note that your recording hand can swing toward your Vivaxis.

1. Prepare by removing glasses, jewelry, watches, mobile phones, tight clothing, and shoes, unless they have leather or rubber soles.

2. Do the short form of the neutralizing exercise. (See exercise 2.)

3. Hold your spine erect and your head level, keep your feet well apart and your eyes open, because light is the carrier wave for connecting with anything in the environment.

4. Turn in a full circle without visualizing any particular direction. Allow your arm to move toward your Vivaxis. As you turn, different receptors on your head will link toward your Vivaxis, and if any are disturbed, you will find that the arm will not move toward the Vivaxis when any disturbed receptor is facing in that direction.

5. To isolate the disturbed receptor, you will probably need to use the testing finger systematically to test each of the brain receptors on the disturbed quadrant of the head. This means doing a simple mathematical calculation (such as 2 x 2 = 4), while finding the points shown on figure 20 and noting which receptors give a disturbed circular motion in the recording arm.

Correction of Disturbed Receptors

Since you now know how to find the energy layers, you can correct any disturbed receptor. Stand on the selected force flow, preferably Force Flow 1 or 3. Face in the direction of your Vivaxis and then jar the disturbed receptor by tapping it lightly with the fingers or a stick while your head is tilted sideways out of your Vivaxis channel. Then align immediately in the usual manner to restore energies to the receptor.

Testing Receptors
for Movement

Specific receptors in the brain groups are associated with each movable part of the body. The voluntary receptors in the brain groups concerned with a particular part of the body will respond when that body part is moving. As the brain instructs a part to move, a line of energy that Fran called a "wave train" moves along a definite path from a voluntary brain receptor to a particular receptor associated with that body part. (See figure 60.)

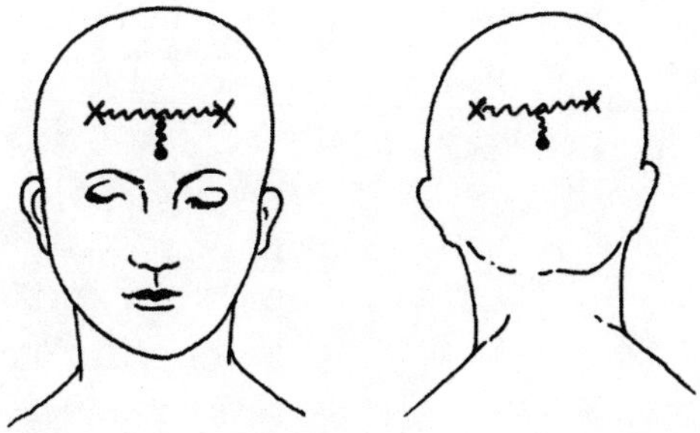

Try this for yourself by testing your knee movement. First find a brain receptor on your forehead by doing a simple calculation (2 x 2 = 4) until your recording arms moves.

Figure 60. The pathways from a brain receptor to knee receptor. Subject charts the "track" associated with movement by moving the limb and noting the response in the recording hand when touching the receptors associated with that movement. First, you need to find a receptor associated with the part being tested.

Adapted from a figure in *Healing through Earth Energies* by Judy Jacka, 1996.

Find the voluntary receptor at one side of that brain receptor. Then flex your knee while moving your testing finger lightly along the track (as shown in figure 60) until your recording hand stops. This will be the knee receptor.

The energy track for movement will probably vary, depending on your position relative to your Vivaxis, but if the knee receptor is disturbed, you will observe a circular motion in your recording hand as your testing finger moves along the track.

Testing the movement in any part of the body is a fairly lengthy business, because you have to find the track on your cranium associated with the body part. However, in cases of paralysis, it is obviously worth the effort. Each limb is connected to specific receptors in one of the four quadrants of the head. To correct energy blocks in specific areas, it is also necessary to find the associated terminal points on your fingers and toes, because they may be disturbed. When you are testing the receptors on the ends of fingers and toes, you obviously will not be able to touch them at the same time the other hand is recording. This means that you must use your eyes to locate these points rather than touch them with the fingertip; alternatively, have a friend help out.

In relation to knee movement, one brain and knee receptor will be associated with forward movement, one pair with backward movement, one pair with upward motion, and the final pair with downward motion. These pairs will swap their functions, depending on the direction you face.

It is easy to imagine the possibilities for corrective work in cases of paralysis if these basic techniques were accepted in conventional medicine. Fran described some cases in which she retrained paralyzed people to walk again after helping them to find and correct their disturbed receptors. The connection of a wave link to our Vivaxis appears to explain why brain receptors can control the direction of movement for the various parts of the body. As I mentioned earlier, when you face your Vivaxis channel, you are like a radio set that has been tuned to *your* specific frequency. In all types of paralysis, there is an interruption to the Vivaxis.

In figure 61, you can see how the energies in your head line up when you face toward your Vivaxis. This indicates the effect of bringing all your energies into one direction when you face the exact direction of your Vivaxis. This is a stimulating effect that results from the coherence taking place. You can liken this effect to the powerful effect of laser light, which develops when all the light rays point in the same direction. For this reason, do not align to your Vivaxis every day, as you might then bring in too much energy.

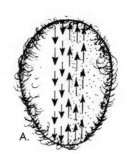 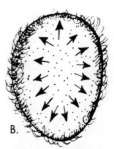

Figure 61. Wave vectors when aligned (A) and not aligned (B) to the Vivaxis channel. A. Direction of wave vectors with your head level and aligned with Vivaxis. The energies run side by side in opposite directions; these directions change at the midline of your skull. B. Directions of vectors when not aligned, showing the scattered effect.

Reprinted from *Healing through Earth Energies* by Judy Jacka, 1996.

EXERCISE 17

Exploring More Important Receptors

Research involving the minerals associated with receptors on the body is only in the very early stages, but discussion of this issue will help you understand some of the mineral relationships with organs and tissues. Since Fran's death, the Canadian group has done a lot of work in this area. I have not been able to duplicate all their work. The reason for this may be that the placement of certain minerals varies from person to person. However, there has been enough work done by Vivaxis researchers to indicate there are many more mineral receptors on our bodies than those first discovered by Fran.

In this section, you will learn to find and monitor receptors associated with the adrenal and thyroid glands, tongue, and jaw. An exercise for some of the eye receptors follows. There also are receptors associated with appetites for food and sex. Eventually, we will have a map of mineral receptors associated with all the organs and tissues of the body.

As you explore the different receptors on your body for various body functions, you will start to understand the working of your body energies and the patterns of energy that are revealed. Just explore a bit at a time so as not to suffer from overload. Test your receptors on different days at odd times when you have a few moments. You will find that you start to become aware of many body energies and to see how they are affected by different situations and environments. All of this is yet another aspect of the Vivaxis connection.

Every part of your body is represented by receptors in some part of the mouth. For instance, the two vital receptors located on either side of the top of the head have their two associated receptors on the roof of the mouth at the back of the soft palate; these are in direct line with that key to the central nervous system called the hypothalamus. It is important to know about these receptors, as they often need correction after dental work. Another relationship exists between the tip of the tongue and the base of the spine. In cases of severe pain or disability in any part of the body, improvement will only be temporary until all the associated receptors are found and treated.

Test your receptors on different days at odd times when you have a few moments. You will find that you start to become aware of many body energies and to see how they are affected by different situations and environments. All of this is yet another aspect of the Vivaxis connection.

Tongue Receptors

There are many receptors on the tongue that are associated with body movement and function. (See figure 62.) No doubt this is why Chinese medicine uses the tongue for diagnosis. There also are a number of receptors on the right side of the nose; these are associated with tongue movement. Lightly touch these receptors with your testing finger while moving your tongue in and out of your mouth. Your recording hand will register a strong response. If you test the left side of your nose, nothing happens. You can locate receptors for tongue movement

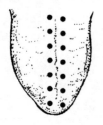

Figure 62. Receptors on the tongue. Half have a clockwise motion and half a counterclockwise motion when we test the energy by holding the recording hand.

Reprinted from *Healing through Earth Energies* by Judy Jacka, 1996.

on your nose, your head, and also on your toes and fingers. If your tongue was paralyzed after an accident or a cerebral vascular event, these receptors need to be found and corrected.

You can perform an interesting test by visualizing a favorite food as you move your sensing finger down the center of your tongue. When you get to the food, or appetite, receptor, your recording arm will move strongly. There also is a sex receptor nearby that can be tested by visualizing enjoyable sex. Areas on the tongue for the fingers and toes can be found by concentrating on these digits.

These correspondences between receptors and our inner organs explain why so many practitioners and clients find value and healing through different types of bodywork. Massage, facial therapy, and acupressure must stimulate many internal organs and tissues during the course of treatment. This stimulation occurs through the various pathways or meridians that lead from the surface receptors or acupuncture points to their associated organs.

Adrenal Receptors

There are points at the end of each eyebrow that are associated with the adrenal glands, which sit on top of the kidneys. They are associated with energy levels and are very important endocrine glands that are often affected by the stress of twenty-first-century living. This is a very simple exercise to test for adrenal stress. The adrenal gland receptors emit the frequencies of the elements copper and selenium.

Using your testing finger, touch the end of one eyebrow and visualize first copper and then selenium to find the positions of these elements on the end of each eyebrow. If the end of one eyebrow records the frequency of copper, the other end will register selenium. The positions on the other eyebrow will be reversed. Record the positions as you did for the fingertips. (See figure 63.) If there is a disturbance in these glands, you may observe a circulating movement in your recording hand when touching the receptors and visualizing the appropriate element. Correct this disturbance with the usual technique of jarring and aligning to your Vivaxis.

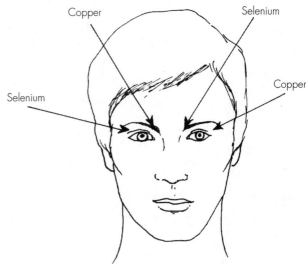

Figure 63. The copper and selenium receptors. The positions may be reversed on some people.

It is interesting to have a friend test your energy via the adrenal receptors when standing first in a healthy environment and then in a situation in which you become static. Place a fingertip on an adrenal receptor while your friend finds that the muscle tests strongly. Cause static in your field by standing under a light that is turned on; the same muscle will test weakly. You could test your own adrenal points by comparing the strength of movement in your recording hand when touching the adrenal points with the tip of your testing finger.

Selenium and copper receptors are located on the top of your head and on the soles of your feet. These are important indicators as to whether you can digest carbohydrates and protein. The selenium receptors on your head and the copper receptors on your feet are activated at the minor period, which is why you should align for selenium at this time for enhanced immunity. A reversal occurs at the major period, and the copper receptors on your head and selenium on your feet are stimulated. Fran found that the selenium frequency relates to protein metabolism and copper to carbohydrate metabolism. On this basis, one wonders whether sufferers of *Candida albicans* (thrush) have disturbed copper receptors, because

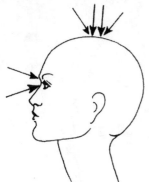

they seem to suffer Candidiasis in conjunction with an inability to digest carbohydrates. Figure 64 shows the position for food and sex receptors on the head. The smaller arrows show the food receptors associated with selenium and protein digestion.

Receptors for the Thyroid and Parathyroid Glands

Figure 64. Apetite receptors for food and sex. The larger arrows indicate the sex receptors and are associated with chromium horizontal groups. The smaller arrows indicate the food receptors and are associated with selenium.

Reprinted from *Healing through Earth Energies* by Judy Jacka, 1996.

The thyroid gland is situated in front of the larynx, or voice box, and the parathyroids are found embedded in the four corners of the thyroid. These are important structures to check for disturbances. The thyroid is connected with our metabolic activities, and the parathyroids are connected with the balance of calcium. I have found the iodine and chromium receptors to be in numerous places across the surface of the thyroid gland. You can test this fact by scanning your thyroid while thinking of these elements. When you scan a part of the body on yourself or others, you can either do it by looking at the part or by thinking of it. If the subject is yourself, you can, if preferred, look in the mirror.

Calcium + zinc frequencies on parathyroid

Calcium + silica frequencies on parathyroid

Iodine and chromium frequencies in parathyroid

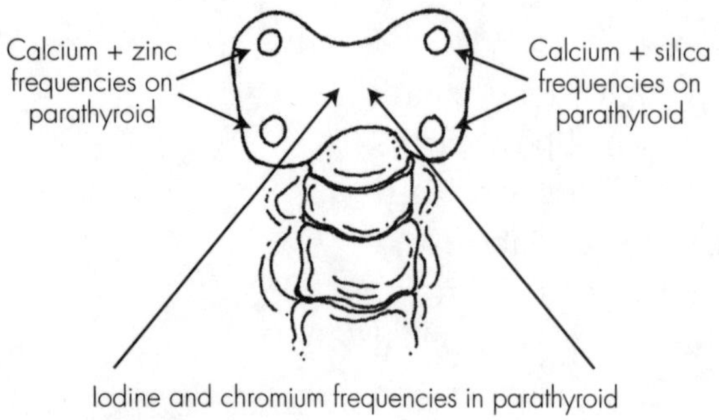

Figure 65. The thyroid and parathyroid glands and associated frequencies. The positions may be reversed on some people.

Apart from the frequency of calcium, the parathyroids on one side have frequencies for silica and on the other side for zinc. The position of these elements will vary from person to person. (See figure 65.) Fran suggested checking the bones in the cervical (neck) area to see if they respond to the frequencies of silica and zinc. If disturbances are found, the following exercise should be undertaken, as this exercise can often correct problems of the thyroid.

1. Scan the cervical vertebrae (in your neck) for disturbances.

2. Face the direction for silica while holding a silica tablet obtained from a health food store in your mouth.

3. Press and release the affected bone area at least six times and also apply pressure inside the mouth to your palate and teeth.

4. Repeat for zinc and also iodine if those receptors are found to be disturbed. A kelp tablet can be used when you face the direction for iodine and a zinc tablet when you face the direction for zinc.

Jaw Receptors

We find the same duo of elements here as in gravitational and magnetic groups composing this duo. You will remember that it also was repeated on the sides of the hands. Receptors on one side of the jaw relate to the magnetic group, with iron as the main element, and those on the other side of the jaw are associated with the gravitational group, which features zinc or iodine. A dividing line is located at the center line of both upper and lower jaw. (See figure 66.)

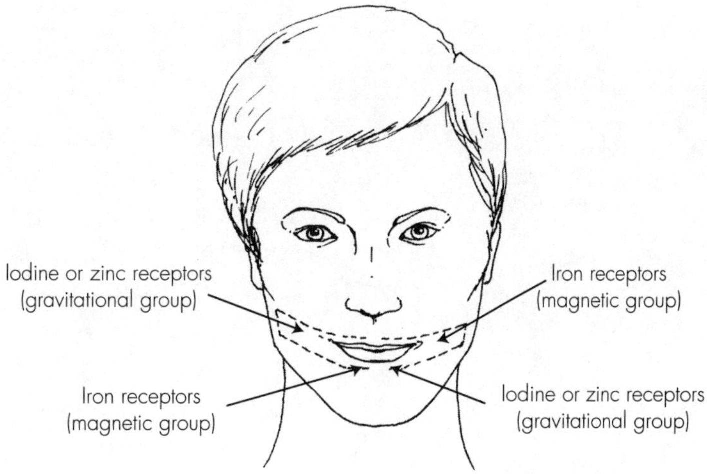

Iodine or zinc receptors (gravitational group)

Iron receptors (magnetic group)

Iron receptors (magnetic group)

Iodine or zinc receptors (gravitational group)

Figure 66. Jaw receptors. Note how the frequencies alternate as they do around the eyes and eyebrows. The position may be reversed on some people.

Cobalt Receptors

The cobalt receptors form a band around your head with a vertical wave on one side and a horizontal wave on the other. Cobalt is one of the elements associated within Force Flow 1, and these receptors often become disturbed from the effects of television. Here is a small research exercise we can conduct with our children: determine how much television they can watch before their cobalt receptors become disturbed. The distance from the television set would also need to be taken into account. As oxygen is the mate of cobalt on Force Flow 1, oxygen receptors are also located around the head near the cobalt band. (See figure 67.)

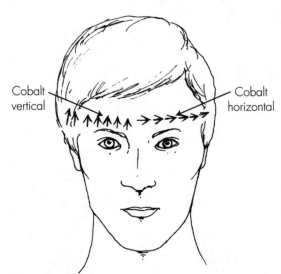

Cobalt vertical

Cobalt horizontal

Figure 67. Cobalt receptors. Cobalt receptors are in a band just above the eyebrows and feature horizontal waves on one side and vertical on the other. These will switch with each other, depending on the direction you are facing.

1. Having obtained a small sample of cobalt powder from a chemical warehouse, absorb the wavelength by looking at the sample of gray powder. Then study figure 67 and observe where the cobalt receptors can be found on the head of your child, as follows.

2. Think of cobalt while looking at the cobalt band on your children's heads. Follow this band around the head with your eyes while continuing to think of cobalt; do this before they watch television. If the cobalt receptors are working properly, you will obtain a back and forth movement in your recording hand while thinking of cobalt and looking at these receptors. Remember to hold your hand in the horizontal position to find which side of the head has the horizontal

flow (see arrows on figure 67) and in the vertical position to find the vertical flows on the other side of the head. The arrangement may vary from person to person, depending on how they are positioned in terms of their Vivaxis. The flows will change at the center front and back points of the head.

3. After your children have been looking at television for one or two hours, check their cobalt receptors again. If the receptors are disturbed, experiment by making the children sit further away from the television screen next time you test.

4. The simplest way to correct their disturbed receptors is to apply water that has been treated on the force flows to their heads. (See exercise 25.) Just put a bit on the palm of your hand and rub it over the head. Then check the receptors again.

Receptors for Gases

Receptors for gases such as hydrogen, nitrogen, argon, ozone, and chlorine were found in the 1990s by the Canadian Vivaxis research group in a diagonal line beginning in front of the ear and moving up to the temple area. (See figure 68.) The research group found corresponding elements on the sternum for each of the gases: zirconium for oxygen, boron for hydrogen, and bromine for nitrogen.

These gases have only recently been considered as having a role in healthy human functioning, so more research will need to be conducted before the significance of these frequencies is fully understood in relation to our health. The Canadian researchers found that swimming in a chlorinated pool can upset the chlorine receptors on the head; they found that the corresponding receptors on the sternum were also affected. This makes us wonder about the effect of constantly showering in chlorinated water. Soaking in a bath or pool appears to have a worse effect than showering.

Receptors for Memory and Imagination

All our body functions appear to have their associated receptors. Finding disturbances in these receptors, such as those for memory, will obviously be significant in conditions like attention deficit disorder in children and in types of dementia, such as Alzheimer's. It is likely that correcting disturbed memory receptors in elderly people could alleviate their memory problems.

As our magnetic group of receptors corresponds to memory, we can touch or look at one of the elements in this group, such as copper or iron, when memorizing and note the movement of our recording hand. For instance, to find one of these groups, think of iron while lightly moving your testing finger down one side of your forehead. Alternatively, look at a fingertip that has the magnetic group; then memorize something while touching or looking at this receptor. There should be a movement in the other recording hand.

The Canadian researchers found that swimming in a chlorinated pool can upset the chlorine receptors on the head; they found that the corresponding receptors on the sternum were also affected. This makes us wonder about the effect of constantly showering in chlorinated water.

Our imagination is related to the gravitational group of receptors. This is not surprising when you consider the relationship between the element zinc and the gonads and between iodine and the thyroid/throat chakra connection that is associated with creative pursuits. To test your imagination, note the movement in your recording hand as you touch a gravitational group of elements, which will always contain either iodine or zinc, or just look at the iodine or zinc fingertip while using your imagination. Remember, the other main group is that named magnetic group that resonates to the frequencies of iron, copper, silver, nickel, and gold.

Logical, or linear, thinking stimulates our horizontal chromium groups, which are found throughout the lines of the triple groups described in exercise 6 and also are found in the center of all the brain receptors. Creative thinking stimulates the vertical chromium receptors also found in the same triple groups and brain receptors. This can be tested by touching a chromium horizontal group on the forehead while counting or multiplying or by thinking of something creative while touching a vertical group.

In summary, we have examined some of the receptors associated with different organs and tissues. They are all like tiny electrical transformers that receive the electrical energies needed by the body for different functions. If they become disturbed by chemical, psychic, or electromagnetic factors, they no longer transmit energy but subside into a chaotic state that could be likened to a short circuit in your household gadgets. They no longer can function.

You have now learned how all body functions, both voluntary and involuntary, are associated with these receptors, which are all related to different mineral frequencies. You can diagnose disturbed receptors and use the technique described for their correction. In particular, you can assess the state of your brain receptors, which need to be in good working order for the correct functioning of all the body organs via the acupuncture meridian system.

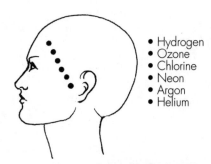

- Hydrogen
- Ozone
- Chlorine
- Neon
- Argon
- Helium

Figure 68. Gas receptors on the side of the forehead

Printed originally in the Vivaxis Energies Research International (VERIS) newsletter, date unknown. Reprinted in *Healing through Earth Energies* by Judy Jacka, 1996.

Testing Your Vision

This is an optional exercise, but an interesting one, because it gives us an understanding of how shortsightedness and longsightedness are associated with mineral frequencies and force flows. The eyes are an area of prime importance for health and well-being. For eye problems, we need to test all the receptors around each eye to see if there is a good response to the elements. Any dead spots should receive applications of energized water and should be jarred before aligning.

There may, of course, be other disturbed head receptors in relation to sight. Other points of interest in relation to minerals and the eye is the finding that the center of one pupil will respond to a vertical chromium flow and the other to a horizontal one. In addition to our energy work with the eyes, we need to have the appropriate minerals and vitamins in our diets, such as chromium, magnesium, and vitamins A, B, and C.

The natural vision exercises based on the Bates method can be combined with this energy work. Fran agreed with the findings of the natural vision practitioners that wearing glasses as little as possible is preferable. She found that the minerals in the glasses disturbed the vision over a period of time, because wearing glasses means constantly receiving frequencies through our eyes from the minerals in the glass. These minerals are present as part of the manufacturing process of the glasses. These are the minerals associated with near-sightedness and farsightedness in their normal parameters. It appears that a deficiency in either can result in excessive nearsightedness (magnesium) or excessive farsightedness (phosphorus). The natural vision therapists find that the more we rely on glasses, the weaker the eyes become. Generally, it has been found that Vivaxis aligning, the use of energized water, and the correction of any disturbed receptors around the eye can all improve the eyesight.

Fran agreed with the findings of the natural vision practitioners that wearing glasses as little as possible is preferable. She found that the minerals in the glasses disturbed the vision over a period of time because wearing glasses means constantly receiving frequencies through our eyes from the minerals in the glass. Vivaxis aligning, the use of energized water, and the correction of any disturbed receptors around the eye can all improve the

Fran found that our normal near vision is connected with magnesium receptors and normal far vision with phosphorus receptors. These receptors are found just inside the bony orbit of the eye. The key elements for eyesight are located at these receptor sites, and the positions of these elements are reversed for each eye. (You will remember that the key elements on the fingers were reversed for each hand as are the adrenal receptors on the ends of the eyebrows.) One eye will be found to have magnesium receptors across the top and phosphorus underneath, while the positions will be reversed for the other eye. (See figure 69.)

In my naturopathic practice, I use a combination of magnesium and phosphorus in the form of one of the twelve tissue salts, specifically, magnesium phosphate, the main tissue salt for stress. The naturopathic understanding of myopia is that the muscles and ligaments controlling the eyeball are

Phosphorus receptors

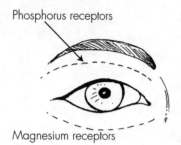

Magnesium receptors

Magnesium receptors

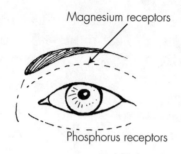

Phosphorus receptors

Figure 69. Testing your vision. Diagram of the eye showing Mg. and P receptors. Note how the receptors are reversed from eye to eye. They may also be reversed from person to person. The bony orbit around the eye has frequencies of magnesium and phosphorus—one element is above and one below. The positions for these elements are reversed from one eye to the other.
- Close vision—your recording arm responds to visualization of magnesium.
- Far vision—your recording arm responds to phosphorus.

Reprinted from *Healing through Earth Energies* by Judy Jacka, 1996.

in a state of tension. I prescribe this tissue salt for clients more than any other combination for all types of body stress, not just the eyes.

Here is how to test your vision:

1. Place the tip of your recording finger just inside the bony orbit below one eye to determine the position for the minerals around each eye. Visualize magnesium and note if there is a response in the recording hand. If not, move the recording finger to the bony orbit above the eye and retest. Make a chart for the positions of magnesium and phosphorus above and below each eye.

2. While scanning the ground in front of your feet, lightly place your index finger on a magnesium receptor and move your eyes gradually further away. At a distance of between fifteen and twenty feet, but perhaps less for very shortsighted people, your recording arm will cut out and the phosphorus vibration will take over. This means that you will need to move your testing finger to a phosphorus receptor on the bony orbit to obtain further response in your recording arm. Continue the scanning process for farsightedness in the same way. Mark the ground where magnesium cuts out and compare it later with the other eye.

3. Repeat these steps for the other eye, remembering that the position of the elements is reversed. You may find that your eyes differ in their response to the elements, because it is common to have one eye with shorter or longer sight than the other.

4. To strengthen the eyes, stand facing your Vivaxis in preparation for aligning.

5. Hold your head tilted out of the Vivaxis channel while applying ice cubes wrapped in plastic to the ends of your fingers, toes, and eyes for a few seconds each. (Eye receptors terminate in the fingers and toes.)

6. Align immediately to your Vivaxis in the usual manner.

Treating the Common Cold and Other Infections

Fran found that there is always a disturbance to the lymphatic glands on one side of the body *before* any infection. You may remember from information about aligning to the Vivaxis that the fluids of the body, including the lymphatic fluids, are stimulated for twenty minutes after aligning. The lymphatic glands are part of the immune system, and therefore regular aligning to the Vivaxis can keep the immune system alert.

At the first sign of a virus, whether it's a simple cold, the flu, or any other infection, the following exercise may be useful. Ice is used to stimulate the affected body part before aligning. The exercise can also be used for insect stings and bites; if no ice is available, the area should be tapped firmly with a small stick or spoon. This exercise has been found to cut short the duration of a cold. It may need to be repeated one or two hours after the first time.

1. Stand on Force Flow 1 and stimulate the sinus receptors, which are on the ends of your toes, by shuffling and pressing them on the ground.

2. Wrap ice cubes in plastic and stimulate the sinus receptors, which are also located on the ends of your fingers, by holding the ice on each fingertip for a few seconds. Gently press the cubes around your sinus cavities on the sides of your nose and around your eyes and ears. In the case of other infections that do not involve the sinuses, hold the ice on the lymph glands under the arms and in the groin on both sides instead of on the sinus points.

3. Align to your Vivaxis as usual and inhale and exhale deeply in each of the four positions. For colds and flu, swallow twice in each direction to flex throat muscles and to direct magnetic energies to the throat.

This procedure may need to be repeated in two hours, and for best results to cut short the infection, this technique needs to be used at the *first* sign of the cold, flu, or other infection.

Observing the Effect of Unwanted Thoughts

Fran made the interesting discovery that many psychic people have holes in their magnetic and gravitational layers. This problem means that these people do not have the normal shielding to help prevent unwanted energies from impinging on their nervous system and consciousness. Usually, she found that the cranium lacks a normal Vivaxis field, and the subject therefore is not able to keep out other people's thoughts. We need to distinguish this type of unwanted psychism from the higher psychism gained through study, meditation, and reflective thought. The latter is the slow and correct type of spiritual development whereby the student learns to receive or reject energies at will.

The following exercise demonstrates the effect of thoughts on a person who lacks adequate shielding in some part of the body, usually the head or throat. The exercise involves the person being tested, A, the tester, B, and the person who will project thoughts periodically toward A, C. This exercise doesn't "treat" the problem, but it does highlight it.

1. Person A does the neutralizing exercise and is scanned by B to make sure there are no foreign fields. All three persons must have cleared circuits.

2. All parties must stand out of their Vivaxis channels; B stands about four feet from A, with hands held down by her sides, ready for testing.

3. B scans the skull of A, and her recording hand should give the normal back and forth response.

4. At periodic intervals without A and B knowing when, C will project her thoughts into A for thirty seconds or more. During these times, B will find that her hand circulates around to indicate a disturbance when looking at the head of A.

5. A should then reinstate the field in her skull by the usual method of jarring and then immediately aligning to her Vivaxis. She must then cut short the effect of aligning by the short neutralizing exercise so as not to drain energies from persons B and C.

6. B will now find that when C projects thoughts, there is no longer a disturbed pattern received from A.

PART THREE

Practical Exercises for Balancing the Energies of Your Environment

Introduction

The following exercises are designed to restore balance to the energies in your environment, as these also impinge on or compromise your Vivaxis connection. We are aware that in this twenty-first century, our planet is chemically and electromagnetically disturbed as never before in our known history. Factories and industrial complexes pour toxic effluent into our air, seas, rivers, and ground. Radioactive waste is added through accidents, such as happened in past years in California and Chernobyl, Russia. Ionizing radiation occurs in the workplace and home from television terminals and smoke sensors. The environment also becomes disturbed from natural occurrences such as earthquakes, volcanoes, and weather patterns.

In our homes, synthetic fabrics in our furnishings and chemicals in our water supply add to our problems. Paints on walls and surfaces can also act as disturbing irritants. Our cars also have interiors featuring plastics and upholstery that give off fumes. Those of us who have clients for some type of therapy have possible problems from foreign fields created when doing body work on patients or when using diagnostic equipment.

The skills described in this section can help you monitor disturbances and take appropriate measures in many cases to correct disturbances. First, I describe an exercise for the self-protection of therapists. This is especially useful for anyone doing bodywork such as massage, sacrocranial therapy, kinesiology, or acupressure. Then I give a description of how to monitor the health of a person on both the health-giving and detrimental force flows. This can be very useful for assessing the effect of pharmaceutical drugs for deficiencies of minerals. In addition, the energy field of the client can be scanned for foreign fields, X-rays, normal ion flow, and disturbances of brain receptors.

I then describe (in exercise 24) how to inactivate home, clinic, office, and car, using the inactivating powder treated by the force flows. Then comes an exercise explaining how to treat water for drinking so that it contains all the force flows. This water can be used for improving our health by taking it internally and can also be used as an inactivator in the absence of inactivating powder. There also is instruction for healing a disturbed room using salt and fresh water.

Exercises involving the wider environment include monitoring the ground before and after earthquakes and monitoring your environment for radiation. A further exercise teaches you how to find a ley line or a watercourse, using your hands or a dowsing rod. Exercise 28 gives tips to keep yourself balanced while traveling in planes and staying in hotels. Finally, there is a suggested menu of exercises to help you sort out the priorities of making your Vivaxis connection.

Self-Protection

The most important consideration when treating or evaluating the energy field of another person is to have protection against unintentionally forming a foreign field. So, whether you are trying to evaluate problems with family, friends, or as a therapist with clients, certain measures should be taken.

Not many practitioners will have immediate access to the energy layers at their place of work. However, as therapists, we have all had the experience of being drained or exhausted by certain people. This process occurs when the patient, friend, or relative unconsciously drains the energy from the energy field of the therapist to boost their own energy.

If, as a therapist, you are doing body work, especially if you hold bilateral points on the patient, (for example, polarity therapy), a foreign field can be created. This creates a permanent link between you and the patient and causes severe energy depletion and, frequently, chaotic energy interference between the Vivaxis of each of you. In other words, as individuals, you no longer have a clear link to your own Vivaxis. A polarity therapist or a masseur could accumulate a number of foreign fields over a period of some years. This may be one reason why some therapists suffer what is commonly called "burn out." Several techniques can be used to alleviate or prevent these problems:

1. The short-form neutralizing exercise (see exercise 2) should be performed after each consultation and especially after body work such as polarity therapy, massage, chiropractic, or kinesiology. The short version of neutralizing is undertaken for about one minute. The connection made between the meridians of your fingertips and the strong circuit made by pressing your ankles and knees together brings in your own Vivaxis energies and cancels out those of another person.

2. Regular aligning to your Vivaxis and drinking energized water are two practices that can strengthen your own energies when you have to work with a lot of people. You can keep a check on your ion flow and key brain receptors so as to establish the integrity of your energies.

3. In addition, if you are doing regular body work, it is a good idea to inactivate the treatment couch after each patient session by going over it with the inactivator material as described for houses and cars in exercise 24. I also recommend inactivating the area over any electronic device used for diagnostic treatment. As with body work, therapists using electronic equipment should also do the quick version of the neutralizing exercise after each patient session. The possibility always exists of creating a foreign field through holding an electrode that is connected with another person via electrical circuitry.

Those who have undergone a diagnostic or treatment procedure such as an electrocardiograph, X-ray, diathermy, ultrasound, encephalogram, CT scan, or nuclear magnetic resonance should check their ion flow or have it checked by another person and undertake the necessary clearing and energizing procedures.

Checking Others on the Energy Layers

One of the problems you are likely to develop when you establish any kind of sympathetic rapport with an unwell person is that you can pick up that condition yourself. Checking people *indirectly* via the energy layers protects you from being drained of energy or from acquiring the condition of the other person, as can happen if you scan their body directly.

This section of skills is of special use for all therapists, but it will also be useful for parents and individuals who may be helping relatives and friends in health areas. It is a means to assess deficiencies of particular elements and also the presence of toxic elements. I have given a few examples of the findings in particular ailments such as diabetes, high blood pressure, and senile dementia.

Follow the procedure outlined for checking yourself on the energy layers

One of the problems you are likely to develop when you establish any kind of sympathetic rapport with an unwell person is that you can pick up that condition yourself. Checking people indirectly via the energy layers protects you from being drained of energy or from acquiring the condition of the other person, as can happen if you scan their body directly.

(see exercise 10), except that you need to visualize the other person instead of yourself as you scan down the bands. There are certain times when you may be unable to detect any response from a person on any of the force flows. This usually occurs when the person is concentrating hard on some subject. So you need to check at another time when they are in a more relaxed state.

Pharmaceutical Drugs

Disturbances can also occur from taking pharmaceutical drugs for a long time. In these latter cases, we will not only record disturbances on the main health-giving force flows, but the subject will also register on the detrimental force flows that are below the main health-giving flows. (See exercise 7.) If someone registers on detrimental force flows, it means that when we scan down the force flows while thinking of that person, we will get a positive response in the recording hand at a particular place on these flows. This will establish that there is a detrimental element present, but not necessarily which one. We could then hold their pharmaceutical medication in our hand, and if that is the disturbing frequency previously noted, we will continue to get a strong back and forth movement in the recording hand while we are visually observing the same position on the force flows.

Many kinesiologists ask the person to hold that medication in their hand and then "muscle test" the person to see if their arm becomes weaker when holding the medicine during muscle testing. The advantage of the Vivaxis method is that the person does not have to be present, provided we can visualize that person while scanning the detrimental force flows with or without holding the drug. So, if someone has been on medical drugs for a long time, you will find they will register on areas below the main band near detrimental elements, depending on the drug concerned. To find the exact position of any prescribed drug, hold a sample in one hand and scan down below the main force flows until your recording hand responds.

Visualize the person who takes a drug at the place you have marked for it, and if a response occurs in the recording hand, you can assume the person is adversely affected by the drug in question. Of course, there will be situations where a person must take drugs for serious life-threatening diseases. The type of energy evaluation we do here merely indicates why so many drugs have side effects as well as the importance of finding natural remedies wherever possible.

Depression

When a person is severely depressed, I have found they only register on Force Flows 1 through 3. They have become so enclosed and cut off from the living world by their worry and introspective state that they also cut themselves off from the life-giving flows of Mother Earth. It seems amazing that the energy field of some depressed people does not register on several energy bands for year after year and yet they survive. However, they are never missing off Force Flows 1 through 3, the central bands, except during major and minor periods when Force Flow 1 disappears. I assume that their depression has prevented their energy field from receiving some of the health-giving frequencies of the force flows. Such people have literally closed down their energy field except to the minimum level of energies necessary for survival. This becomes a vicious circle, as the deficiency of some of the mineral frequencies will increase their depression.

High Blood Pressure

Blood pressure drugs always cause the hand to move in a circular motion on the magnesium force flow when you visualize the person concerned on that level. It may be that blood pressure problems are associated with disturbances of the magnesium receptors. The connection between magnesium and myopia has also been mentioned. (See exercise 18.) You will recall that the magnesium receptors around the eyes were associated with the type of tension that causes short sight.

As with all the minerals, there also are other magnesium receptors on the body. I had thought that magnesium receptors in relation to blood pressure may be located in the area above the adrenal glands, but to date I have not found this to be so. Then I checked around the heart itself near the sternum and above the nipples on both sides of the body. The usual way to locate receptors is to visualize the element and then move your testing finger lightly around the chosen area until you record a response. About two inches above the left nipple, I found a magnesium receptor. On the corresponding point on the right side, I found a phosphorus receptor. The point on the left is very close to the heart. It is significant that minor chakras also are found at these points above the nipple. Checking in the area of the breasts brings up the amusing speculation: where to look in the case of sagging breasts? Do the points correspond to the skeletal structure or to soft tissues? Obviously each person has to be individually assessed.

Magnesium relaxes structures in the body. High blood pressure often results from tension and overactivity in the sympathetic nervous system, which in turn causes arterial contraction and therefore an increase in blood pressure. Stress hormones are involved in this sympathetic nervous response. I have no doubt that other magnesium receptors exist and that they will be found to influence other organs and tissues. The need for adequate magnesium is a prime consideration in our stressed society.

Drinking energized water can reduce blood pressure very quickly in some cases. The water should be rolled on all layers but finished on the magnesium layer, and the person concerned should stand on the magnesium layer to drink about half a cup.

Diabetes

Diabetes is a common disorder that I have checked in relation to the force flows. Zinc and chromium are two minerals associated with blood sugar imbalance in diabetes. The zinc receptors seem to be the most significant, and this is illustrated by diabetics showing a disturbance on Force Flow 4. But diabetics also have a disturbance on Force Flow 3; this relates to the solar plexus, which rules the function of the pancreas in an esoteric sense. This central chakra governs all the digestive organs. Diabetes may be a good example of the fact that in most diseases there is an inner and outer factor. In diabetes, the inner factor is the state of the solar plexus chakra, and the outer factor is the inherited tendency in the genes and, possibly, a bad diet. The significance of the outer factor is illustrated by the enormous increase of diabetes in the Australian Aborigines when they began eating large quantities of refined sugars.

Dementia and Spinal Sublaxations

In cases of dementia in the elderly, I have found that the recording hand registers a circular motion on all force flows. This circular movement sometimes relates to spinal impediments, which need chiropractic or similar adjustment. It is interesting to have a client with a known back problem and to check this person on the energy flows before doing body work to correct the misalignment. I have found that before I conduct the body work, my recording hand registers a disturbed circular motion on all force flows even if the problem is located at a particular spinal segment. But within minutes of the correction, a normal recording will be observed on all force flows.

This could be a very simple way for osteopaths, chiropractors, and facial therapists to check their work with clients.

So, if a therapist has the force flows marked somewhere on their clinic walls, they have a means to immediately assess the success of their treatment apart from the experience of the client. This is useful because the client does not always experience immediate benefit from the treatment.

Intimacy

A few years ago, I did some interesting research with couples, watching their connection to the force flows while they were giving each other hugs. In every case, as soon as the couple hugged, it became impossible to monitor either person individually on the energy layer. This occurs because a temporary circuit is formed between the two people that disconnects their individual circuits to their Vivaxis. It would be ridiculous to suggest that people should stop hugging, but I wonder about the effect on the energy field of those persons who have intimate relations with a number of partners. Does this maintain the energy field of such a person in constant chaos, and is this a new argument for at least serial monogamy?

It could well be that we supplement the energies of each other at times, and perhaps this replaces the need for our connection to the Vivaxis during short periods. What happens when two incompatible energy fields live and sleep in close proximity year after year? If one partner has a chaotic energy field, does this always affect the field of the other? There are large areas of research yet to be undertaken.

EXERCISE 23

Scanning Others for Disturbances

Although it is preferable to teach people to assess their own energies, there are occasions when a therapist knows that a person has an energy block of some kind, and no natural therapies seem to be working. In this situation, we may not have access to the energy layers and need to scan the person directly without the protection of the energy layers. Before starting any type of scanning, check for solunar flow time. Both the tester and subject should be standing out of their Vivaxis directions to prevent false readings.

Scanning for Ion Flow

Ask the client to close her eyes and count slowly to one hundred; this takes her mind off you and the scanning process. Scan her back and front for ion flow. If your recording arm stops at some part, this usually points to a complete lack of ion flow and means the field is out of the bone. The remedy is to get the client to do the carbon exercise (exercise 1).

Alternatively, your hand may go round and around, indicating chaotic energies. In this case, you should encourage the person to exercise on the energy bands after jarring the affected part and then to drink energized water. Ideally, the client should be trained to find their own Vivaxis so that they can align regularly, thus keeping themselves in a state of balanced energies.

It should be noted that there usually is a corresponding disturbance on the skull that accompanies any disturbance found on the body. The head should be carefully checked after finding the body disturbance. This area must then also be corrected, even if no sensation or problems are noted by the individual concerned.

Scanning for Foreign Fields

There may be a foreign field, if when you test a person for ion flow, the recording hand moves in a circular direction when scanning any spot on the body. Check this possibility by testing for a vertical flow. Hold the fingers of your recording hand in the vertical position (pointing skyward) while scanning that same place on the person. If your hand moves back and forth in this position, you can conclude that a foreign field is attached to that part of the body, as you have now established that both a chaotic horizontal wave and a vertical wave exist.

The most appropriate technique for removal of a foreign field is the long neutralizing exercise (exercise 2). The affected person should repeat this exercise on at least three successive days. Check afterward to ensure that the foreign field is eradicated. You should observe a good ion flow on all parts of the body except on the exact midline. The person can then align to their Vivaxis.

Scanning for X-rays

After a person has cleared themselves with carbon to erase the effects of X-rays, it may be useful for someone else to scan them for normal responses to the carbon frequencies, especially in the X-rayed areas. Often a person cannot check their own energies at this stage of their Vivaxis work. Here's how you can help them:

1. Ask the person to stand, eyes closed, so that they are not facing any of the four quadrants of their Vivaxis, or directly into true north and south—the directions for carbon and calcium. This negates the possibility of a false positive for carbon.

2. The person then shuts their eyes and visualizes carbon, while the tester scans the X-rayed areas.

3. If the person's bones are responding correctly to the carbon/calcium frequencies, you should record a strong response in your recording hand from a carbon wave flowing throughout the body of the subject. If there is no response in your recording hand in some parts of the body, the subject's carbon are atoms in a state of imbalance, and the clearing exercise for X-rays must be conducted again.

4. Ask the person to strongly flex or move the part concerned. Your recording hand should register a normal ion flow during the movement.

Scanning the Brain Receptors

Wherever possible, it is best to get people to check their own brain receptors, but in the case of therapists, they may need to check their clients. The following guidelines must then be followed so that the therapist receives an accurate picture:

1. Your subject sits in a chair, with their head visible to the tester. The subject sits, legs apart and uncrossed,

and with a hand on each thigh. This is to stop the person from forming a closed circuit, which would negate the testing process.

2. Ask your subject to shut their eyes to keep out other influences and to hold their head tilted slightly to one side to avoid aligning to their Vivaxis. The person then counts or multiplies while being tested.

3. The testing place must be on neutral ground and not directly under an electric light.

4. You, the tester, must stand so as to be testing receptors that are lower than your own head. Also, keep your own head slightly tilted to one side to avoid connecting with your own Vivaxis. All your own brain receptors must be in good working order; otherwise you may simply record a disturbance in your own receptor.

5. Scan each of the thirty-six main brain receptors of your subject (see figure 20, page 113) and note the response in your recording hand. A circulating movement in the hand denotes a disturbed receptor, which can be treated by jarring it before the subject aligns to their Vivaxis.

6. After you have scanned the subject, you and the client should do the neutralizing exercise (the short one will do—see exercise 2) to give protection from remaining linked to each other. Wherever possible, people should be trained to do their own checking and scanning.

When the subtle currents of etheric energy are disturbed in the body, the logical process is to attend to the etheric body and then to give the vitamins, minerals, and herbs to sustain the physical body. At present, people are taking far more vitamins and minerals than they need,

probably because their energy receptors for these substances are disturbed. However, natural remedies are certainly superior to drugs for most health disturbances,
because they have no side effects.

Inactivating Your Environment

The science of Vivaxis is obviously connected intimately to our environment in terms of both the force flows in the energy layers and our personal connection to the Earth. Since the industrial age began, we have suffered a severe interference to our environment from chemicals and electrical or electronic sources. The procedures in this section were developed by Fran to recreate a healthy energy environment.

You have already used the energy layers to inactivate or treat plastic and nylon articles. Now it is time to extend this activity into the larger environment. It is possible to carry a purifying activity from the energy flows to other environments. One of the first exercises I ask seminar participants to undertake is to inactivate the harmful vibrations of modern buildings and human-made substances in their homes and cars. Disturbances in our environment may come from paints, furnishings, household detergents used in cleaning, glues and varnishes on household floors, and plastics. You will notice a different feeling to your environment after completing this process of inactivating.

Inactivating Your Home and Office

Make an "inactivator" bag by mixing a heaped table-spoon of calcium ascorbate (vitamin C) with about one pound of organic wheat bran. Seal this mixture tightly in a strong, clear plastic bag and place it on each force flow for about half a minute. The ascorbate powder appears to absorb all the frequencies of the force flows and to retain them for years, provided it does not become damp. Research has shown this vitamin to be involved with electron transfer in the cell. It therefore is sensitive to energy transfer. So perhaps this exercise is not as eccentric as it sounds. The vitamin C is used in the form of calcium ascorbate, because it lasts much longer when exposed to air than does vitamin C in the form of ascorbic acid powder.

One of the first exercises I ask seminar participants to undertake is to inactivate the harmful vibrations of modern buildings and human-made substances in their homes and cars. You will notice a different feeling to your environment after completing this process of inactivating.

Test the furnishings in your house for ion flow. Use your eyes for scanning and note the response in the recording hand. Disturbed furnishings will cause the recording hand to move in a circular fashion instead of the healthy back and forth motion. Alternatively, there may be a complete lack of movement. It is interesting to test different furnishings such as carpets, chairs, and beds for ion flow. Many disturbances will be found, except in the case of completely natural substances like untreated timber, wool, straw, and cotton. All painted surfaces will tend to give disturbed recordings, as will wallpapers, synthetic carpets, and floors sealed with polyurethane compounds.

After testing, swing the inactivator bag systematically over all areas, starting at the back of each room and moving away from areas just inactivated. Ideally, the process is undertaken on the roof, because everything below the roof would then be treated. This could certainly be carried out on a flat roof, but it may be a hazardous exercise if the roof is too steep! Allow a few moments for the energies to settle before retesting. Your arm should give a healthy back and forth movement after treating the area concerned.

Use the same technique for your car. In most cases, this can be done by swinging the bag over the car from the outside. It may be wise to undertake these activities when the neighbors are not watching! Many people comment on the difference in the atmospheres of their homes, offices, and cars after treatment with the inactivator bag. They feel the room is more peaceful and harmonious. The bag should not be stored next to where people sleep or on any vibrating household items such as washing machines or refrigerators.

You can also inactivate food substances to remove the frequencies of cadmium, lead, or mercury (often present in fish). The inactivator bag does not, of course, remove the physical molecules of these harmful elements, but harmful vibrations or frequencies corresponding to the element in question seem to disappear permanently. Note however, that if the article to be inactivated is actually on the detrimental force flow that you are seeking to eradicate, the inactivating will not work. By the same token, it can therefore become "reinfected," if it is subject to a detrimental force flow after it has been inactivated.

It is necessary to clarify here the various responses we have in our recording hand. If we are not thinking of anything in particular, normal healthy energy will be recorded as a back and forth movement. The direction of this movement is not important, but it is usually toward and away from the side of the body unless we are facing our Vivaxis. An energy disturbance from a detrimental substance will usually give a circulating movement. However, if you are visualizing a particular substance such as lead and it is present in the testing sample, you will get a back and forth movement, which is literally saying "yes," lead is present. Your hand therefore responds to your intention, whether testing for normal energy as in ion flow or testing for a particular element that is visualized.

As a research exercise, test whether various objects contain harmful substances. For instance, look at small bottles of leaded and unleaded gasoline and test which contains lead by visualizing lead (think of lead weights). If lead is present, your recording arm should give a positive back and forth response when visualizing for lead. The responses should then be recorded and some of the samples containing lead should be inactivated by a person not involved with the testing. The samples could then be retested and the results compared.

You could also test unsprayed fruit and vegetables from organic farms and compare it with supermarket produce. There is no end to the small projects you can undertake to test the effect of the Vivaxis flows and the energy layers. Your body is a most sensitive instrument for diagnosis. The inactivator material eventually will cease to work, which can be assessed by testing objects before and after inactivating. I have found that the inactivator material can retain its potency for years, but when it loses its inactivating effect, the material should be burned in case it retains a tendency to interact adversely with new inactivating material.

> *You could also test unsprayed fruit and vegetables from organic farms and compare it with supermarket produce. There is no end to the small projects you can undertake to test the effect of the Vivaxis flows and the energy layers. Your body is a most sensitive instrument for diagnosis.*

Earth energies are quite powerful, so a few notes of caution are appropriate here. Two inactivators should not be stored in a house, office, or car. This is because lines of force are formed between the two inactivator bags. If a person works or sleeps in a line between two inactivators, their body energies may be disturbed. The same energies from the energy layers can be used to deflect harmful but naturally occurring phenomena such as underground water streams, which will be described below when we look at other environmental issues.

Creating and Testing for Safe Places in the Home

1. Check that you are in a solunar flow period and check your ion flow.

2. Inactivate every room, using the inactivator material to remove disturbances from paint, floor coverings, and so on. Note that acrylic carpets cannot be inactivated.

3. Stand at the doorway of each room and systematically scan for ion flow in the room. If you find an energy disturbance, take note of its position. Is it confined to one spot or does it follow a course across the room? If the disturbance is only in one area, it possibly is a Hartmann and Curry grid intersection. If it is moving right across the room, it may be an electrical cable if the disturbance is less than twelve inches wide. An underground watercourse is usually several feet wide, but not always.

4. Move beds, study desks, or favorite armchairs to areas free of disturbances.

5. Note where your domestic animals sleep and remember that dogs avoid energy disturbances, whereas cats seem to be attracted to such spots.

Energizing Water

One of the simple ways you can use the energies of the energy layers is to treat water on the energy flows. Water appears to absorb Earth energies very readily, as has been demonstrated in research associated with homeopathy. After the thirtieth dilution (meaning one part homeopathic substance to one hundred parts of water repeated thirty times), there are no physical molecules of the substance left. Yet we know from our clinical work that these very high dilutions can have a powerful effect in restoring health. By energizing water on the force flows, the resonance of the various elements seems to be imprinted on the water for a considerable time. By drinking the water daily, the molecular balance of the elements in your body can be restored. You can also absorb the health-giving elements more adequately from your food.

By energizing water on the force flows, the resonance of the various elements seems to be imprinted on the water for a considerable time. By drinking the water daily, the molecular balance of the elements in your body can be restored. You can also absorb the health-giving elements more adequately from your food.

Like every form of therapy involving energies, take care not to overdose. This is why homeopathic doses are administered sparingly: to avoid confusion or the creation of excess energies. It is best to use the energized water no more than once daily except in cases of acute disorders such as sore throat, inflamed bowel, or other acute infections. In such cases, a few mouthfuls of water every couple of hours should be taken. If you have an infection or illness, you may need to dose yourself with the treated water more often than otherwise.

Method for Energizing Water to Drink

1. Choose a time when environmental conditions are stable and test for balanced ion flow and for solunar flow period. If you are able to do the exercise between 10 a.m. and 2 p.m., the valuable White Flows can be included.

2. Fill a jar with rainwater or filtered water. Use a jar that measures at least six inches tall so that when placed on its side, it will cover the vertical energy bands in addition to the horizontal flows. The material of the lid can be tin or plastic.

3. If it is between 10 a.m. and 2 p.m., roll the water from the top of the White Flow to the bottom of the lower White Flow on the energy layers. At other times, roll the jar between the top of the magnesium band to the bottom of the phosphorus band. If you need more negative ions, finish rolling the jar and drink the water while you stand on the magnesium flow. If you need more positive ions, finish rolling the jar and drink the water while standing on the phosphorus layer.

4. Now test the water, using visualization of the essential elements such as calcium, magnesium, zinc, iron,

chromium, and so on. Your recording arm will move back and forth for as long as you visualize each element, providing the frequency of the element is present in the energized water.

5. Drink about half a cup.

Without the White Flows, the energized water will retain the frequencies absorbed from the energy bands for about fifteen minutes but will lose its potency fairly quickly after you place the bottle on the ground. Therefore, drink it immediately after the rolling procedure. If the water is rolled between 10 A.M. and 2 P.M. to include the White Force Flows, the water retains the frequencies for weeks, provided it is placed away from electromagnetic interference.

The Canadian research group found that a bottle of distilled water rolled up the body from two inches below the navel to just above the eyebrows became imprinted with all the frequencies of the Vivaxis layers currently present in that person. In the case of disturbed receptors on the person concerned, this method proved valuable for detecting missing frequencies. To diagnose in this way, the jar was first rolled on the person and then placed upright on a table. The testing group then visualized each element to see if it was present in the water. If a deficiency was found, the subject then faced the compass direction for that element and aligned to that particular element (as described in exercise 12).

The research group also created a field containing all the health-giving frequencies by energizing two similar-sized bottles of water on the energy layers and placing the jars about six feet apart on a level surface. They measured the field created between the bottles by visualizing the elements above and between the jars. The height of the field between the jars was found to be about half the distance between the jars. The experimenters energized themselves by sitting for some moments in this field. This

could be a useful exercise if you were not able to go outside to stand on the energy layers. It is possible that the
same benefit could be obtained by drinking a few mouthfuls of energized water when necessary.

The energized water can, in addition, be used as an
inactivator by placing it in a bag and using as described
above in the technique for inactivating the environment.
Never drink the water that has been used for inactivating;
discard it as soon as you have completed the inactivating.
Using water for inactivating food and drink can be very
useful if you don't have calcium ascorbate and bran.

As mentioned above in the section on inactivating,
take care not to have two bottles of inactivating water or
material such as the treated ascorbate powder in your
house or office permanently, because the field between
the jars could be disturbing on a permanent basis. The
field could also be imbalanced at those times of the day
when Force Flows 1 and 4 cancel each other out. So it is
fine to experiment with two jars of water, but at least one
should be discarded after the experiment is finished.
More of a good thing is not always wise!

Water that is not distilled or filtered may contain various minerals, both healthy and otherwise. The only fil-
tering method that removes all foreign substances is
reverse osmosis, which passes the water under pressure
through a very fine membrane to remove pollutants, even
bacteria. The popular and cheap water purifiers that have
carbon filters remove a few substances, but they won't
remove substances that are more fully dissolved in the
water. Water from an underground source is usually rich
in those elements from the surrounding rocks and soil
and cannot be used for the above exercises.

Creating a Compatible Wave Field for Your Home or Office

Fran found that a consistently compatible and
health-giving field could be maintained, despite changes

in the environment, by the following arrangement of salt and sodium bicarbonate:

Place two sealed jars of soda six inches apart in an east/west direction outside the house. Place the jars on a bed of charcoal on ground that is slightly lower than the floor of the lowest room. Place the sealed jar of salt six feet away and three feet higher than the soda. The compatible field will extend about six hundred feet in all directions, and the soda will not deteriorate for many months. Any area below the jars is not included in the compatible field. The field only operates in daylight. Keep any other jars of soda and salt in a dark cupboard so that conflicting wave fields are not formed. (See figure 34.)

Healing a Disturbed Room Using Salt and Fresh Water

The following technique is useful in a hotel or lecture room where jars of salt and soda cannot be placed outside. Because of atmospheric changes, Sick Building Syndrome, and earthquakes, which affect the energy field over wide areas, we sometimes need to balance the energies in such a public room. It is difficult for people to concentrate on a lecture if the ion flow in a room is severely disturbed by the above factors.

The following exercise illustrates the relation of ion flow to magnetic north and south. A strong inactivating influence spreads around the jars and up to the ceiling of the room. This technique is also useful for reaching pollutants in the ceiling, which are hard to access by the normal inactivating procedure described earlier.

1. Test for normal ion flow in the room.

2. Dissolve one teaspoon of pure sea salt to half a liter or one pint of purified water and stir with a wooden spoon or shake until dissolved. Pour into a jar and freeze the water.

3. Take a second jar of frozen fresh water. The jars must be at least twelve inches apart and are placed in line between magnetic north and south with the salt water north of the fresh water. Notice that we are copying the arrangement of the water that is found at the north and south poles—salt in the north and fresh in the south. Remove jars if the atmosphere becomes too saturated with negative ions. A strong inactivating influence spreads around the jars and up to the ceiling of the room.

Earthquakes and Radiation

Earthquake Activity

Disturbances before an earthquake may occur even days before the actual quake. It has been noted that animals become very restless some hours beforehand. The effect usually dissipates fairly quickly after the quake, unless there are aftershocks. We can pick up these disturbances many thousands of miles from the epicenter. I have registered severe disturbances in Melbourne from the last major Japanese and Los Angeles quakes, but I have not yet learned how to identify the direction of their activity. We can make this analysis of the ground if we find the energy in our environment is very disturbed, and especially if our Vivaxis appears to be at right angles to its usual direction. Imbalance of ion flow in the environment may be another indicator.

The best way to test for earthquake activity is to sense the motion of your hands when held at your sides while looking at your feet. Near the time of earthquake activity, each hand will move in a circular motion opposite to the other hand. Volcanic activity will often register the same effect. The feet are obviously sensing energy that comes through the ground. I also hear a low-frequency sound coming from the Earth for some weeks before a quake.

Observing and Testing for Radiation

Radiation can be present in the atmosphere after nuclear testing. If you find that the ion flow at any time is severely disturbed, scan the sky while holding your hands by your side. Both hands will record this disturbance by moving in a circular motion, first one way and then the other. Presumably, underground atomic testing would produce the same response in your hands if the disturbance traveled to your area.

According to Fran's research, Force Flow 2 (the chromium vertical band) can protect against and even provide an antidote to the effects of radiation. It may be useful to know this fact if you are in a crisis situation involving radiation. My theory is that those few persons who were at the center of the Hiroshima blast and yet survived unharmed into old age may have been standing on such a layer at the time. No explanation has ever been given for their escape from illness and injury.

Safeguards to Protect against Computer Radiation

If you use computers every day but have a good diet and take antioxidants such as vitamins A, C, and E, any negative effects from computer radiation will be considerably minimized. Another practical suggestion is to use a movable keyboard that can stretch back at least eighteen inches from the screen. This moves you further from the electromagnetic field. Laptop computers with liquid crystal screens are a preferable alternative, because they do not emit ionizing radiation as the television screens of most computer terminals do. Modern computers are now designed to emit far less radiation than computers did in the first twenty years of their production.

The Canadian research group found that a protective field from computer radiation could be established with the frequencies of selenium and copper. They wound copper wire around a selenium tablet and placed it near the computer. They found the field created extended at least three feet in all directions from the tablet. Presumably, to measure this field they visualized the frequency of selenium of copper while moving the eyes outward from the tablet, using the recording hand to gauge a response. It would then be simple to remove the tablet well away from the computer and then to test for ion flow, which is usually found to be disturbed near computers. The positive effect from this field on the body has a strengthening effect on the adrenal glands and kidneys.

Another practical measure to improve the office environment is to install a negative ion generator to balance the constant stream of positive ions emitted by computers and air-conditioning. Have a short break every half hour away from the computer. In addition, take the antioxidants vitamin A, vitamin C, and grapeseed extract to protect against the free radical effect of ionizing radiation. Free radical damage involves cell membranes and can have mutagenic effects on cells. Vitamin B complex gives general energy to combat tiredness from office work.

EXERCISE 27

Finding a Ley Line
or Watercourse

This is an optional exercise for those interested in expanding their understanding of Earth energies. It is interesting to compare the different types of energy flows in our environment, and energy in a ley line is quite powerful.

You will need to search in an area that is not built up with typical small suburban blocks. National parks are suitable areas for finding a ley line. Establish the general area by means of landmarks such as very large or unusual tree formations, or perhaps in relation to a single standing stone. However, not all such markers will be on a ley line. We also can use our subtle sense of intuitive knowing. If the opportunity presents, I recommend that you first start this type of sensing at a large cathedral or temple that is some centuries old, and therefore that is likely to have been sited by a master builder.

1. Scan across either end and each side of the building to find the direction where normal ion flow is not present. Mark where ion flow begins and ends.

2. Stand in the middle of the flow and allow your body to register the direction of the energy flowing in the ley line. The line probably will be on the longitudinal axis of the building. If possible, revisit the site after the next new or full moon and recheck the direction of the flow, because it usually reverses every two weeks in keeping with new and full moons.

3. Some people feel comfortable locating ley lines with dowsing rods. If you prefer this method, hold the rods in front of your body so that they are in a parallel position as you approach the building. Think "ley line" as you approach and note the position where the rods swing outward. When dowsing and hence visualizing water, the same movement will occur when you reach the edge of the watercourse. (See figure 70, on page 368—note that the watercourse below the ground will not be visible and is shown here to illustrate the movement of the rods.)

4. Turn at right angles so that you face into the flow or have your back to it, depending on the direction of the flow. The tips of the rods will swing in the direction of the flow and remain parallel. As you move along with the flow, the tips will turn to follow the direction of the ley line. figure 70 indicates how the rods swing outward when you approach the edge of a watercourse or ley line.

I prefer to use my arms, hands, and body rather than the rods, but the rods are easier to use if you are charting a ley line over a long distance in a moving car. Only an experienced dowser could undertake such a task, but it was successfully managed by Hamish Miller and Paul Broadhurst for the purpose of charting the famous St. Michael line across southern England.

The dowser has to completely concentrate on the energy in question, because there are many side lines that may

feed in to the ley line or watercourse you are charting. By concentrating intensely on the task, you automatically block out other phenomena, such as other watercourses, electrical cables, and water pipes, that could affect your accuracy. If you dowse without giving it your full attention, you may pick up a number of energy factors, but you will not know what they represent.

Figure 70. Dowsing a watercourse or ley line. Note that although the watercourse is shown here for figurematic purposes, we are really dealing with an underground watercourse that cannot be seen above ground. Whether dowsing an underground watercourse or ley line, the dowsing technique will be the same and the dowser needs to think of water or ley lines while walking over the ground and testing

Once you have practiced finding ley lines on a known ancient site, and when you feel confident, move into a country area and start to sense for signs connected with trees and rocks. Sometimes you will find them in the least expected places. I was touring with friends in northeast Greece and we found a place to stay at a small hotel near the sea. I was gazing out from my balcony across the small backyard when I saw a strange yellow stone standing by itself. It had the usual shape of a standing stone, although there was nothing else of significance in sight.

I could detect no normal ion flow associated with the stone, and sure enough, with further checking I found it was situated on a ley line. The stone had probably been placed there a long time ago by someone to mark the line. The present owners would have been oblivious of the fact, but they may have been attracted by the special energy that would have been apparent to a sensitive person.

EXERCISE 28

Hints for Travelers

When traveling, it is useful to know the general directions of north, south, east, and west, because then you will always be aware of the general direction of your Vivaxis. Traveling rapidly, as in jets, or over long distances, can tend to skew your perception of your Vivaxis direction, which may appear to be at right angles to its true direction. Therefore, it is wise to exercise on the central Force Flows 1 through 4 after a disturbance like jet traveling or other electrical or magnetic interferences. These interferences have not prevented me from finding the energy layers after I have traveled.

Find some gently sloping land and locate Force Flow 1 after arriving at your destination; you can then proceed to check for the direction of your Vivaxis. Hopefully the direction you find coincides with your rough evaluation of compass directions, and you can then proceed to align to your Vivaxis. If the direction still appears to be at right angles, it is probably necessary to stress (jar) the key points on your skull while exercising further on the force flows. Affected points could be the top of the head, roof of mouth, bridge of nose, and mastoid bone behind the ear. If there is no suitable land around the hotel on which to ground yourself and find the energy layers, a public park usually is nearby.

Ask for a room as far away as possible from hotel elevators and power cable wells. The room next to an elevator always contains a strong electromagnetic field. When I taught in Athens, I regularly stayed in an apartment where my room was next to the elevator well. After my first visit and following two disturbed nights, I realized the cause of my problem and slept the other way around in the bed so that my feet, rather than my head, were in the disturbed energy field. Over the last two decades, during which I have traveled a great deal, I have found that checking ion flows and a discriminating choice of hotels and apartments have allowed me to travel without any loss of energy and with a minimum of jet lag.

To avoid the worst of the electromagnetic field effects from jet engines, sit in the midline of the plane. The disturbance is minimized by the extra distance from the engines and by the buffering effect provided by the not-so-fortunate people who have chosen the seats near the windows on either side of the plane. As most people prefer the window and aisle seats it is always easy to obtain a seat in the middle, presuming you're flying in a 747 with four or so seats in the middle of the plane and between the aisles. (The other advantage is that it is the most likely place to have a spare seat or two adjacent for lying down during long night flights.)

Suggested Menu of Exercises

After looking at so many possible exercises for working the Vivaxis connection, I have chosen a menu for regular use. This is because not all the exercises are necessary for everyone, and the general reader may find it useful to follow the suggested guidelines for use. Use discrimination as to how often you do some of these exercises, for too much energy can be as damaging as too little. This applies to any work with subtle energies.

You will see that some of these procedures only need to be conducted once, such as marking the force flows on the ground or on a vertical surface. The procedure would only need to be repeated if rain or other damage to our markings made it necessary. The inactivating of house and car only needs to be done once, unless new furnishings are added. Guidelines for the frequency of the main exercises such as aligning to the Vivaxis are included.

It will only take you a few minutes a week to keep up your Vivaxis skills once you have mastered the main principles, and this menu will help to keep you to the essentials.

1. Inactivate your house, car, and office after checking the energies in each and note the differences afterward. Recheck from time to time as new furniture and fittings are added.

2. Become more aware of the environment and learn to check different environments as you travel around. Carefully check for normal ion flow around a new house or apartment before you decide to move in. Be especially careful of electrical installations nearby and make sure that the associated energy fields are checked on a clear day when they are at their maximum size.

3. Introduce the suggested safeguards for working with computers and other equipment with electromagnetic fields. Insist on adequate air-conditioning in offices, as all electrical equipment tends to saturate the atmosphere with positive ions. Photocopiers of some older designs give off ozone, which also disturbs the atmosphere.

4. Establish and mark the different force flows near your house for personal use, for inactivating pollutants in food, and for energizing water. Whenever possible, place groceries and foodstuffs for a minute or so on the energy layers and force flows after purchase.

5. Mark a vertical band on a tree, post, or wall for ease in checking both yourself and others. Ground markings have a habit of disappearing with keen lawn mowers and foul weather, but are, of course, necessary for our own body work.

6. Regularly check yourself by standing on the force flows, and at least twice a week, align to your Vivaxis on the force flow that seems most suitable on that day.

7. When you feel your concentration or memory is poor, do the exercise for the memory receptors.

8. Repeat the carbon exercise after new X-rays, CT scans, and ultrasounds, and align as soon as possible to your Vivaxis.

9. Test regularly for north and south in your environment and whenever going on holidays, and also remain aware of the movement of the tides and your experiences with meditation at these times.

10. Repeat the neutralizing exercise after any medical diagnostic procedure where electrodes are placed on your body, for instance during electrocardiographs or diathermy. Women should do this exercise after electrolysis for hair removal. Assume after any surgery that you have been placed in an electrical circuit for one reason or another. Become proficient at testing for foreign fields. You also need to exercise on the energy layers and drink energized water after having received any anesthesia.

11. Drink energized water at least twice a week and use the force flows regularly as general purification for water used in cooking and drinking.

12. Practice identifying the various mineral receptors on your body and the left and right hand spins of the receptors in the triple groups.

13. Begin to practice becoming aware of ley lines, underground watercourses, and the Hartmann and Curry grids and other unusual energy fields.

14. If you are a therapist, learn how to check other people's receptors and become proficient at relating

health problems involving particular minerals with disturbances in people, as observed on the energy bands.

15. Regularly check your brain receptors to monitor interference picked up from clients. Remember to do the short neutralizing exercise at regular intervals during the day's consulting. Spend one minute inactivating the treatment couch after each use.

16. Regard all this energy work with your Vivaxis connection as an exciting adventure you cannot miss!

Postscript

Now you have seen how extensive and vital the Vivaxis connection is and how to make it a health-giving part of your life. It takes only a few moments each day to check your energy fields and to do strengthening energy work. You are now in a position to monitor yourself and others with respect to their energy flows and mineral status and to have an understanding as to how the energy layers reflect the frequencies of minerals, herbs, and homeopathic remedies that have traditionally been used to restore health and balance. Observations of the detrimental force flows enable you to personally monitor any buildup of toxic waste that could threaten life and health in yourself and others. You also have skills to check the body receptors or acupuncture points in a far more detailed way than through pulse diagnosis as used by acupuncturists. In addition, when needed, you can create a new Vivaxis.

As a natural therapist, I have used therapies for decades to give people more energy. However, in conjunction with our psychological state, our basic physical lifestyle and environment must be understood as the *backdrop* for any therapeutic aid. If we compromise the integrity of our body energies, the effect of vitamins, minerals, herbs, homeopathy, or Vivaxis energies is greatly diminished. The effect is then like pouring water into a bottomless pit. Some of the ways we diminish our health include poor diet, a noisy and polluted environment, introducing conflicting energies from human-made electrical sources, and negative thoughts and emotions. So our first task on the road to better health is to free the body from those disturbances that cause a conflict of energies.

At the beginning of this book, I said my experience with Earth energies was the most amazing adventure in healing I had yet encountered. As I continue to deepen my understanding of the Vivaxis connection and my understanding of the electrical polarities of humanity and of our earthly home, the web of life connecting us all becomes increasingly revealed to my inner and outer sight. I rejoice afresh in these earthly insights and the opportunity to share this living pattern—the Vivaxis connection—with others.

About the Author

Judy Jacka is best known for her work in natural therapies, in which she has consulted, lectured, written, and taught for thirty years. She also has a lifelong interest in the metaphysical teachings of H. P. Blavatsky and Alice Bailey and is a senior worker in the Arcane school. Her esoteric interests have been expressed through writing and teaching about subtle forms of healing.

In this book, Judy Jacka has integrated the Vivaxis teachings and information about Earth energies with her long experience of natural therapies and the ancient wisdom teachings about subtle energies. She has succeeded in making a working synthesis of many aspects of Earth energies.

Judy has taught the Vivaxis techniques revealed in this book since 1980 in Australia, New Zealand, Canada, and Europe.

Index

Hampton Roads Publishing Company

... for the evolving human spirit

Hampton Roads Publishing Company
publishes books on a variety of subjects,
including metaphysics, health, integrative medicine,
visionary fiction, and other related topics.

For a copy of our latest catalog, call toll-free
(800) 766-8009, or send your name and address to:

Hampton Roads Publishing Company, Inc.
1125 Stoney Ridge Road
Charlottesville, VA 22902

e-mail: hrpc@hrpub.com
Website: www.hrpub.com